SOLUTIONS MANUAL

for the

ELECTRICAL ENGINEERING REFERENCE MANUAL

Fifth Edition

Raymond B. Yarbrough, P.E.

PROFESSIONAL PUBLICATIONS, INC.
Belmont, CA 94002

In the ENGINEERING REFERENCE MANUAL SERIES

Engineer-In-Training Reference Manual
    Engineering Fundamentals Quick Reference Cards
    Engineer-In-Training Sample Examinations
    Mini-Exams for the E-I-T Exam
    1001 Solved Engineering Fundamentals Problems
    E-I-T Review: A Study Guide
Civil Engineering Reference Manual
    Civil Engineering Quick Reference Cards
    Civil Engineering Sample Examination
    Civil Engineering Review Course on Cassettes
    Seismic Design of Building Structures
    Seismic Design Fast
    Timber Design for the Civil P.E. Examination
    Fundamentals of Reinforced Masonry Design
246 Solved Structural Engineering Problems
Mechanical Engineering Reference Manual
    Mechanical Engineering Quick Reference Cards
    Mechanical Engineering Sample Examination
    101 Solved Mechanical Engineering Problems
    Mechanical Engineering Review Course on Cassettes
    Consolidated Gas Dynamics Tables
Electrical Engineering Reference Manual
    Electrical Engineering Quick Reference Cards
    Electrical Engineering Sample Examination
Chemical Engineering Reference Manual
    Chemical Engineering Quick Reference Cards
    Chemical Engineering Practice Exam Set
Land Surveyor Reference Manual
Petroleum Engineering Practice Problem Manual
Expanded Interest Tables
Engineering Law, Design Liability, and Professional Ethics
Engineering Unit Conversions

In the ENGINEERING CAREER ADVANCEMENT SERIES

How to Become a Professional Engineer
The Expert Witness Handbook—A Guide for Engineers
Getting Started as a Consulting Engineer
Intellectual Property Protection—A Guide for Engineers
E-I-T/P.E. Course Coordinator's Handbook
Becoming a Professional Engineer
Engineering Your Start-Up

SOLUTIONS MANUAL for the ELECTRICAL ENGINEERING REFERENCE MANUAL
Fifth Edition

Printed in the United States of America

ISBN: 0-912045-12-4

Library of Congress Catalog Card Number: 89-62329

Professional Publications, Inc.
1250 Fifth Avenue, Belmont, CA 94002
(415) 593-9119

Current printing of this edition (last number): 5 4 3 2

TABLE OF CONTENTS

Notice To Examinees

MATHEMATICS

1. Convert 1101.011_2 to a decimal number.

$$1 \times 2^3 = 8$$
$$1 \times 2^2 = 4$$
$$0 \times 2^1 = 0$$
$$1 \times 2^0 = \underline{1}$$
$$= 13$$
$$0 \times 2^{-1} = 0$$
$$1 \times 2^{-2} = 0.25$$
$$1 \times 2^{-3} = \underline{0.125}$$
$$= 0.375$$

$$1101.011_2 = \boxed{13.375_{10}}$$

2.
$$(4 + j5)(2 + j3) = 8 + j12 + j10 + j^2 15$$
$$= 8 - 15 + j(12 + 10)$$
$$= \boxed{-7 + j22}$$

3. (a)
$$4 + j5 = \sqrt{(4)^2 + (5)^2} \, \underline{/\tan^{-1}\left(\frac{5}{4}\right)}$$
$$(4 + j5)^* = \sqrt{(4)^2 + (5)^2} \, \underline{/\tan^{-1}\left(-\frac{5}{4}\right)}$$
$$(4 + j5)(4 + j5)^* = (4)^2 + (5)^2 = \boxed{41}$$

(b)
$$(4 + j5)(4 + j5)^* = (4 + j5)(4 - j5)$$
$$= 16 - j20 + j20 - j^2 25$$
$$= 16 + 25 = \boxed{41}$$

4.
$$\left(\frac{1}{2 - j3}\right)\left(\frac{2 + j3}{2 + j3}\right) = \frac{2 + j3}{(2)^2 + (3)^2}$$
$$= \boxed{\frac{2 + j3}{13}}$$

5.
$$\left(\frac{4 + j5}{2 - j3}\right)\left(\frac{2 + j3}{2 + j3}\right) = \frac{8 + j12 + j10 + j^2 15}{4 + 9}$$
$$= \frac{-7 + j22}{13}$$
$$= \boxed{1.776 \, \underline{/107.7^\circ}}$$

6. The numbers shown are used in subsequent calculations, so rounding errors will occur.

$$A = 4 + j5 = 6.4 \, e^{j0.896}$$
$$B = 2 - j3 = 3.6 \, e^{-j0.983}$$
$$\frac{A}{B} = \frac{6.4}{3.6} e^{j(0.896 + 0.983)}$$
$$= 1.778 e^{j1.879}$$

The exponent is in radians.

$$\frac{A}{B} = \boxed{1.778 \, \underline{/107.7^\circ}}$$

7.
$$\frac{1}{x(x + 1)} = \frac{A}{x} + \frac{B}{x + 1}$$

Using cross multiplication,

$$\frac{Ax + A + Bx}{x(x + 1)} = \frac{1}{x(x + 1)}$$
$$A = 1$$
$$A + B = 0$$
$$B = -1$$

$$\frac{1}{x(x + 1)} = \boxed{\frac{1}{x} - \frac{1}{x + 1}}$$

8.
$$f(x) = \frac{4x^2 + 5x + 2}{x^2(x + 1)}$$
$$= \frac{A}{x} = \frac{B}{x^2} + \frac{C}{x + 1}$$

Using cross multiplication,

$$f(x) = \frac{Ax(x + 1) + B(x + 1) + Cx^2}{x^2(x + 1)}$$
$$= \frac{(A + C)x^2 + (A + B)x + B}{x^2(x + 1)}$$

Matching coefficients of x in the numerator,

$$A + C = 4$$
$$A + B = 5$$
$$B = 2$$
$$A = 3$$
$$C = 1$$

$$f(x) = \boxed{\frac{3}{x} + \frac{2}{x^2} + \frac{1}{x + 1}}$$

9.
$$f(x) = \frac{5x^2 + 11x + 20}{x(x^2 + 2x + 5)}$$
$$= \frac{A}{x} + \frac{Bx + C}{x^2 + 2x + 5}$$
$$= \frac{Ax^2 + 2Ax + 5A + Bx^2 + Cx}{x(x^2 + 2x + 5)}$$
$$= \frac{(A + B)x^2 + (2A + C)x + 5A}{x(x^2 + 2x + 5)}$$

Matching numerator coefficients of x,

$$A + B = 5$$
$$2A + C = 11$$
$$5A = 20$$
$$A = 4$$
$$B = 1$$
$$C = 3$$

$$\boxed{f(x) = \frac{4}{x} + \frac{x + 3}{x^2 + 2x + 5}}$$

10.
$$(s + 1)^2 = s^2 + 2s + 1$$

$$
\begin{array}{r}
s + 2 \\
s^2 + 2s + 1 \overline{\smash{)}\, s^3 + 4s^2 + 6s + 2} \\
\underline{s^3 + 2s^2 + s} \\
2s^2 + 5s + 2 \\
\underline{2s^2 + 4s + 2} \\
s
\end{array}
$$

$$\frac{s^3 + 4s^2 + 6s + 2}{(s + 1)^2} = \boxed{s + 2 + \frac{s}{(s + 1)^2}}$$

11. Let $x = \theta/2$.

$$\theta = 2x$$
$$\cos 2x = 2\cos^2 x - 1$$
$$= 1 - 2\sin^2 x$$
$$\sin^2 x = \left(\frac{1}{2}\right)(1 - \cos 2x)$$
$$\cos^2 x = \left(\frac{1}{2}\right)(1 + \cos 2x)$$
$$\sin^2 \frac{\theta}{2} = \boxed{\left(\frac{1}{2}\right)(1 - \cos\theta)}$$
$$\cos^2 \frac{\theta}{2} = \boxed{\left(\frac{1}{2}\right)(1 + \cos\theta)}$$

12. (a) In the range $1 < I < 10$, curve a is a constant value of 50.

$$V = \boxed{50}$$

(b) In the range $0 < I < 4.5$, curve b has a slope of $-10/4.5$ with an intercept at $I = 0$, $V = 100$. Using the slope intercept form,

$$V = -\frac{10}{4.5}I + 100 \quad 0 < I < 4.5$$

In the range $5.5 < I < 10$, the slope appears to be approximately $-90/5$, passing through $V = 0$, $I = 10$. Using the point-slope form,

$$\frac{V - 0}{I - 10} = -\frac{90}{5}$$

$$V = \boxed{-18I + 180 \quad 5.5 < I < 10}$$

(c) Over the range $0 < I < 2$, the voltage is zero, or

$$V = 0 \quad 0 < I < 2$$

Over the range $3 < I < 4.5$, curve c passes through point $I = 4.5, V = 100$, and if extended would intersect $V = 0$ axis at $I \cong 2.4$. Using the two-point method,

$$\frac{V - 0}{I - 2.4} = \frac{100 - 0}{4.5 - 2.4}$$

$$V = \boxed{\frac{100}{2.1}I - \frac{240}{2.1} \quad 3 < I < 4.5}$$

13.
$$\frac{du}{dx} = 2\cos x - 3\sin x = 0$$
$$\tan x = \frac{2}{3}$$

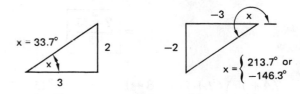

In the range $-90° < x < 90°$, minimax is at $x = 33.7°$

$$\frac{d^2u}{dx^2} = -2\sin x - 3\cos x \text{ (evaluated at } x = 33.7°)$$
$$= -1.11 - 2.50 < 0$$

$$\boxed{33.7° \text{ is a maximum.}}$$

14.

$$\bar{u} = \frac{1}{b-a} \int_a^b u(x)\,dx \qquad \text{(Eq. 1.66)}$$
$$u = e^{-2x} \cos \pi x$$
$$b = 1$$
$$a = 0$$
$$\bar{u} = \int_0^1 e^{-2x} \cos \pi x \, dx$$

Use Eq. 1.04.

$$\bar{u} = \left[\frac{e^{-2x}}{(2)^2 + \pi^2} \right] (-2\cos \pi x + \pi \sin \pi x) \Big|_{x=0}^{x=1}$$

$$= \left(\frac{e^{-2}}{4 + \pi^2} \right) (-2\cos \pi + \pi \sin \pi)$$

$$+ \left(\frac{-e^0}{4 + \pi^2} \right) (-2\cos 0 + \pi \sin 0)$$

$$= \left(\frac{e^{-2}}{4 + \pi^2} \right) (2 + 0) + \left(\frac{-e^0}{4 + \pi^2} \right) (-2 + 0)$$

$$= \frac{2e^{-2} + 2}{4 + \pi^2} = \boxed{0.164}$$

15.

$$b\frac{dv}{dt} + cv = 0 = d$$
$$b = 0.01$$
$$c = 0.0025$$
$$v = \frac{d}{c} + \left[v(0) - \frac{d}{c} \right] e^{\frac{-c}{b}t}$$
$$v(0) = 100$$
$$\frac{b}{c} = 4$$
$$v(t) = \boxed{100\, e^{-\frac{t}{4}}\ \text{V}}$$

16. Let $i = I_0 + I_1 e^{\alpha t}$.

$$\frac{di}{dt} = \alpha I_1 e^{\alpha t}$$
$$\frac{d^2 i}{dt^2} = \alpha^2 I_1 e^{-\alpha t}$$

$$\alpha^2 I_1 e^{\alpha t} + 5\alpha I_1 e^{\alpha t} + 4(I_0 + I_1 e^{\alpha t}) = 2$$

$$4I_0 = 2 \text{ or } I_0 = 0.5$$

$$(\alpha^2 + 5\alpha + 4)I_1 e^{\alpha t} = 0$$
$$(\alpha^2 + 5\alpha + 4) = 0$$
$$\alpha = -1$$
$$\alpha = -4$$

$$i = 0.5 + Ae^{-t} + Be^{-4t}$$
$$i(0) = 0.5 + A + B = 1.7$$
$$\frac{di(0)}{dt} = -A - 4B = 0$$
$$A = 1.6$$
$$B = -0.4$$
$$i(t) = \boxed{0.5 + 1.6e^{-t} - 0.4e^{-4t}\ \text{A}}$$

17. Let $i = I_0 + I_1 e^{\alpha t}$.

$$\frac{di}{dt} = \alpha I_1 e^{\alpha t}$$
$$\frac{d^2 i}{dt^2} = \alpha^2 I_1 e^{\alpha t}$$

$$\alpha^2 I_1 e^{\alpha t} + 2\alpha I_1 e^{\alpha t} + I_0 + I_1 e^{\alpha t} = 0.25$$
$$I_0 = 0.25$$

$$\alpha^2 + 2\alpha + 1 = 0$$
$$\alpha = 1$$
$$i = 0.25 + Ae^{-t} + Bte^{-t}$$
$$\frac{di}{dt} = -Ae^{-t} + Be^{-t} - Bte^{-t}$$
$$i(0) = 0.8 = 0.25 + A$$
$$A = 0.55$$
$$\frac{di(0)}{dt} = 0 = -A + B$$
$$B = 0.55$$
$$i(t) = \boxed{0.25 + 0.55(1 + t)e^{-t}\ \text{A}}$$

18.

$$v(t) = V_0 + V_1 e^{\alpha t}$$
$$\frac{dv}{dt} = \alpha V_1 e^{\alpha t}$$
$$\frac{d^2 v}{dt^2} = \alpha^2 V_1 e^{\alpha t}$$

$$(\alpha^2 + 3\alpha + 6.25)V_1 e^{\alpha t} + 6.25V_0 + 12.5 = 0$$
$$V_0 = -2$$
$$\alpha^2 + 3\alpha + 6.25 = 0$$
$$\alpha = -1.5 \pm j2$$
$$v(t) = -2 + Ae^{-1.5t} \cos 2t + Be^{-1.5t} \sin 2t$$
$$\frac{dv}{dt} = (2B - 1.5A)e^{-1.5t} \cos 2t - (2A + 1.5B)e^{-1.5t} \sin 2t$$
$$v(0) = 10 = -2 + A$$
$$A = 12$$

$$\frac{dv}{dt}(0) = 0 = 2B - 1.5A$$

$$B = 9$$

$$v(t) = \boxed{-2 + (12\cos 2t + 9\sin 2t)e^{-1.5t} \ \text{V}}$$

19.

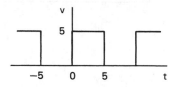

The average value is $a_0/2$.

$$a_0 = \frac{2}{T}\int_{-5}^{5} v\,dt = \left(\frac{2}{10}\right)(25) = 5$$

$$a_n = \frac{2}{T}\int_{-5}^{5} v\cos\left(\frac{2\pi}{T}\right)nt\,dt$$

$$= \left(\frac{2}{10}\right)\int_{0}^{5} 5\cos\left(\frac{2\pi}{10}\right)nt\,dt$$

$$= \left(\frac{5}{\pi n}\right)(\sin\pi n - \sin 0) = 0$$

Because this is an odd function (when the average value is removed), there will be no cosine terms in the series.

$$b_n = \frac{2}{T}\int_{-5}^{5} v\sin\left(\frac{2\pi}{T}\right)nt\,dt$$

$$= \left(\frac{2}{10}\right)\int_{0}^{5} 5\sin\left(\frac{2\pi}{10}\right)nt\,dt$$

$$= \left(\frac{2}{10}\right)\left(-\frac{10}{2\pi n}\right)5\cos\left(\frac{2\pi}{10}\right)nt\Big|_{t=0}^{5}$$

$$= \left(\frac{-5}{\pi n}\right)(\cos\pi n - 1)$$

$$\cos\pi n = (-1)^n$$

$$b_1 = \left(\frac{-5}{1\pi}\right)[(-1)^1 - 1] = \frac{10}{\pi}$$

$$b_2 = \left(\frac{-5}{2\pi}\right)[(-1)^2 - 1] = 0$$

$$b_3 = \left(\frac{-5}{3\pi}\right)[(-1)^3 - 1] = \frac{10}{3\pi}$$

$$b_4 = 0$$

$$b_5 = \frac{10}{5\pi}$$

$$b_7 = \frac{10}{7\pi}, \ \text{etc.}$$

$$v(t) = \frac{5}{2} + \frac{10}{\pi}\sin\left(\frac{\pi}{5}t\right) + \frac{10}{3\pi}\sin\left(\frac{3\pi}{5}t\right)$$

$$+ \frac{10}{5\pi}\sin\pi t + \cdots$$

$$= \boxed{\frac{5}{2} + \sum_{m=1}^{\infty}\frac{10}{(2m-1)\pi}\sin\frac{2m-1}{5}\pi t \ \text{V}}$$

20.

$$\mathcal{L}\left\{\frac{df}{dt}\right\} = sF(s) - f(0)$$

$$\mathcal{L}\left\{\frac{d^2f}{dt^2}\right\} = s^2 F(s) - sf(0) - \frac{df}{dt}(0)$$

$$\mathcal{L}\left\{\frac{d^2i}{dt^2}\right\} = s^2 I(s) - 0.5s - 50$$

$$\mathcal{L}\left\{\frac{di}{dt}\right\} = sI(s) - 0.5$$

$$\frac{0.02}{s} = \boxed{\begin{array}{l} 10^{-6}s^2 I - 0.5 \times 10^{-6}s - 50 \times 10^{-6} \\ +2 \times 10^{-4}sI - 10^{-4} + I \end{array}}$$

21. This is manipulated to obtain

$$I(s) = \boxed{(0.5)\left[\frac{s^2 + 300s + 4\times 10^4}{s(s^2 + 200s + 10^6)}\right] \ \text{A-s}}$$

22. $(0.5)\left[\dfrac{s^2 + 300s + 4\times 10^4}{s(s^2 + 200s + 10^6)}\right] = \dfrac{A}{s} + \dfrac{Bs + C}{s^2 + 200s + 10^6}$

Using cross multiplication,

$$s^2(A+B) + s(200A+C) + 10^6 A = 0.5s^2 + 150s + 2\times 10^4$$

$$A = 2\times 10^{-2}$$

$$200A + C = 150$$

$$C = 146$$

$$A + B = 0.5$$

$$B = 0.48$$

$$I(s) = \boxed{\frac{0.02}{s} + \frac{0.48s + 146}{s^2 + 200s + 10^6} \ \text{A-s}}$$

23.
$$b^2 - 4ac = 200^2 - 4 \times 10^6 < 0$$

The system is underdamped.

$$s^2 + 200s + 10^6 \rightarrow (s+100)^2 + (995)^2$$

$$0.48s + 146 \rightarrow (0.48)(s+100) + (995)(0.098)$$

This is done to form the terms

$$\mathcal{L}\left\{ e^{-at} \sin bt \right\} = \frac{b}{(s+a)^2 + b^2}$$

$$\mathcal{L}\left\{ e^{at} \cos bt \right\} = \frac{s+a}{(s+a)^2 + b^2}$$

$$I(s) = \frac{0.02}{s} + \frac{(0.48)(s+100)}{(s+100)^2 + (995)^2} + \frac{(0.098)(995)}{(s+100)^2 + (995)^2}$$

The inverse transform gives

$$i(t) = \boxed{\begin{array}{l} 0.02 + 0.48e^{-100t}\cos 995t \\ +0.098e^{-100t}\sin 995t \text{ A} \end{array}}$$

24. It is convenient to rewrite the expression.

$$f\left(\frac{pT}{2N}\right) = \sum_{k=0}^{7} e^{-jk\frac{\pi}{2}} e^{jkp\frac{\pi}{4}} = \sum_{k=0}^{7} e^{jk\frac{\pi}{2}\left(\frac{p}{2}-1\right)}$$

Beginning with $p = 0$,

$$f(0) = \sum_{k=0}^{7} e^{-j\frac{\pi}{2}k} = \sum_{k=0}^{7} (-j)^k$$

$$= 1 - j - 1 + j + 1 - j - 1 + j$$

$$= 0$$

At $p = 1$, with $N = 4$,

$$f\left(\frac{T}{8}\right) = \sum_{k=0}^{7} e^{jk\frac{\pi}{2}\left(\frac{1}{2}-1\right)} = \sum_{k=0}^{7} e^{-j\frac{\pi}{4}k}$$

$$= 1 + e^{-j\frac{\pi}{4}} + e^{-j\frac{\pi}{2}} + e^{-j\frac{3\pi}{4}} + e^{-j\pi}$$

$$+ e^{-j\frac{5\pi}{4}} + e^{-j\frac{6\pi}{4}} + e^{-j\frac{7\pi}{4}}$$

This can be viewed on the complex plane.

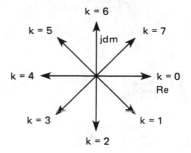

These components cancel each other.

$$f\left(\frac{T}{8}\right) = 0 \quad (p = 1)$$

At $p = 2$,

$$f\left(\frac{T}{4}\right) = \sum_{k=0}^{7} e^{jk\frac{\pi}{2}(1-1)} = \sum_{k=0}^{7} 1 = 8$$

At $p = 3$,

$$f\left(\frac{3T}{8}\right) = \sum_{k=0}^{7} e^{jk\frac{\pi}{2}\left(\frac{3}{2}-1\right)} = \sum_{k=0}^{7} e^{j\frac{k\pi}{4}}$$

This is the complex conjugate of $f\left(\frac{T}{8}\right)$, so it is also zero.

At $p = 4$,

$$f\left(\frac{T}{2}\right) = \sum_{k=0}^{7} e^{jk\frac{\pi}{2}\left(\frac{4}{2}-1\right)}$$

$$= \sum_{k=0}^{7} e^{jk\frac{\pi}{2}} = \sum_{k=0}^{7} (j)^k$$

$$= 1 + j - 1 - j + 1 + j - 1 - j = 0$$

At $p = 5$,

$$f\left(\frac{5T}{8}\right) = \sum_{k=0}^{7} e^{jk\frac{\pi}{2}\left(\frac{5}{2}-1\right)} = \sum_{k=0}^{7} e^{j\frac{3\pi}{4}k}$$

$$= 1 + e^{j\frac{3\pi}{4}} + e^{j\frac{3\pi}{2}} + e^{j\frac{9\pi}{4}} + e^{j3\pi}$$

$$+ e^{j\frac{15\pi}{4}} + e^{j\frac{9\pi}{2}} + e^{j\frac{21\pi}{4}}$$

This can also be viewed on the complex plane.

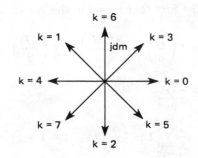

This cancels, so

$$f\left(\frac{5T}{8}\right) = 0$$

At $p = 6$,

$$f\left(\frac{3T}{4}\right) = \sum_{k=0}^{7} e^{jk\frac{\pi}{2}\left(\frac{6}{2}-1\right)}$$

$$= \sum_{k=0}^{7} e^{j\pi k} = \sum_{k=0}^{7} (-1)^k$$

$$= 1 - 1 + 1 - 1 + 1 - 1 + 1 - 1 = 0$$

At $p = 7$,

$$f\left(\frac{7T}{8}\right) = \sum_{k=0}^{7} e^{jk\frac{\pi}{2}\left(\frac{7}{2}-1\right)} = \sum_{k=0}^{7} e^{j\frac{5\pi}{4}k}$$

$$= \sum_{k=0}^{7} e^{-j\frac{3\pi}{4}k}$$

The result is the same as for $5T/8$.

$$f\left(\frac{7T}{8}\right) = 0$$

Then,

$$f\left(\frac{pT}{2n}\right) = \boxed{\left\{\begin{array}{ll} 8 & \text{for } p = 2 \\ 0 & \text{otherwise} \end{array}\right\}}$$

25.

p	0	1	2	3	4	5	6	7
$f\left(\frac{pT}{2N}\right)$	5	5	5	5	0	0	0	0

$$N = 4$$

$$C_k = \frac{1}{2N} \sum_{p=0}^{2N-1} f\left(\frac{pT}{2N}\right) e^{-j\frac{\pi kp}{N}}$$

$$f\left(\frac{4T}{8}\right) = f\left(\frac{5T}{8}\right) = f\left(\frac{6T}{8}\right) = f\left(\frac{7T}{8}\right) = 0$$

Keep only the first four terms in the summation.

$$f(0) = f\left(\frac{T}{8}\right) = f\left(\frac{2T}{8}\right) = f\left(\frac{3T}{8}\right) = 5$$

$$C_k = \frac{5}{8} \sum_{p=0}^{3} e^{-j\frac{\pi kp}{4}}$$

$$C_o = \frac{5}{8} \sum_{p=0}^{3} 1 = \left(\frac{5}{8}\right)(1 + 1 + 1 + 1) = 2.5$$

$$C_1 = \frac{5}{8} \sum_{p=0}^{3} e^{j\frac{\pi}{4}p}$$

$$= \left(\frac{5}{8}\right)\left(e^{-0} + e^{-j\frac{\pi}{4}} + e^{-j\frac{\pi}{2}} + e^{-j\frac{3\pi}{4}}\right)$$

$$= 1.633 e^{-j\frac{3\pi}{8}}$$

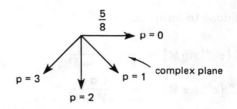

$$C_2 = \frac{5}{8} \sum_{p=0}^{3} e^{-j\frac{\pi}{2}p}$$

$$= \left(\frac{5}{8}\right)\left(e^{-0} + e^{-j\frac{\pi}{2}} + e^{-j\pi} + e^{-j\frac{3\pi}{2}}\right)$$

$$= 0$$

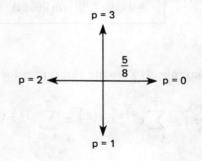

$$C_3 = \frac{5}{8} \sum_{p=0}^{3} e^{-j\frac{3\pi}{4}p}$$

$$= \left(\frac{5}{8}\right)\left(e^0 + e^{-j\frac{3\pi}{4}} + e^{-j\frac{3\pi}{2}} + e^{j\frac{9\pi}{4}}\right)$$

$$= 0.676 e^{-j\frac{\pi}{8}}$$

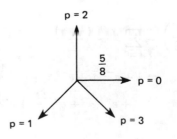

This is rewritten as

$$f\left(\frac{pT}{8}\right) = 2.5$$
$$+ (1.633)\left\{ e^{j\left(\frac{\pi}{4}p - \frac{3\pi}{8}\right)} + e^{-j\left(\frac{\pi}{4}p - \frac{3\pi}{8}\right)} \right\}$$
$$+ (0.676)\left\{ e^{j\left(\frac{3\pi}{4}p - \frac{\pi}{8}\right)} + e^{-j\left(\frac{3\pi}{4}p - \frac{\pi}{8}\right)} \right\}$$

$e^{jx} + e^{-jx} = 2\cos x$ obtains

$$\boxed{f\left(\frac{pT}{8}\right) = \begin{array}{l} 2.5 + 3.266\cos\left(\frac{\pi}{4}p - \frac{3\pi}{8}\right) \\[2mm] + 1.352\cos\left(\frac{3\pi}{4}p - \frac{\pi}{8}\right) \end{array}}$$

In Prob. 19,

$$\frac{a_0}{2} = 2.5$$
$$b_1 = \frac{10}{\pi} = 3.18 < 3.266$$
$$b_3 = \frac{10}{3\pi} = 1.06 < 1.352$$

> The discrete Fourier series exactly matches the values at the sampled points. The ordinary Fourier series converges on the values with an infinite number of terms. Thus, using only three terms of the ordinary Fourier series results in some error.

$$C_4 = \frac{5}{8}\sum_{p=0}^{3} e^{j\pi p}$$
$$= \left(\frac{5}{8}\right)(1 - 1 + 1 - 1) = 0$$
$$C_5 = \frac{5}{8}\sum_{p=0}^{3} e^{-j\frac{5\pi}{4}p}$$
$$= 0.676\, e^{j\frac{\pi}{8}}$$

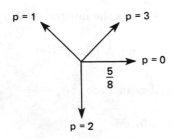

$$C_6 = \frac{5}{8}\sum_{p=0}^{3} e^{-j\frac{3\pi}{2}p}$$
$$= \left(\frac{5}{8}\right)(1 + j - 1 - j) = 0$$
$$C_7 = \frac{5}{8}\sum_{p=0}^{3} e^{-j\frac{7\pi}{4}p}$$
$$= 1.633\, e^{j\frac{3\pi}{8}}$$

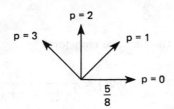

$$f\left(\frac{pT}{8}\right) = \sum_{k=0}^{7} C_k e^{j\frac{\pi}{4}kp}$$
$$= 2.5 + 1.633 e^{-j\frac{3\pi}{8}} e^{j\frac{\pi}{4}p} + 0.676 e^{-j\frac{\pi}{8}} e^{j\frac{3\pi}{4}p}$$
$$+ 0.676 e^{j\frac{\pi}{8}} e^{j\frac{5\pi}{4}p} + 1.633 e^{j\frac{3\pi}{8}} e^{j\frac{7\pi}{4}p}$$

but $e^{j\frac{5\pi}{4}p} = e^{-j\frac{3\pi}{4}p}$

and $e^{j\frac{7\pi}{4}p} = e^{-j\frac{\pi}{4}p}$

26. Brute force takes $(4096)^2 = (2N)^2$. FFT takes $2N(L+D)$ where $LD = 2N$ or $D = 2N/L$. The number is minimized.

$$\text{no. multiplied} = 2N\left(L + \frac{2N}{L}\right)$$
$$\frac{\partial}{\partial L}\left\{ 2N\left(L + \frac{2N}{L}\right) \right\} = 2N\left(1 - \frac{2N}{L^2}\right)$$

This is minimax at $L^2 = 2N$.

$$\frac{\partial^2}{\partial L^2}\left\{ 2N\left(L + \frac{2N}{L}\right) \right\} = (2N)^2\ \frac{2}{L^3} > 0$$

Minimum is at $L^2 = 2N$.

$$L = D = \sqrt{4096}$$

The ratio of multiples is

$$\frac{(4096)^2}{(4096)(2\sqrt{4096})} = \frac{\sqrt{4096}}{2} = 32$$

> The FFT will take no more than 1/32 the time of the brute force method.

27.

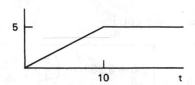

$$f(t) = 0.5u(t) - 0.5(t - 10)u(t - 10)$$

$$\int_{-\infty}^{\infty}(t - \tau)e^{-bt}u(t - \tau)dt$$

$$= e^{-b\tau}\int_{-\infty}^{\infty}(t - \tau)e^{-b(t-\tau)}u(t - \tau)d(t - \tau)$$

$$= e^{-b\tau}\int_{0}^{\infty}xe^{-bx}dx$$

$$\int xe^{-bx}dx = -\frac{bx + 1}{b^2}e^{-bx}$$

For this case, the Laplace and Fourier transforms differ only in b.

$$\text{Laplace:} \quad b \to s$$
$$\text{Fourier:} \quad b \to j\omega$$

The integrations are carried out using the dummy variable x.

$$\mathcal{L}\left\{f(t)\right\} \text{ or } F\left\{f(t)\right\}$$

$$\int_{A}^{\infty}0.5tu(t)e^{-bt}dt - \int_{A}^{\infty}(0.5)(t - 10)u(t - 10)e^{-bt}dt$$

$$= 0.5\int_{0}^{\infty}te^{-bt}dt - 0.5e^{-10b}\int_{0}^{\infty}xe^{-bx}dx$$

$$= (-0.5)\left(\frac{bt + 1}{b^2}\right)e^{-bt}\bigg|_{t=0}^{\infty}$$

$$+ (0.5e^{-10b})\left(\frac{bx + 1}{b^2}\right)e^{-bx}\bigg|_{x=0}^{\infty}$$

At the upper limit, the exponential term dominates to make that part zero. The result is then obtained substituting for b.

$$\mathcal{L}\left\{f(t)\right\} = \left(\frac{0.5}{s^2}\right)\left(1 - e^{-10s}\right)$$

$$F\left\{f(t)\right\} = \left[\frac{0.5}{(j\omega)^2}\right]\left(1 - e^{-j10\omega}\right)$$

$$= \left(-\frac{0.5}{\omega^2}\right)\left(1 - e^{-j10\omega}\right)$$

28. The transform of a pulse from $t = 0$ to τ is

$$\int_{-\infty}^{\infty}\{u(t) - u(t - \tau)\}e^{-bt}dt = \int_{0}^{\tau}e^{-bt}dt = \frac{1}{b}\left(1 - e^{-\tau b}\right)$$

(a) Laplace transform:

$$F(s) = 0.5\frac{1}{s}\left(1 - e^{-10s}\right)$$

Theorem:

$$\mathcal{L}\left\{\int_{0}^{t}f(t')dt'\right\} = \frac{1}{s}F(s)$$

For the finite ramp as the integral of this pulse,

$$0.5\frac{1}{s^2}\left(1 - e^{-10s}\right)$$

This is obtained as in Prob. 27.

(b) Fourier transform:

$$F(\omega) = 0.5\frac{1}{j\omega}\left(1 - e^{-j10\omega}\right)$$

Theorem:

$$F\left\{\int_{0}^{t}f(t')dt'\right\} = \frac{1}{j\omega}F(\omega)$$

Taking the finite ramp as the integral of this pulse, obtain as in Prob. 27,

$$\boxed{\frac{0.5}{(j\omega)^2}(1 - e^{-j10\omega})}$$

29. $h(t)$ has the Laplace transform

$$\mathcal{L}\left\{e^{-0.2t}\sin 0.2t\right\} = \frac{0.2}{(s + 0.2)^2 + (0.2)^2}$$

This is its transfer function.

The output $G(s)$ is the product of the transformed input and the transfer function.

$$G(s) = \left(\frac{0.5}{s^2}\right)\left(1 - e^{-10s}\right)\left[\frac{0.2}{(s + 0.2)^2 + (0.2)^2}\right]$$

This is expanded in partial fractions.

$$G(s) = (1 - e^{-10s})\left[\frac{A}{s} + \frac{B}{s^2} + \frac{Cs + D}{(s + 0.2)^2 + (0.2)^2}\right]$$

By cross multiplication, $A, B, C,$ and D are found.

$$A = -6.25$$
$$B = 1.25$$
$$C = 6.25$$
$$D = 1.25$$

This provides

$$G(s) = \left(\frac{1 - e^{-10s}}{0.16}\right)\left[-\frac{1}{s} + \frac{0.2}{s^2} + \frac{s + 0.2}{(s + 0.2)^2 + (0.2)^2}\right]$$

The time response is then found.

$$g(t) = \left|\begin{array}{l}[6.25u(t)](0.2t - 1 + e^{-0.2t}\cos 0.2t) \\ \quad - 6.25u(t - 10)[(0.2)(t - 10) - 1 \\ \quad + e^{(0.2)(t-10)}\cos(0.2(t - 10))]\end{array}\right|$$

30. It is necessary to find the transform of $e^{-0.2t} \times \sin 0.2t$. From the fundamental Fourier transformation identities table,

$$e^{jat}f(t) \longleftrightarrow F(\omega - a)$$

From Euler's equation,

$$\sin at = \frac{e^{jat} - e^{-jat}}{2j}$$

$$f(t)\sin at \longleftrightarrow \frac{1}{2j}[F(\omega - a) - F(\omega + a)]$$

From the Fourier transform pairs table,

$$F\{u(t)e^{at}\} = \frac{1}{j\omega + a}$$

By substituting into the derived transform,

$$F\{u(t)e^{-at}\sin at\} = \frac{1}{2j}\left[\frac{1}{j(\omega - a) + a} - \frac{1}{j(\omega + a) + a}\right]$$

$$= \frac{a}{(j\omega + a)^2 + a^2}$$

This is the Fourier transfer function. From Prob. 28(b), the output is

$$G(\omega) = \left[\frac{0.5}{(j\omega)^2}\right]\left(1 - e^{-j10\omega}\right)\left[\frac{0.2}{(j\omega + 0.2)^2 + (0.2)^2}\right]$$

This is expanded by partial fractions to give

$$G(\omega) = \frac{(1 - e^{-j10\omega})}{0.16}$$

$$\times \left[-\frac{1}{j\omega} + \frac{0.2}{(j\omega)^2} + \frac{j\omega + 0.2}{(j\omega + 0.2)^2 + (0.2)^2}\right]$$

From the Fourier transform pairs and fundamental Fourier transformation identities tables,

$$F\{u(t)e^{-at}\cos bt\} = \frac{j\omega + a}{(j\omega + a)^2 + b^2}$$

The result is as in Prob. 29.

$$g(t) = \left|\begin{array}{l}[6.25u(t)][0.2t - 1 + e^{-0.2t}\cos 0.2t] \\ \quad - 6.25u(t - 10)[(0.2)(t - 10) - 1 \\ \quad + e^{(0.2)(t-10)}\cos(0.2(t - 10))]\end{array}\right|$$

LINEAR CIRCUIT ANALYSIS

Warmup 1

$$\rho_{20} = 1.08 \times 10^{-6} \ \Omega \cdot m$$
$$\alpha_{20} = 0.017/°C$$
$$\text{(i.e. per degree C)}$$

$A = 5.07 \times 10^{-8} \ m^2$ (from Ex. 2.1)

At 100°C,

$$\rho_{100} = (1.08 \times 10^{-6}) \ [1 + 0.017(100 - 20)]$$
$$= 2.549 \times 10^{-6} \ \Omega \cdot m$$

$$R_{100} = 1 \ \Omega = \frac{\rho_{100} l}{A}$$

$$l = \frac{5.07 \times 10^{-8} \ \Omega \cdot m^2}{2.55 \times 10^{-6} \ \Omega \cdot m} = \boxed{0.0199 \ m}$$

$$R_{20} = \left(\frac{\rho_{20}}{\rho_{100}}\right)(1) = \frac{1.08 \ \Omega^2 \cdot m}{2.55 \ \Omega \cdot m} = \boxed{0.424 \ \Omega}$$

Warmup 2

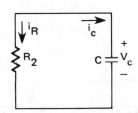

As the switch was closed for a long time, the capacitor was charged to

$$v_C = \frac{R_2}{R_1 + R_2} V_s = V_C(0^+)$$

(a) When the switch is opened, the voltage causes

$$t = 0^+ : i_R = \frac{v_C}{R_2} = \frac{V_s}{R_1 + R_2}$$

But that is $-i_C$, so

$$i_C = \boxed{-\frac{V_s}{R_1 + R_2}} \ \text{(at } t = 0^+)$$

(b)
$$i_C = C\frac{dv_C}{dt}$$
$$\frac{dv_C}{dt} = \frac{i_C}{C}$$

$$\left.\frac{dv_C}{dt}\right|_{t=0^+} = \boxed{-\frac{V_s}{C(R_1 + R_2)}}$$

(c) After a long time, the capacitor will discharge through R_2, so

$$v_C(\infty) = \boxed{0}$$

Warmup 3

At $t = 0$, the current is V_s/R_1. This does not change instantaneously.

(a) $i_L(0^+) = \boxed{\dfrac{V_s}{R_1} \ A}$

(b)
$$v_L = L\frac{di_L}{dt} = -R_2 i_L$$

$$\frac{di_L}{dt}(0^+) = \boxed{-\left(\frac{R_2}{L}\right)\left(\frac{V_s}{R_1}\right) \ A/s}$$

(c) $v_L(0^+) = \boxed{-\dfrac{R_2}{R_1} V_s \ V}$

Warmup 4

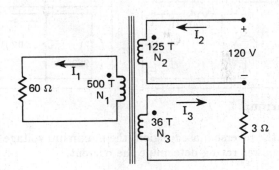

$$\frac{V}{N} = \frac{120 \ V}{125} = \frac{V_1}{500} = \frac{V_3}{36}$$
$$V_1 = 480 \ V$$
$$V_3 = 34.6 \ V$$
$$N_1 I_1 + N_3 I_3 = N_2 I_2$$

$$I_2 = \left(\frac{500}{125}\right)\left(\frac{480 \ V}{60 \ \Omega}\right) + \left(\frac{36}{125}\right)\left(\frac{34.6 \ V}{3 \ \Omega}\right) = 35.3 \ A$$

$$I_1 = \frac{480 \ V}{60} = 8 \ A$$

$$I_3 = \frac{34.6 \ V}{3 \ \Omega} = 11.5 \ A$$

Current ratings must exceed these values.

PROFESSIONAL PUBLICATIONS, INC. ● Belmont, CA

Warmup 5

The voltage at $i = 0$ is 10 V, and at $i = 6$ A it appears to be 9.1 V. Using the two-point formula for a line,

$$\frac{v - 10\text{ V}}{i - 0\text{ A}} = \frac{9.1\text{ V} - 10\text{ V}}{6\text{ A} - 0\text{ A}} : 6v - 60\text{ V} = (-0.9\ \Omega)i$$

$$v = 10\text{ V} - 0.15i \qquad\qquad i = 66.7\text{ A} - \frac{v}{0.15}$$

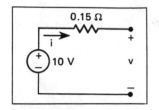
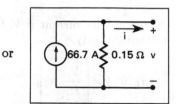

or

Warmup 6

A 1% reduction of 5 V is 0.05 V. The source has 5.05 V at no current, and 5.0 V at 25 A. The two-point line equation is

$$\frac{5.05\text{ V} - 5.0\text{ V}}{0 - 25\text{ A}} = \frac{5.05\text{ V} - v}{0 - i}$$

Thevenin		Norton
$v = 5.05\text{ V} - 0.002\ \Omega\,i$		$i = 2525\text{ A} - \dfrac{v}{0.002\ \Omega}$

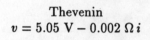
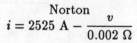

or

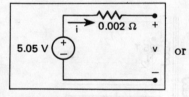
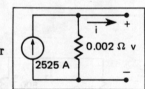

Warmup 7

For the reverse biased region, the maximum voltage and the power rating determine the current.

$$I_{\text{rev-max}} = \frac{2\text{ W}}{-5.6\text{ V}}$$

Two points (v, i) are $(-5.6\text{ V}, -2/5.6\text{ A})$ and $(-5.5\text{ V}, 0\text{ A})$.

Using the two-point line formula,

$$\frac{-5.6\text{ V} - (-5.5\text{ V})}{\left(\dfrac{-2\text{ A}}{5.6} - 0\text{ A}\right)} = \frac{v - (-5.5\text{ V})}{i - 0\text{ A}}$$

Solving for v, $v < -5.5$ V.

$$v = -5.5\text{ V} + (0.28\ \Omega)i$$

In the range $-5.5\text{ V} < v < 0.6\text{ V}$, $i = 0$ A.

For $v > 0.6$ V, diodes have rated current at a voltage of 1.4 V.

Using the two-point line formula,

$$\frac{1.4\text{ V} - 0.6\text{ V}}{1\text{ A} - 0\text{ A}} = \frac{v - 0.6\text{ V}}{i - 0\text{ A}}$$

$$v = 0.6\text{ V} + (0.8\ \Omega)i$$

Using ideal diodes, a complete equivalent circuit is formed.

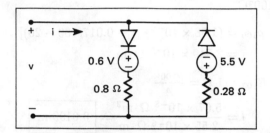

Warmup 8

The equations are in the form of z-parameters.

$$z_{11} = 250\ \Omega$$
$$z_{21} = -100\ \Omega$$
$$z_{12} = 5\ \Omega$$
$$z_{22} = 25\ \Omega$$

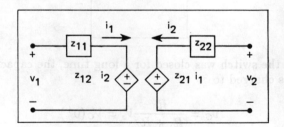

Warmup 9

$$v_{eb} = i_e(r_e + r_b) + i_c r_b$$
$$v_{cb} = (i_c + \alpha i_e)r_c + (i_c + i_e)r_b$$
$$\quad\;\; = i_e(\alpha r_c + r_b) + i_c(r_c + r_b)$$

Put in matrix form,

$$\begin{bmatrix} v_{eb} \\ v_{cb} \end{bmatrix} = \begin{bmatrix} r_e + r_b & r_b \\ \alpha r_c + r_b & r_b + r_c \end{bmatrix} \times \begin{bmatrix} i_e \\ i_c \end{bmatrix}$$

Inverting,

$$\begin{bmatrix} i_e \\ i_c \end{bmatrix} = \begin{bmatrix} y_{ib} & y_{rb} \\ y_{fb} & y_{ob} \end{bmatrix} \times \begin{bmatrix} v_{eb} \\ v_{cb} \end{bmatrix}$$

The determinant of the coefficient matrix is

$$\Delta = \begin{vmatrix} r_e + r_b & r_b \\ \alpha r_c + r_b & r_c + r_b \end{vmatrix} = \left\{ \begin{array}{c} r_e(r_c + r_b) \\ + r_b r_c (1-\alpha) \end{array} \right\}$$

Using Cramer's rule for i_e,

$$\Delta i_e = \begin{vmatrix} v_{eb} & r_b \\ v_{cb} & r_b + r_c \end{vmatrix} = \left\{ \begin{array}{c} (r_b + r_c)v_{eb} \\ -r_b v_{cb} \end{array} \right\}$$

$$y_{ib} = \frac{r_b + r_e}{\Delta} = \boxed{\frac{1}{re + \dfrac{r_b r_c}{r_b + r_c}(1-\alpha)}\ \text{S}}$$

$$y_{rb} = \frac{-r_b}{\Delta} = \boxed{\frac{-1}{r_e\left(1 + \dfrac{r_c}{r_b}\right) + r_c(1-\alpha)}\ \text{S}}$$

Finding i_c,

$$\Delta i_c = \begin{vmatrix} r_e + r_b & v_{eb} \\ \alpha r_c + r_b & v_{cb} \end{vmatrix} = \left\{ \begin{array}{c} -(\alpha r_c + r_b)v_{eb} \\ +(r_e + r_b)v_{cb} \end{array} \right\}$$

$$y_{fb} = \boxed{\frac{-(\alpha r_c + r_b)}{r_e(r_c + r_b) + r_c r_b(1-\alpha)}\ \text{S}}$$

$$y_{ob} = \boxed{\frac{r_e + r_b}{r_e(r_c + r_b) + r_c r_b(1-\alpha)}\ \text{S}}$$

Warmup 10

From Ex. 2.11, the photodiode current was

$$i = 0.7\ \mu\text{A} + (0.0192\ \mu\text{A})I_L$$

I_L is in footcandles.

The photodiode is in a circuit with a 5-V source and 10kΩ resistance.

$$v = 5\ \text{V} - (10\ \text{k}\Omega)i$$

The output is taken across the 10kΩ resistor.

$$v_{\text{out}} = (10^4\ \Omega)i$$

$$= \boxed{(10^{-2}\ \frac{\text{V}}{\mu\text{A}})\left[0.7\ \mu\text{A} + \left(0.0192\ \frac{\mu\text{A}}{\text{f.c.}}\right)I_L\right]\ \text{V}}$$

The output voltage is limited to range from 0 V to 5 V.

$$0 \le \left(10^{-2}\frac{\text{V}}{\mu\text{A}}\right)\left[0.7\ \mu\text{A} + \left(0.0192\ \frac{\mu\text{A}}{\text{f.c.}}\right)I_L\right] \le 5\ \text{V}$$

The maximum I_L is

$$I_{L,\max} = \frac{(500)\left(V \times \dfrac{\mu\text{A}}{\text{V}}\right) - 0.7\ \mu\text{A}}{\left(0.0192\ \dfrac{\mu\text{A}}{\text{f.c.}}\right)} = 26{,}005\ \text{f.c.}$$

Its range is $\boxed{0 \le I_L \le 26\ \text{kf.c.}}$

Warmup 11

$$\frac{V_{\text{out}} - 0.95\ \text{V}}{T - 0^\circ\text{C}} = \frac{0.6\ \text{V} - 0.95\ \text{V}}{100\ \text{V} - 0^\circ\text{C}} = -0.0035\ \text{V}/^\circ\text{C}$$

$$V_{\text{out}} = 0.95\ \text{V} - \left(0.0035\ \frac{\text{V}}{^\circ\text{C}}\right)T$$

$$v_f = V_{\text{out}} + (0.3\ \Omega)i_f$$

$$v_f = \boxed{0.95\ \text{V} - (0.0035\ \text{V}/^\circ\text{C})T + (0.3\ \Omega)i_f}$$

Warmup 12

$$v_y = \frac{I_x B_Z}{wqn}$$

$$= \frac{0.1 B_Z}{(5\times 10^{-3}\ \text{m})(1.6\times 10^{-19}\ \text{C}/e)(10^{19}\ (e/\text{m}^3))}$$

$$= (12.5\ \text{V/T})B_Z$$

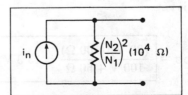

Warmup 13

From Ex. 2.20,

$$v_{\text{Th}} = \left(\frac{1000}{3}\right)\left(\frac{N_2}{N_1}\right)v_{\text{in}}$$

$$Z_{\text{Th}} = (10^4\ \Omega)\left(\frac{N_2}{N_1}\right)^2 = Z_n$$

$$i_n = \frac{v_{\text{Th}}}{Z_{\text{Th}}} = \frac{\left(\dfrac{1000}{3}\right)\left(\dfrac{N_2}{N_1}\right)v_{\text{in}}}{(10^4\ \Omega)\left(\dfrac{N_2}{N_1}\right)^2}$$

$$= \left(\frac{1}{30\ \Omega}\right)\left(\frac{N_1}{N_2}\right)v_{\text{in}}$$

Warmup 14

$$R_L \to Z_{Th}^* = 8\ \Omega$$

$$R_L = \left(\frac{N_2}{N_1}\right)^2 (10^4\ \Omega) = 8\ \Omega$$

$$\left(\frac{N_1}{N_2}\right)^2 = \boxed{1250 = (35.35)^2}$$

Warmup 15

From Ex. 2.22 with $Z_1 = jX_1$ and $Z_2 = jX_2$,

$$V_{Th} = \frac{jX_2}{50\ \Omega + j(X_1 + X_2)} V_s$$

$$Z_{Th} = \frac{jX_2(50 + jX_1)}{50\ \Omega + j(X_1 + X_2)}$$

$$X_1 = 0.2\omega$$

$$X_2 = -\frac{10^6}{\omega}$$

For DC,

$$\omega = 0$$
$$X_1 \to 0$$
$$X_2 \to -\infty$$

$$V_{Th}\Big|_{\omega=0} = \frac{-j\infty V_{DC}}{50\ \Omega + j(0 - \infty)} = 20\ \text{V}$$

$$Z_{Th}\Big|_{\omega=0} = \frac{-j\infty(50 + j0)}{50\ \Omega + j(0 - \infty)} = 50\ \Omega$$

$$\omega = 2236\ \text{rad/s}$$
$$X_1 = 447.2\ \Omega$$
$$X_2 = -447.2\ \Omega$$

$$V_{Th} = \left(\frac{-j447.2\ \Omega}{50\ \Omega}\right) V_\omega$$

$$Z_{Th} = \frac{(-j\,447.2\ \Omega)(50\ \Omega + j447.2\ \Omega)}{50\ \Omega}$$

$$= 4000\ \Omega - j447.2\ \Omega$$

$$v_s = 20\ \text{V} + 5\cos 2236t\,\Omega$$

DC voltage is

$$V_{DC} = \boxed{\frac{(20\ \text{V})((100\ \Omega)}{100\ \text{V} + 50\ \Omega} = 13.3\ \text{V}}$$

Phasor voltage is

$$V_{AC} = (5\ \text{V})\left(\frac{-j447.2\ \Omega}{50\ \Omega}\right)\left(\frac{100\ \Omega}{100\ \Omega + Z_{Th}}\right)$$

$$= \frac{-j4472}{4100 - j447.2} = 1.08\underline{/-83.8°}\ \text{V}$$

$$v_{100} = \boxed{13.3\ \text{V} + 1.08\cos(2236t - 83.8°)\ \text{V}}$$

Warmup 16

$$r_b + R_e = 210\ \Omega$$
$$-\beta r_c + r_e \to -1.25 \times 10^5\ \Omega$$
$$r_c + R_e = 2510\ \Omega$$
$$i_2 = -10^{-3} v_{out}$$

(a) $v_{in} = (210\ \Omega)i_1 + (10)(-10^{-3} v_{out})$

(b) $v_{out} = -(1.25 \times 10^5\ \Omega)\,i_1 + (2510)(-10^{-3} v_{out})$

from (b) $i_1 = (-2.808\ \text{S})(10^{-5} v_{out})$

into (a) $v_{in} = -1.59 \times 10^{-2} v_{out}$

$$\frac{v_{out}}{v_{in}} = \boxed{-62.9}$$

Warmup 17

The upper circuit is

$$i_{in} = \frac{v_{in} - v_{out}}{R_f} = -i_{out}$$

$$\begin{bmatrix} i_{in,1} \\ i_{out,1} \end{bmatrix} = \begin{bmatrix} \dfrac{1}{R_f} & -\dfrac{1}{R_f} \\ -\dfrac{1}{R_f} & \dfrac{1}{R_f} \end{bmatrix} \times \begin{bmatrix} v_{in} \\ v_{out} \end{bmatrix}$$

The lower circuit is

$$i_{in} = \frac{1}{r_b} v_{in}$$

$$i_{out} = g_m v_{in} + \frac{1}{rc} v_{out}$$

$$\begin{bmatrix} i_{in,2} \\ i_{out,2} \end{bmatrix} = \begin{bmatrix} \dfrac{1}{r_b} & 0 \\ g_m & \dfrac{1}{r_c} \end{bmatrix} \times \begin{bmatrix} v_{in} \\ v_{out} \end{bmatrix}$$

The total currents are sums.

$$\begin{bmatrix} i_{in} \\ i_{out} \end{bmatrix} = \begin{bmatrix} i_{in,1} \\ i_{out,1} \end{bmatrix} + \begin{bmatrix} i_{in,2} \\ i_{out,2} \end{bmatrix}$$

$$\begin{bmatrix} i_{in} \\ i_{out} \end{bmatrix} = \boxed{\begin{bmatrix} \dfrac{1}{R_f} + \dfrac{1}{r_b} & -\dfrac{1}{R_f} \\ g_m - \dfrac{1}{R_f} & \dfrac{1}{R_f} + \dfrac{1}{r_c} \end{bmatrix} \times \begin{bmatrix} v_{in} \\ v_{out} \end{bmatrix}}$$

Concentrate 1

From the 100-Ω load, the Thevenin impedance is

$$Z_{\text{Th}} = \frac{Z_2(50\ \Omega + Z_1)}{50\ \Omega + Z_1 + Z_2}$$

For maximum power transfer, $Z_{\text{Th}} = Z_L^* = 100\ \Omega$. Z_1 and Z_2 should be reactive. Let $Z_1 = jX_1$ and $Z_2 = jX_2$. Substituting into Z_{Th},

$$100\ \Omega = \frac{jX_2(50\ \Omega + jX_1)}{50\ \Omega + j(X_1 + X_2)}$$
$$5000 + j100(X_1 + X_2) = -X_1X_2 + j50X_2$$

Equating real parts,

$$X_1X_2 = -5000$$

Equating imaginary parts,

$$100X_1 + 100X_2 = 50X_2$$
$$X_2 = -2X_1$$
$$-2X_1^2 = -5000\ \Omega$$
$$X_1 = \pm 50\ \Omega$$
$$X_2 = \mp 100\ \Omega$$

(a) $X_1 = +50\ \Omega$
$X_2 = -100\ \Omega$
$2000\,L_1 = 50\ \Omega$

$$L_1 = \boxed{25\ \text{mH}}$$

$$\frac{1}{2000\,C_2} = 100\ \Omega$$

$$C_2 = \boxed{5\ \mu\text{F}}$$

(b) $X_1 = -50\ \Omega$
$X_2 = 100\ \Omega$

$$\frac{1}{2000\,C_1} = 50\ \Omega$$

$$C_1 = \boxed{10\ \mu\text{F}}$$

$$2000\,L_2 = 100\ \Omega$$

$$L_2 = \boxed{50\ \text{mH}}$$

Concentrate 2

$$i_1 = \left(\frac{1\ \text{V}}{500\ \Omega}\right)(v_4 - v_3) = (0.002\ \text{S})(v_4 - v_3)$$
$$i_2 = \frac{v_3}{500\ \Omega} = (0.002\ \text{S})v_3$$

KCL at node 1,

$$v_1\left(\frac{1}{1000\ \Omega} + \frac{1}{1000\ \Omega}\right) - v_3\left(\frac{1}{1000\ \Omega}\right) = -50i_1$$

$$0.002v_1 - 0.001v_3 = (-0.1)(v_4 - v_3)$$
$$2v_1 - 101v_3 + 100v_4 = 0$$

KCL at node 2,

$$v_2\left(\frac{1}{1000\ \Omega} + \frac{1}{1000\ \Omega}\right) - v_3\left(\frac{1}{1000\ \Omega}\right) = 50i_2$$

$$0.002v_2 - 0.001v_3 = 0.1v_3$$
$$2v_2 - 101v_3 = 0$$

KCL at node 3,

$$-\frac{v_1}{1000\ \Omega} - \frac{v_2}{1000\ \Omega} - \frac{v_4}{500\ \Omega}$$
$$+ v_3\left[(2)\left(\frac{1}{500\ \Omega}\right) + (3)\left(\frac{1}{1000\ \Omega}\right)\right]$$
$$= (50)(i_1 - i_2) = (0.1)(v_4 - v_3) - 0.1v_3$$
$$= 0.1v_4 - 0.2v_3$$

$$-v_1 - v_2 + 207v_3 - 102v_4 = 0$$

KCL at node 4,

$$v_4\left(\frac{1}{50\ \Omega} + \frac{1}{50\ \Omega} + \frac{1}{500\ \Omega}\right) - v_3\frac{1}{500\ \Omega} = \frac{v_s}{50\ \Omega}$$
$$10v_s = -v_3 + 21v_4$$

The matrix equation is

$$\begin{bmatrix} 0 \\ 0 \\ 0 \\ 10v_s \end{bmatrix} = \begin{bmatrix} 2 & 0 & -101 & 100 \\ 0 & 2 & -101 & 0 \\ -1 & -1 & 207 & -102 \\ 0 & 0 & -1 & 21 \end{bmatrix} \times \begin{bmatrix} v_1 \\ v_2 \\ v_3 \\ v_4 \end{bmatrix}$$

From the node 2 equation,

$$v_3 = \frac{2}{101}v_2$$

From the node 4 equation,

$$v_4 = \frac{10v_s + v_3}{21} = \frac{10}{21}v_s + \frac{2}{2121}v_2$$

PROFESSIONAL PUBLICATIONS, INC. ● Belmont, CA

Substituting into the node 1 equation,

$$2v_1 - \frac{4042}{2121}v_2 = -\frac{1000}{21}v_s$$

Substituting into the node 3 equation,

$$-v_1 + \frac{6369}{2121}v_2 = \frac{1020}{21}v_2$$

Rationalizing,

$$2121v_1 - 2021v_2 = -50,500v_s$$
$$-2121v_1 + 6369v_2 = 103,020v_s$$

Adding,

$$v_2 = \frac{52,520}{4348}v_s$$

Substituting,

$$v_1 = -\frac{53,480}{4348}v_s$$
$$v_1 - v_2 = -24.4v_s$$
$$A = \boxed{-24.4}$$

Concentrate 3

Note: $i_1 = 2\text{ V}/300\text{ }\Omega = (2/300)$ A. Reflect the 200-Ω load to the transformer's primary winding.

$$R'_L + \left(\frac{4}{1}\right)^2 (200\text{ }\Omega) = 3200\text{ }\Omega$$

The $50\,i_1$ current source divides, so

$$i'_L = \left(\frac{1000\text{ }\Omega}{R'_L + 1000\text{ }\Omega + 200\text{ }\Omega}\right) 50\,i_1 = \frac{50}{4.4}i_1$$
$$1i_L = 4\,i'_L$$
$$i_L = \frac{50}{1.1}i_1 = \left(\frac{50}{1.1}\right)\left(\frac{2}{300}\text{ A}\right)$$
$$i_L = \boxed{\frac{1}{3.3}}\text{ A}$$

Concentrate 4

$$\text{Let } Z_s = R + jX \qquad \text{(Thevenin}$$
$$\text{note } V_s\big|_{\text{o.c.}} = 120\text{ V} \qquad \text{equivalent)}$$
$$V_L = V_s\frac{Z_L}{Z_L + R + jX}$$

Only magnitude is measured.

With $Z_L = 60\text{ }\Omega$,

$$72\text{ V} = (120\text{ V})\left(\frac{60\text{ }\Omega}{|60\text{ }\Omega + R + jX|}\right)$$
$$(60\text{ }\Omega + R)^2 + X^2 = 10^4\text{ }\Omega^2$$

With $Z_L = j60\text{ }\Omega$,

$$51.43\text{ V} = (120\text{ V})\left(\frac{60\text{ }\Omega}{|R + j(X + 60\text{ }\Omega)|}\right)$$
$$R^2 + (X + 60\text{ }\Omega)^2 = 1.96 \times 10^4\text{ }\Omega^2$$

With $Z_L = -j60\text{ }\Omega$,

$$360\text{ V} = (120\text{ V})\left(\frac{60\text{ }\Omega}{|R + j(X - 60\text{ }\Omega)|}\right)$$
$$R^2 + (X - 60\text{ }\Omega)^2 = 400\text{ }\Omega^2$$

The last two equations are expanded.

$$R^2 + X^2 + 120X + 3600 = 1.96 \times 10^4\text{ }\Omega^2$$
$$R^2 + X^2 - 120X + 3600 = 400\text{ }\Omega^2$$
$$X = 80\text{ }\Omega$$

Substituting into the last unexpanded equation,

$$R^2 + (80\text{ }\Omega - 60\text{ }\Omega)^2 = 400\text{ }\Omega^2$$

R is negligible. For $Z_L = -j120\text{ }\Omega$,

$$|V| = (120\text{ V})\left|\frac{-j120\text{ }\Omega}{j80\text{ }\Omega - j120\text{ }\Omega}\right|$$

$$\text{or } |V| = \boxed{360\text{ }V_{\text{RMS}}}$$

Concentrate 5

$$R_2 = (1.5\text{ k}\Omega) \quad (\text{ at } 25°\text{C})$$
$$R_1 = (1.5\text{ k}\Omega)\left[1 - \left(\frac{0.04}{°\text{C}}\right)(T - 25°\text{C})\right]$$
$$R_1 = 1.8\text{ k}\Omega \quad (\text{at } 20°\text{C})$$
$$R_1 = 1.2\text{ k}\Omega \quad (\text{at } 30°\text{C})$$

The meter sees a Thevenin source of

$$v_{\text{Th}} = \left(\frac{1\text{ k}\Omega}{R_1 + 1\text{ k}\Omega}\right)(24\text{ V}) \quad \left(\frac{1\text{ k}\Omega}{R_2 + 1\text{ k}\Omega}\right)(24\text{ V})$$

At 20°C,

$$v_{\text{Th}} = \left(\frac{1}{2.8} - \frac{1}{2.5}\right)(24\text{ V}) = -1.029\text{ V}$$

At 30°C,

$$v_{\text{Th}} = \left(\frac{1}{2.2} - \frac{1}{2.5}\right)(24 \text{ V}) = 1.309 \text{ V}$$

To find the Thevenin impedance, the 24-V source is shorted. The meter then sees R_1 in parallel with 1 kΩ on the left, and R_2 in parallel with 1 kΩ on the right. These two parallel combinations add in series to give the Thevenin impedance.

$$Z_{\text{Th}} = \frac{(1 \text{ k}\Omega)R_1}{1 \text{ k}\Omega + R_1} + \frac{(1 \text{ k}\Omega)R_2}{1 \text{ k}\Omega + R_2}$$

At 20°C,

$$Z_{\text{Th}} = \frac{1.8 \text{ k}\Omega}{2.8} + \frac{1.5 \text{ k}\Omega}{2.5} = 1.243 \text{ k}\Omega$$

At 30°C,

$$Z_{\text{Th}} = \frac{1.2 \text{ k}\Omega}{2.2} + \frac{1.5 \text{ k}\Omega}{2.5} = 1.145 \text{ k}\Omega$$

The meter current (positive to the right) will be

$$i_{\text{meter}} = \frac{v_{\text{Th}}}{Z_{\text{Th}} + 800 \ \Omega}$$

(a) At 20°C,

$$i_{\text{meter}} = \frac{-1.029 \text{ V}}{1243 \ \Omega + 800 \ \Omega} = \boxed{-0.504 \text{ mA}}$$

(b) At 30°C,

$$i_{\text{meter}} = \frac{1.309 \text{ V}}{1145 \ \Omega + 800 \ \Omega} = \boxed{+0.673 \text{ mA}}$$

Concentrate 6

The Thevenin equivalent to the left of the 1-mH inductor is

$$V_{\text{oc}} = 5000 KE = V_{\text{Th}}$$
$$I_{\text{sc}} = \frac{KE}{2}$$
$$R_{\text{Th}} = \frac{V_{\text{oc}}}{I_{\text{sc}}} = 10,000 \ \Omega$$

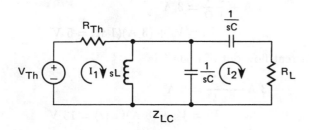

Lumping $sL \| 1/sC$ into a single impedance,

$$Z_{LC} = \frac{sL\dfrac{1}{sC}}{sL + \dfrac{1}{sC}} = \frac{sL}{s^2 LC + 1}$$

The loop equations are

$$V_{\text{Th}} = (R_{\text{Th}} + Z_{LC})I_1 - Z_{LC}I_2$$
$$0 = -Z_{LC}I_1 + \left(Z_{LC} + \frac{1}{sC} + R_L\right)I_2$$

Using Cramer's Rule,

$$I_2 = \frac{V_{\text{Th}}}{\dfrac{1}{sC} + R_{\text{Th}} + R_L + \dfrac{R_{\text{Th}}}{Z_{LC}}\left(\dfrac{1}{sC} + R_L\right)}$$

$$E_0 = R_L I_2$$

$$= \frac{s^2 R_L \dfrac{V_{\text{Th}}}{R_{\text{Th}}}}{s^3 CR_L + s^2\left(2 + \dfrac{R_L}{R_{\text{Th}}}\right) + s\left(\dfrac{R_L}{L} + \dfrac{1}{CR_{\text{Th}}}\right) + \dfrac{1}{LC}}$$

Substituting values,

$$E_0 = \frac{200\,KEs^2}{(4 \times 10^{-7}s^3) + 2.04s^2 + (5 \times 10^5 s) + (10)^{12}}$$

This makes $E_0 = E$, with $s \rightarrow j\omega$.

$$-200\,K\omega^2 = (-j4 \times 10^{-7}\omega^3) - (2.04\omega^2 + j5 \times 10^5\omega) + (10)^{12}$$

The imaginary part must vanish.

$$(-4 \times 10^{-7}\omega^3) + (5 \times 10^5\omega) = 0$$
$$\omega^2 = 1.25 \times (10)^{12}$$
$$-200\,K\omega^2 = -2.04\omega^2 + (10)^{12}$$

$$K = \frac{2.04}{200} - \frac{(10)^{12}}{200\omega^2} = \frac{2.04}{200} - \frac{1}{(200)(1.25)}$$

$$= \boxed{0.0062}$$

$$\omega = \sqrt{1.25} \times 10^6$$

$$= \boxed{1.12 \times 10^6 \text{ rad/s}}$$

Concentrate 7

Initially the transformer appeared as

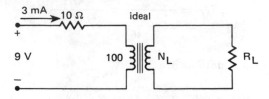

The input impedance is

$$\frac{9 \text{ V}}{3 \text{ mA}} = 3 \text{ k}\Omega$$

$$= 10 \ \Omega + \left(\frac{100}{N_L}\right)^2 R_L$$

$$\frac{R_L}{N_L^2} = \frac{2990 \ \Omega}{10^4} = 0.299 \ \Omega$$

When the short occurs, assuming n turns are shorted out, the transformer circuit has an added tertiary winding of n turns. The load resistance of this winding is

$$R_t = \left(\frac{10 \ \Omega}{100 \ T}\right) n = \frac{n}{10} \ \Omega$$

Likewise, the primary winding has been reduced by n turns, and its resistance decreased by $n/10$.

The new circuit is

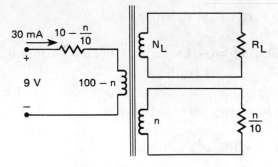

The 100-n turn primary sees two parallel loads.

$$\left(\frac{100 - n}{N_L}\right)^2 R_L$$

$$\left(\frac{100 - n}{n}\right)^2 \left(\frac{n}{10}\right)$$

When combined in parallel, these are

$$R_p = \frac{(0.299 \ \Omega)(100 - n)^2}{1 + 2.99n}$$

The total input impedance is

$$\frac{9 \text{ V}}{30 \text{ mA}} = 10 \ \Omega - \frac{n}{10} \ \Omega + \frac{(0.299 \ \Omega)(100 - n)^2}{1 + 2.99n}$$

From this, $n = 2.9$.

> The number of shorted turns must then be 3.

Concentrate 8

Superposition is useful here. First, apply a current source to inject a current of 1 A into node a. This current divides equally, so each resistor attached to node a will have 1/4 A of current.

As a separate procedure, use a different 1-A source to draw current from node b. This source will draw 1/4 A from each of the resistors attached to node b.

Now superpose the two results. Note that 1/4 A flows from node a to node b due to the first source, and 1/4 A flows from node a to node b because of the second source, so a total of 1/2 A flows from node a to node b.

Because they are equal the two current sources can be put in series, injecting 1 A at node a and drawing 1 A from node b. This is accompanied by a voltage drop of $1/2 \text{ A} \times 1 \ \Omega = 1/2 \text{ V}$.

> The apparent resistance from node a to node b is 0.5 Ω.

Concentrate 9

(a)

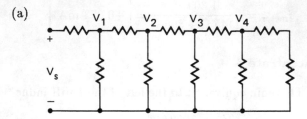

Assume 1 A flows down through right-hand R.

$$V_4 = 2 \text{ V}$$

Current flow out of node 4 is

$$1 \text{ A} + \frac{2 \text{ V}}{1 \ \Omega} = 3 \text{ A}$$

$$V_3 = V_4 + (3 \text{ A})(1 \ \Omega) = 5 \text{ V}$$

Current flow out of node 3 is

$$3 \text{ A} + \frac{5 \text{ V}}{1 \ \Omega} = 8 \text{ A}$$

$$V_2 = V_3 + (8 \text{ A})(1 \ \Omega) = 13 \text{ V}$$

Current flow out of node 2 is

$$8\text{ A} + \frac{13\text{ V}}{1\text{ }\Omega} = 21\text{ A}$$

The voltage at node 1 is

$$13\text{ V} + (21\text{ A})(1\text{ }\Omega) = 34\text{ V}$$

Current flow out of node 1 is

$$21\text{ A} + \frac{34\text{ V}}{1\text{ }\Omega} = 55\text{ A}$$

The voltage, V_s, is

$$V_s = 34\text{ V} + (55\text{ A})(1\text{ }\Omega) = 89\text{ V}$$

The input impedance is

$$Z_{\text{in}} = \frac{89\text{ V}}{55\text{ A}} = \boxed{1.62\text{ }\Omega}$$

(b) To obtain output impedance, input is shorted.

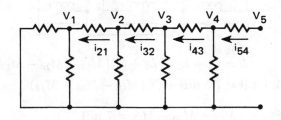

Assume $V_1 = 1$ V.

$$I_{21} = 2\text{ A}$$
$$V_2 = 3\text{ V}$$
$$I_{32} = 2\text{ A} + 3\text{ A}$$
$$V_3 = 3\text{ V} + 5\text{ V} = 8\text{ V}$$
$$I_{43} = 5\text{ A} + 8\text{ A}$$
$$V_4 = 8\text{ V} + 13\text{ V} = 21\text{ V}$$
$$I_{54} = 13\text{ A} + 21\text{ A}$$
$$V_5 = 21\text{ V} + 34\text{ V} = 55\text{ V}$$

$$\boxed{Z_{\text{out}} = \frac{55\text{ V}}{13\text{ A} + 21\text{ A}} = 1.62\text{ }\Omega}$$

Concentrate 10

Obtain the source conversion of a 3-A source in parallel with 40 Ω to a voltage source of 120 V in series with 40 Ω.

Add the series 20-Ω resistor to find the circuit

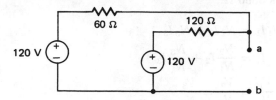

With a-b open, no current flows in either source, so $V_{\text{oc}} = 120$ V. With a-b shorted, the current is

$$I_{\text{sc}} = \frac{120\text{ V}}{60\text{ }\Omega} + \frac{120\text{ V}}{120\text{ }\Omega} = 3\text{ A}$$

Thevenin resistance is

$$\frac{V_{\text{oc}}}{I_{\text{sc}}} = \frac{120\text{ V}}{3\text{ A}} = 40\text{ }\Omega$$

(a)

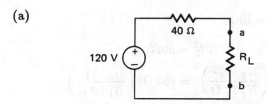

(b) Maximum power is delivered when

$$R_L = R_{\text{Th}} = 40\text{ }\Omega$$
$$P_L = I^2 R_L = \left(\frac{120\text{ V}}{80\text{ }\Omega}\right)^2 (40\text{ }\Omega) = \boxed{90\text{ W}}$$

(c) When $R_L = 20$,

$$P_L = \left(\frac{120\text{ V}}{60\text{ }\Omega}\right)^2 (20\text{ }\Omega) = \boxed{80\text{ W}}$$

(d) When $R_L = 80$,

$$P_L = \left(\frac{120\text{ V}}{120\text{ }\Omega}\right)^2 (80\text{ }\Omega) = \boxed{80\text{ W}}$$

Timed 1

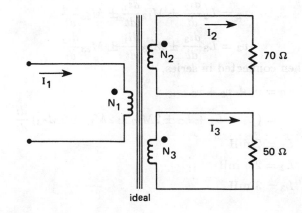

Maximum power is transmitted when the primary presents $3500 \ \Omega$.

$$N_1 I_1 = N_2 I_2 + N_3 I_3$$

$$I_1 = \frac{N_2}{N_1} I_2 + \frac{N_3}{N_1} I_3$$

$$\frac{V_1}{N_1} = \frac{V_2}{N_2} = \frac{V_3}{N_3}$$

$$I_2 = \frac{V_2}{70 \ \Omega} = \frac{N_2}{N_1} \frac{V_1}{70 \ \Omega}$$

$$I_3 = \frac{V_3}{50 \ \Omega} = \frac{N_3}{N_1} \frac{V_1}{50 \ \Omega}$$

$$I_1 = \frac{N_2}{N_1} \left(\frac{N_2}{N_1} \frac{V_1}{70 \ \Omega} \right) + \frac{N_3}{N_1} \left(\frac{N_3}{N_1} \frac{V_1}{50 \ \Omega} \right)$$

$$= \left[\left(\frac{N_2}{N_1} \right)^2 \left(\frac{1}{70 \ \Omega} \right) + \left(\frac{N_3}{N_1} \right)^2 \left(\frac{1}{50 \ \Omega} \right) \right] V_1$$

For equal loading,

$$70 I_2^2 = 50 I_3^2$$

$$(70 \ \Omega) \left(\frac{N_2}{N_1} \frac{V_1}{70 \ \Omega} \right)^2 = (50 \ \Omega) \left(\frac{N_3}{N_1} \frac{V_1}{50 \ \Omega} \right)^2$$

$$\left(\frac{N_2}{N_1} \right)^2 \left(\frac{1}{70 \ \Omega} \right) = \left(\frac{N_3}{N_1} \right)^2 \left(\frac{1}{50 \ \Omega} \right)$$

$$I_1 = \left(\frac{2}{70 \ \Omega} \right) \left(\frac{N_2}{N_1} \right)^2 V_1$$

$$Z = (35 \ \Omega) \left(\frac{N_1}{N_2} \right)^2 = 3500 \ \Omega$$

$$\frac{N_1}{N_2} = \boxed{10}$$

$$\left(\frac{N_1}{N_3} \right)^2 (25 \ \Omega) = 3500 \ \Omega$$

$$\frac{N_1}{N_3} = \sqrt{140} = \boxed{11.83}$$

Timed 2

$$v_1 = L_1 \frac{di_1}{dt} \pm M_{12} \frac{di_2}{dt} \pm M_{13} \frac{di_3}{dt}$$

$$v_2 = L_2 \frac{di_2}{dt} \pm M_{12} \frac{di_1}{dt} \pm M_{23} \frac{di_3}{dt}$$

$$v_3 = L_3 \frac{di_3}{dt} \pm M_{13} \frac{di_1}{dt} \pm M_{23} \frac{di_2}{dt}$$

When connected in series,

$$v = v_1 + v_2 + v_3$$

$$= (L_1 + L_2 + L_3 \pm 2M_{12} \pm 2M_{13} \pm 2M_{23}) \frac{di}{dt}$$

$$L_1 = 2 \ \text{mH}$$

$$L_2 = 2.5 \ \text{mH}$$

$$L_3 = 3 \ \text{mH}$$

Test 4:

$$L = L_1 + L_2 + L_3 + (2)(M_{12} + M_{13} + M_{23})$$

$$1.5 \ \text{mH} = 7.5 \ \text{mH} + (2)(M_{12} + M_{13} + M_{23})$$

$$M_{12} + M_{13} + M_{23} = -3 \ \text{mH}$$

Test 5:

$$L = L_1 + L_2 + L_3 + (2)(-M_{12} - M_{23} + M_{13})$$

$$3.5 \ \text{mH} = 7.5 \ \text{mH} + (2)(-M_{12} - M_{23} + M_{13})$$

$$M_{12} + M_{23} - M_{13} = 2$$

$$M_{13} = \boxed{-2.5 \ \text{mH}}$$

Test 6:

$$L = L_1 + L_2 + L_3 + (2)(M_{12} - M_{23} - M_{13})$$

$$21.5 \ \text{mH} = 7.5 \ \text{mH} + (2)(M_{12} - M_{23} - M_{13})$$

$$M_{12} - M_{23} - M_{13} = 7 \ \text{mH}$$

$$M_{12} = \boxed{2 \ \text{mH}}$$

$$M_{23} = \boxed{-2.5 \ \text{mH}}$$

Timed 3

$$M = K \sqrt{L_1 L_2}$$

$$= 0.8 \sqrt{(0.001 \ \text{H})(0.002 \ \text{H})} = 1.131 \ \text{mH}$$

$$\omega M = 1.131 \ \text{k}\Omega$$

$$\omega L_1 = 1 \ \text{k}\Omega$$

$$\omega L_2 = 2 \ \text{k}\Omega$$

Writing Kirchhoff's voltage law equations,

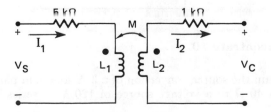

$$V_S = (5 \text{ k}\Omega + j1 \text{ k}\Omega)I_1 - j(1.131 \text{ k}\Omega)I_2$$
$$0.150 = (5 + j1)(1.9771\underline{/-26.6°})I_2 - j(1.131 \text{ k}\Omega)I_2$$
$$V_C = j(1.131 \text{ k}\Omega)I_1 - (1 \text{ k}\Omega + j2 \text{ k}\Omega)I_2$$

With I_1 and I_2 in mA,

$$V_S = (5 + j1)I_1 - j1.131I_2$$
$$V_C = j1.131I_1 - (1 + j2)I_2$$

open circuit: $i_2 = 0$

$$V_{oc} = \left(\frac{j1.131}{5 + j1}\right)V_s$$
$$= (0.222\underline{/78.7°})V_s$$

short circuit: $V_C = 0$

$$I_1 = \left(\frac{1 + j2}{j1.131}\right)I_2$$
$$= (1.9771\underline{/-26.6°})I_2$$

Substituting,

$$I_{sc} = I_2 = (0.0958\underline{/21.3°})V_s \text{ mA}$$

The Thevenin impedance is

(a) $R_{Th} = \frac{V_{oc}}{I_{sc}} = 2.317\underline{/57.4°} \text{ k}\Omega$

$$= \boxed{1.248 + j1.952 \text{ k}\Omega}$$

(b)

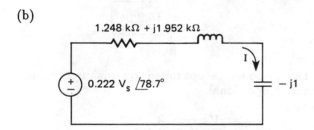

The impedance of the capacitance $(-j1)$ is negligible, so the current is the short-circuit current.

$$I \cong I_{sc} = (0.0958\underline{/21.3°} \text{ k}\Omega)(0.150 \text{ V})$$

$$= \boxed{0.0144\underline{/21.3°} \text{ mA}}$$

(c) The maximum current occurs at series resonance where

$$\frac{1}{10^6 C} = 1.952 \times 10^3$$

or $C = \boxed{0.512 \text{ nF}}$

The current is then

$$I = \frac{(0.222)(0.15 \text{ V})}{1248 \text{ }\Omega} = \frac{0.0333 \text{ V}}{1.248 \text{ k}\Omega} = 0.0267 \text{ mA}$$

Timed 4

The shunt resistivity is 40,000 Ω-mi, for 100 miles.

$$R_{shunt} = \frac{40,000 \text{ }\Omega\text{-mi}}{100 \text{ mi}} = 400 \text{ }\Omega$$

The series resistance is averaged.

$$R_{series} = (100 \text{ mi})\left(\frac{15 \frac{\Omega}{\text{mi}} + 20 \frac{\Omega}{\text{mi}}}{2}\right) = 1750 \text{ }\Omega$$

(a)

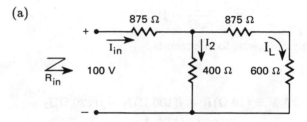

(b) $R_{in} = 875 \text{ }\Omega + \frac{(400 \text{ }\Omega)(1475 \text{ }\Omega)}{400 \text{ }\Omega + 1475 \text{ }\Omega} = 1190 \text{ }\Omega$

$$I_{in} = \frac{100 \text{ V}}{1190 \text{ }\Omega} = \boxed{84 \text{ mA}}$$

(c) By current division,

$$I_L = \left(\frac{400 \text{ }\Omega}{400 \text{ }\Omega + 875 \text{ }\Omega + 600 \text{ }\Omega}\right)(84 \text{ mA}) = \boxed{17.9 \text{ mA}}$$

Timed 5

A Thevenin equivalent circuit is required. (A Norton circuit would also be satisfactory.)

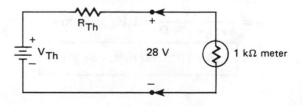

$$V_{Th} - R_{Th}\left(\frac{28 \text{ V}}{1000 \text{ }\Omega}\right) = 28 \text{ V}$$

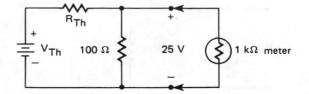

(a) $\quad V_{Th} - R_{Th} \left(\dfrac{25 \text{ V}}{100 \text{ }\Omega} + \dfrac{25 \text{ V}}{1000 \text{ }\Omega} \right) = 25 \text{ V}$

$$R_{Th} = \boxed{12.15 \text{ }\Omega}$$

$$V_{Th} = \boxed{28.34 \text{ V}}$$

(b) $\quad I_{sc} = \dfrac{28.34 \text{ V}}{12.15 \text{ }\Omega} = \boxed{2.33 \text{ A}}$

Timed 6

$$\omega L_1 = 100 \text{ }\Omega$$
$$\omega M = 120 \text{ }\Omega$$
$$\omega L_2 = 200 \text{ }\Omega$$
$$\frac{1}{\omega C} = 100 \text{ }\Omega$$

Taking clockwise loop currents,

Left loop:

$$0.1 \text{ V} = (10 \text{ }\Omega)I_1 + j(100 \text{ }\Omega)I_1 - j(120 \text{ }\Omega)I_2$$
$$- j(100 \text{ }\Omega)(I_1 - I_2)$$

Right loop:

$$0 \text{ V} = -j(100 \text{ }\Omega)(I_2 - I_1) + j(200 \text{ }\Omega)I_2 - j(120 \text{ }\Omega)I_1$$
$$+ (100 \text{ }\Omega)I_2$$

Simplifying,

$$0.1 \text{ V} = (10 \text{ }\Omega)I_1 - j(20 \text{ }\Omega)I_2$$
$$0 \text{ V} = -j(20 \text{ }\Omega)I_1 + (100 \text{ }\Omega + j100 \text{ }\Omega)I_2$$
$$I_1 = \left(\frac{100 \text{ }\Omega + j100 \text{ }\Omega}{j20 \text{ }\Omega} \right) I_2 = (5 \text{ }\Omega - j5 \text{ }\Omega)I_2$$
$$0.1 \text{ V} = (50 \text{ }\Omega - j50 \text{ }\Omega - j20 \text{ }\Omega)I_2$$
$$I_2 = \frac{0.1 \text{ V}}{50 \text{ }\Omega - j70 \text{ }\Omega} = 1.16\underline{/54.5^\circ} \text{ mA}$$
$$i_2(t) = \boxed{1.16 \times 10^{-3} \cos(10^4 t - 54.5^\circ) \text{ A}}$$

Timed 7

(a)

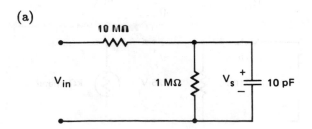

The oscilloscope input impedance is

$$Z_s = \frac{10^6 \text{ }\Omega}{(10^6 \text{ }\Omega)(10^{-11} \text{ F})s + 1} = \frac{10^6 \text{ }\Omega}{10^{-5}s + 1}$$

By voltage division,

$$V_s = \frac{Z_s V_{in}}{Z_s + 10^7 \text{ }\Omega} = \frac{10^4 V_{in}}{s + 1.1 \times 10^5}$$

For the unit step input,

$$V_{in} \rightarrow \frac{1}{s}$$

$$V_s = \frac{10^4}{s(s + 1.1 \times 10^5)} = \frac{A}{s} + \frac{B}{s + 1.1 \times 10^5}$$
$$= \left(\frac{1}{11} \right) \left(\frac{1}{s} - \frac{1}{s + 1.1 \times 10^5} \right)$$

Taking the inverse transform,

$$v_s(t) = \left(\frac{1}{11} \right) (1 - e^{-1.1 \times 10^5 t}) u(t) \text{ V}$$

This reaches 70% of its final value where

$$e^{-1.1 \times 10^5 t} = 0.3$$
$$1.1 \times 10^5 t = \ln \left(\frac{1}{0.3} \right)$$
$$t = \boxed{10.9 \text{ }\mu s}$$

(b) The response is optimized by making the impedances proportional.

$$\frac{V_s}{V_{in}} = \frac{Z_s}{Z_C + Z_s}$$

If $Z_C = 10Z_s$,

$$\frac{V_s}{V_{in}} = \frac{1 \text{ V}}{11 \text{ V}}$$

$$\frac{10^7}{10^7 C_c s + 1} = \frac{10^7}{10^{-5}s + 1}$$

$$C_c = \frac{10^{-5}}{10^7} = 10^{-12} \text{ F}$$

$$C_c = \boxed{1 \text{ pF}}$$

Note: To make the ratio 10:1, $R_c \rightarrow 9 \text{ }M\Omega$.

Timed 8

The capacitive reactance is

$$X_c = \frac{10^6}{0.1\omega} \ \Omega$$
$$= \frac{10^7}{\omega} \ \Omega$$

The impedance at the lower-left branches is

$$\frac{(50 \text{ k}\Omega)\left(-j\dfrac{10^7}{\omega} \ \Omega\right)}{50 \text{ k}\Omega - j\dfrac{10^7}{\omega} \ \Omega}$$

$$\frac{50 \text{ k}\Omega}{(5 \times 10^{-3})j\omega + 1} = Z_{RC}$$

To be in balance, the ratios of impedances must be the same.

$$\frac{5 \text{ k}\Omega}{Z_{RC}} = \frac{R + j\omega L}{100 \ \Omega}$$

$$R + j\omega L = \frac{(5000 \ \Omega)(100 \ \Omega)}{Z_{RC}}$$

$$= 5 \times 10^{-2} j\omega + 10 \ \Omega$$

$$\boxed{R = 10 \ \Omega}$$

$$\boxed{L = 50 \text{ mH}}$$

Timed 9

Designate capacitances by their microfarads.

$$X_4 = -\frac{10^6}{4\omega} \ \Omega$$

$$X_8 = -\frac{10^6}{8\omega} \ \Omega$$

$$X_c = -\frac{1}{\omega C} \ \Omega$$

The impedance of the lower left branches is

$$Z_{RC} = \frac{(10 \text{ k}\Omega)(-jX_4\Omega)}{10 \text{ k}\Omega - jX_4\Omega}$$

To be in balance, the impedance ratios must match.

$$\frac{5 \text{ k}\Omega}{Z_{RC}} = \frac{R - jX_c}{-jX_8}$$

$$R - jX_C = \frac{-jX_8(5 \text{ k}\Omega)}{Z_{RC}}$$

$$= \frac{-jX_8(5 \text{ k}\Omega)}{-jX_4(10 \text{ k}\Omega)}(10 \text{ k}\Omega - jX_4)$$

$$= \frac{X_8}{X_4}\left(\frac{10 \text{ k}\Omega}{2}\right) - j\frac{X_8}{2}$$

$$\boxed{R = 2.5 \text{ k}\Omega}$$

$$\boxed{C = 16 \ \mu\text{F}}$$

Timed 10

The resistance seen from the 12-V source is

$$R = 1 \ \Omega + \frac{(2 \ \Omega)(201 \ \Omega)}{2 \ \Omega + 201 \ \Omega}$$

The voltage across across the bridge is

$$V_{\text{bridge}} = (12 \text{ V})\left[\frac{\dfrac{(2 \ \Omega)(201 \ \Omega)}{2 \ \Omega + 201 \ \Omega}}{1 \ \Omega + \dfrac{(2 \ \Omega)(201 \ \Omega)}{2 \ \Omega + 201 \ \Omega}}\right] = \frac{4824}{605} \text{ V}$$

Using voltage division for each side,

$$V_{xy} = \left(\frac{4824}{605} \text{ V}\right)\left(\frac{1 \ \Omega}{2 \ \Omega} - \frac{101 \ \Omega}{201 \ \Omega}\right) = \frac{-4824}{(605)(402)} \text{ V}$$

$$\boxed{V_{\text{Th}} = -19.8 \text{ mV}}$$

With x and y shorted, the source sees an impedance of

$$R_s = 1 \ \Omega + \frac{(1 \ \Omega)(100 \ \Omega)}{1 \ \Omega + 100 \ \Omega} + \frac{(1 \ \Omega)(101 \ \Omega)}{1 \ \Omega + 101 \ \Omega} = \frac{30,703}{10,302} \ \Omega$$

The source current is

$$I_s = (12 \text{ V})\left(\frac{10,302}{30,703} \text{ S}\right) \text{ A}$$

By current division, the 100-Ω resistance carries.

$$I_{100} = \left(\frac{1 \ \Omega}{101 \ \Omega}\right)I_s = \frac{(12)(102)}{30,703} \text{ A}$$

The 101-Ω resistance carries.

$$I_{101} = \left(\frac{1 \ \Omega}{102 \ \Omega}\right)I_s = \frac{(12)(101)}{30,703} \text{ A}$$

$$I_{xy} = I_{101} - I_{100} = \frac{-12}{30,703} = I_{\text{sc}}$$

$$R_{\text{Th}} = \frac{V_{\text{Th}}}{I_{\text{sc}}} = \frac{(4824)(30,703)}{(12)(605)(402)} \ \Omega$$

$$= \boxed{50.7 \ \Omega}$$

WAVEFORMS, POWER, AND MEASUREMENTS

Warmup 1

$$\int_{\omega t=\theta}^{\theta+2\pi} \sin(\omega t + \alpha)dt$$

$$= -\frac{1}{\omega}\cos(\omega t + \alpha)\Big|_{\omega t=\theta}^{\theta+2\pi}$$

$$= -\frac{1}{\omega}[\cos(\theta + \alpha + 2\pi) - \cos(\theta + \alpha)]$$

$$= -\frac{1}{\omega}[\cos(\theta + \alpha) - \cos(\theta + \alpha)] = \boxed{0}$$

Warmup 2

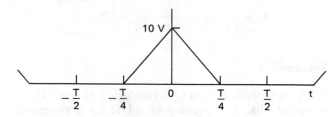

The half-wave rectified waveform is shown. It is described mathematically.

$$v(t) = \begin{cases} 0 & -\dfrac{T}{2} < t < -\dfrac{T}{4} \\ 10 + 40\dfrac{t}{T} & -\dfrac{T}{4} < t < 0 \\ 10 - 40\dfrac{t}{T} & 0 < t < \dfrac{T}{4} \\ 0 & \dfrac{T}{4} < t < \dfrac{T}{2} \end{cases}$$

$$V_{\text{avg}} = \frac{1}{T}\int_{-\frac{T}{4}}^{0}\left(10 + 40\frac{t}{T}\right)dt$$

$$+ \frac{1}{T}\int_{0}^{\frac{T}{4}}\left(10 - 40\frac{t}{T}\right)dt$$

$$V_{\text{avg}} = \frac{1}{T}\left[\left(\frac{1}{2}\right)(10)\left(\frac{T}{2}\right)\right]$$

$$= \frac{1}{T}(\text{area of triangle}) = \boxed{2.5 \text{ V}}$$

$$V_{\text{RMS}}^2 = \frac{1}{T}\int_{-\frac{T}{4}}^{0}\left(10 + 40\frac{t}{T}\right)^2 dt$$

$$+ \frac{1}{T}\int_{0}^{\frac{T}{4}}\left(10 - 40\frac{t}{T}\right)^2 dt$$

The two integrals are the same.

$$V_{\text{RMS}}^2 = \frac{2}{T}\int_{0}^{\frac{T}{4}}\left(100 - 800\frac{t}{T} + 1600\frac{t^2}{T^2}\right)dt$$

$$= \frac{2}{T}\left[100t - \frac{800\,t^2}{2T} + \frac{1600}{3T^2}t^3\right]_{0}^{\frac{T}{4}}$$

$$= (200)\left(\frac{T}{4T}\right) - \left(\frac{800}{T^2}\right)\left(\frac{T^2}{16}\right)$$

$$+ (2)\left(\frac{1600}{3T^3}\right)\left(\frac{T^3}{64}\right)$$

$$V_{\text{RMS}}^2 = 16.667$$

$$V_{\text{RMS}} = \boxed{4.08 \text{ V}}$$

Warmup 3

$$V_{\text{avg}} = \frac{\text{pulse area}}{\text{period}}$$

$$= \frac{(10)(2\text{ V})(1\text{ ms})}{50\text{ ms}} = \boxed{0.4 \text{ V}}$$

$$V_{\text{RMS}}^2 = \frac{1}{T}\int v^2\,dt$$

$$= \frac{(10)(2\text{ V})^2(1\text{ ms})}{50\text{ ms}} = 0.8\text{ V}^2$$

$$V_{\text{RMS}} = \sqrt{0.8\text{ V}^2} = \boxed{0.894 \text{ V}}$$

Warmup 4

The full scale is 9999.

Accuracy, or resolution, is half of the least significant digit, or ±0.5.

$$\text{precision} = \left(\frac{0.5}{9999}\right)(100) = \boxed{0.005\%}$$

PROFESSIONAL PUBLICATIONS, INC. • Belmont, CA

Warmup 5

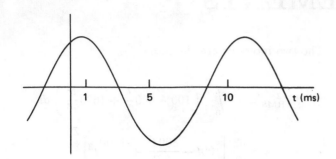

$$\omega = \frac{2\pi}{T} = \frac{2\pi}{0.01} = 200\pi \text{ rad/s}$$

$$10 \text{ ms} = 360°$$

$$1 \text{ ms} = 36°$$

For the sine, the positive zero crossing is at -1.5 ms, or $-54°$.

$$f = \boxed{F_p \sin(200\pi + 54°)}$$

$$= \boxed{F_p \cos(200\pi - 36°)}$$

Warmup 6

Using cosine reference,

$$I_R = \frac{10\underline{/25°} \text{ V}}{25 \text{ }\Omega} = 0.4\underline{/25°} \text{ A}$$

$$= 0.3625 + j0.1690 \text{ A}$$

$$I_L = \frac{10\underline{/25} \text{ V}}{(0.5)(100)\underline{/90°} \text{ }\Omega} = 0.2\underline{/-65°} \text{ A}$$

$$= 0.0845 - j0.1813 \text{ A}$$

$$I_t = 0.447 - j0.0123 \text{ A} = 0.4472\underline{/-1.6°} \text{ A}$$

$$\text{phase angle} = \boxed{-1.6°}$$

The calculations were made on peak values. Divide by $\sqrt{2}$ to get RMS.

$$I_{\text{RMS}} = \frac{0.4472}{\sqrt{2}} \text{ A} = \boxed{0.316 \text{ A}}$$

Warmup 7

Use peak values.

$$S = VI^* = \frac{(10\underline{/25°} \text{ V})(0.4472\underline{/+1.6°} \text{ A})}{2} \text{ VA}$$

$$= 2.236\underline{/26.6°} = 2 + j1 \text{ VA}$$

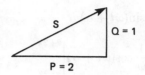

Warmup 8

The capacitance current must cancel the inductance current, so its reactance must be $-j\omega L = -j50 \text{ }\Omega$.

$$X_C = \frac{1}{j\omega C} = \frac{-j}{100C} \rightarrow -j50 \text{ }\Omega$$

$$C = \frac{1}{(50 \text{ }\Omega)(100 \text{ rad/s})} = \boxed{200 \text{ }\mu\text{F}}$$

Warmup 9

With each resistor having a resolution of ±0.5 Ω, the composite has an accuracy of ±1 Ω for a percentage of $435 + 9565 \pm 1 = 10,000 \pm 0.01\%$. The full-scale voltage will be $(10,000 \text{ }\Omega)(1 \text{ mA}) = 10$ V. At half-scale, the meter will read 0.50 mA, with an error range of ±0.005 mA or 1%. The resistor error and meter error add as the square root of the sum of the squares.

$$\boxed{\sqrt{(0.01)^2 + (0.0001)^2}} \, (100) = \boxed{1\% \text{ accuracy}}$$

Warmup 10

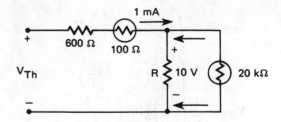

Assuming the meters are perfectly accurate,

$$V_{\text{Th}} = 10 \text{ V} + (0.001 \text{ A})(700 \text{ }\Omega) = 10.7 \text{ V}$$

With 1 mA flowing into 10 V, the equivalent load resistance is 10 V/1 mA = 10 kΩ, so

$$R = \boxed{20 \text{ k}\Omega}$$

Removing the meters, the current flowing will be

$$i = \frac{10.7 \text{ V}}{20{,}600 \text{ }\Omega} = \boxed{0.52 \text{ mA}}$$

Concentrate 1

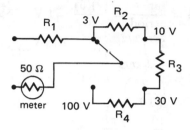

The meter configuration is as shown. With the 1-mA full-scale current,

$$3 \text{ V}: \quad 50 + R_1 = \frac{3 \text{ V}}{1 \text{ mA}} = 3000 \text{ }\Omega$$

$$R_1 = \boxed{2950 \text{ }\Omega}$$

$$10 \text{ V}: \quad R_2 = \frac{7 \text{ V}}{1 \text{ mA}} = \boxed{7000 \text{ }\Omega}$$

$$30 \text{ V}: \quad R_3 = \frac{20 \text{ V}}{1 \text{ mA}} = \boxed{20{,}000 \text{ }\Omega}$$

$$100 \text{ V}: \quad R_4 = \frac{70 \text{ V}}{1 \text{ mA}} = \boxed{70{,}000 \text{ }\Omega}$$

Concentrate 2

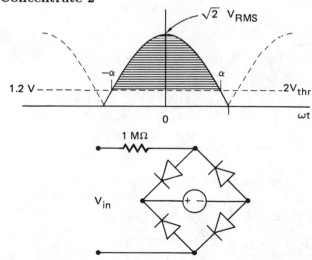

For $|V_{\text{in}}| > 2V_{\text{thr}}$,

$$i = \frac{|V_{\text{in}}| - 2V_{\text{thr}}}{10^6}$$

$$I_{\text{fs}} = 0.125 \text{ mA}$$

$$V_{\text{avg}} = \frac{2}{\pi} \int_0^\alpha (\sqrt{2}\, V_{\text{RMS}} \cos \omega t - 1.2 \text{ V}) d\omega t$$

$$\sqrt{2}\, V_{\text{RMS}} \cos \alpha = 1.2$$

$$V_{\text{avg}} = \left(\frac{2}{\pi}\right) \left[\sqrt{2} V_{\text{RMS}} \sin \omega t - 1.2\omega t \right]_{\omega t = 0}^{\alpha}$$

$$\alpha = \cos^{-1}\left(\frac{1.2 \text{ V}}{\sqrt{2} V_{\text{RMS}}}\right)$$

$$V_{\text{avg}} = \left(\frac{2}{\pi}\right)\left(\sqrt{2}\, V_{\text{RMS}} \sin \alpha - 1.2\alpha\right)$$

For the term 1.2α, α is in radians.

For $V_{\text{RMS}} = 100$ V,

$$V_{\text{avg}} = \left(\frac{200\sqrt{2}}{\pi}\right)(\sin \alpha) - \frac{2.4}{\pi}\alpha \text{ V}$$

$$\alpha = \cos^{-1}\left(\frac{1.2 \text{ V}}{100\sqrt{2} \text{ V}}\right) = 89.5°$$

$$= 0.497\pi \text{ rad}$$

$$V_{\text{avg}} = 90.03 \text{ V} - 1.19 \text{ V} = 88.84 \text{ V}$$

$$\theta_{100} = \left(\frac{88.84 \text{ V}}{125 \text{ V}}\right)(50) = 35.5°$$

For $V_{\text{RMS}} = 90$ V,

$$\alpha = 89.46°$$

$$V_{\text{avg}} = 81.02 \text{ V} - 1.19 \text{ V} = 79.83 \text{ V}$$

$$\theta_{90} = 31.9°$$

For $V_{\text{RMS}} = 80$ V,

$$\alpha = 89.39°$$

$$V_{\text{avg}} = 72.02 \text{ V} - 1.19 \text{ V} = 70.83 \text{ V}$$

$$\theta_{80} = \left(\frac{70.83 \text{ V}}{125 \text{ V}}\right)(50) = 28.3°$$

For $V_{\text{RMS}} = 70$ V,

$$\alpha = 89.31°$$

$$V_{\text{avg}} = 63.02 \text{ V} - 1.19 \text{ V} = 61.83 \text{ V}$$

$$\theta_{70} = \left(\frac{61.83 \text{ V}}{125 \text{ V}}\right)(50) = 24.7°$$

For $V_{\text{RMS}} = 60$ V,

$$\alpha = 89.19°$$

$$V_{\text{avg}} = 54.01 \text{ V} - 1.19 \text{ V} = 52.82 \text{ V}$$

$$\theta_{60} = \left(\frac{52.82 \text{ V}}{125 \text{ V}}\right)(50) = 21.1°$$

For $V_{\text{RMS}} = 50$ V,

$$\alpha = 89.0°$$

$$V_{\text{avg}} = 45.01 \text{ V} - 1.19 \text{ V} = 43.82 \text{ V}$$

$$\theta_{50} = \left(\frac{43.82 \text{ V}}{125 \text{ V}}\right)(50) = 17.5°$$

For $V_{RMS} = 40$ V,

$$\alpha = 88.78°$$
$$V_{avg} = 36.00 \text{ V} - 1.18 \text{ V} = 34.82 \text{ V}$$
$$\theta_{40} = \left(\frac{34.82 \text{ V}}{125 \text{ V}}\right)(50) = 13.9°$$

For $V_{RMS} = 30$ V,

$$\alpha = 88.38°$$
$$V_{avg} = 27.00 \text{ V} - 1.18 \text{ V} = 25.82 \text{ V}$$
$$\theta_{30} = \left(\frac{25.82 \text{ V}}{125 \text{ V}}\right)(50) = 10.3°$$

For $V_{RMS} = 20$ V,

$$\alpha = 87.57°$$
$$V_{avg} = 17.99 \text{ V} - 1.17 \text{ V} = 16.82 \text{ V}$$
$$\theta_{20} = \left(\frac{16.82 \text{ V}}{125 \text{ V}}\right)(50) = 6.7°$$

For $V_{RMS} = 10$ V,

$$\alpha = 85.13°$$
$$V_{avg} = 8.97 \text{ V} - 1.14 \text{ V} = 7.83 \text{ V}$$
$$\theta_{10} = \left(\frac{7.83 \text{ V}}{125 \text{ V}}\right)(50) = 3.1°$$

The scale markings are

V_{RMS}	0 V	10 V	20 V	30 V	40 V	50 V
θ	0	3.1°	6.7°	10.3°	13.9°	17.5°
V_{RMS}	60 V	70 V	80 V	90 V	100 V	
θ	21.1°	24.7°	28.3°	31.9°	35.5°	

Concentrate 3

The signal power is normalized to 1 Ω, so it is in units of volts squared.

$$P_{signal} = \frac{1}{R}\frac{1}{T}\int_T V^2 \, dt$$

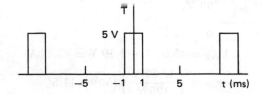

The signal is represented by a Fourier cosine series (even function).

$$v_t = \frac{a_0}{2} + \sum_{n=1}^{\infty} a_n \cos\left(\frac{2\pi}{T}\right) nt$$

$$\frac{a_0}{2} = \frac{\text{area}}{\text{period}} = \frac{(2)(5)}{10} = 1 \text{ V}$$

$$a_n = \frac{2}{T}\int_{-T/2}^{T/2} f(t)\cos\left(\frac{2\pi}{T}\right) nt \, dt$$

$$a_n = \left(\frac{2}{0.01}\right)\int_{-0.001}^{0.001} 5\cos\left(\frac{2\pi}{0.01}\right) nt \, dt$$

$$= \frac{10}{\pi n}\sin\left(\frac{\pi n}{5}\right) \text{ V}$$

The fundamental frequency is $1/T = 100$ Hz. The filter allows only $a_0, a_1, a_2, a_3, a_4,$ and a_5 to pass.

$$a_1 = \frac{10}{\pi}\sin\left(\frac{\pi}{5}\right) = 1.87 \text{ V}$$

$$a_2 = \frac{10}{2\pi}\sin\left(\frac{2\pi}{5}\right) = 1.51 \text{ V}$$

$$a_3 = \frac{10}{3\pi}\sin\left(\frac{3\pi}{5}\right) = 1.01 \text{ V}$$

$$a_4 = \frac{10}{4\pi}\sin\left(\frac{4\pi}{5}\right) = 0.47 \text{ V}$$

$$a_5 = \frac{10}{5\pi}\sin \pi = 0 \text{ V}$$

The "power" is the RMS voltage squared.

$$P_{out} = \frac{1}{R}\left[(1 \text{ V})^2 + \frac{(1.87 \text{ V})^2}{2} + \frac{(1.51 \text{ V})^2}{2}\right.$$
$$\left. + \frac{(1.01 \text{ V})^2}{2} + \frac{(0.47 \text{ V})^2}{2}\right]$$

$$= \frac{1}{R}(4.51) \text{ W}$$

$$P_{in} = \frac{1}{R}\frac{1}{T}\int_{-0.001}^{0.001} 25 \, dt = \frac{1}{R}(5) \text{ W}$$

$$\frac{P_{out}}{P_{in}} = \frac{4.51 \text{ W}}{5 \text{ W}} = \boxed{0.9 \text{ or } 90\%}$$

Concentrate 4

The meter is calibrated to read RMS value while operating from the average of the full-wave rectified sinusoid.

For such a sinusoid,

$$v = \sqrt{2}\, V_{\text{RMS}} \sin \omega t$$

$$V_{\text{avg}} = \frac{1}{T} \int_0^T v\, dt$$

$$= \frac{1}{\pi} \int_0^\pi \sqrt{2}\, V_{\text{RMS}} \sin \omega t\, d\omega t$$

$$= \frac{2\sqrt{2}\, V_{\text{RMS}}}{\pi}$$

The meter is designed to read

$$V_{\text{reading}} = \frac{\pi}{2\sqrt{2}} V_{\text{avg}}$$

For the triangular wave, the average is half the peak.

$$V_{\text{avg}} = \frac{50}{2}\ \text{V}$$

$$V_{\text{reading}} = \left(\frac{\pi}{2\sqrt{2}}\right)\left(\frac{50\ \text{V}}{2}\right) = \boxed{27.8\ \text{V}}$$

Note: The RMS value of the triangle is $V_p/\sqrt{3}$, which is 28.9 V for a 3.8% error.

Concentrate 5

Model the impedance by its reciprocal.

$$I = V(G + jB)$$

As I lags V by 30°,

$$\tan^{-1} \frac{B}{G} = -30°$$

$$B = -G \tan 30°$$

$$P = V^2 G = 200\ \text{W at } 100\ \text{V}$$

$$G = \frac{200\ \text{W}}{10^4\ \text{V}^2} = 0.02\ \text{S}$$

$$B = -0.02 \tan 30°\ \text{S}$$

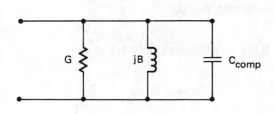

$$Y_C = j\frac{1}{X_C} = j0.02 \tan 30°\ \text{S}$$

$$X_C = \frac{-50}{\tan 30°} = \boxed{-86.6\ \Omega}$$

Concentrate 6

(a) $X_C = \dfrac{-1}{377C} = \boxed{-29.97\ \Omega}$

$\qquad X_L = 377L = \boxed{25.00\ \Omega}$

(b) $Y_G = G = \dfrac{1}{R} = \boxed{0.10\ \text{S}}$

$\qquad Y_C = jB_C = -\dfrac{1}{jX_C} = \boxed{j0.0334\ \text{S}}$

$\qquad Y_L = jB_L = \dfrac{1}{jX_L} = \boxed{-j0.0400\ \text{S}}$

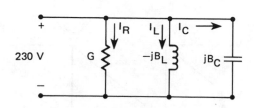

(c) $\quad I_R = (230\ \text{V})G = 23\underline{/0°}\ \text{A}$

$\qquad I_L = (-230\ \text{V})j(0.04\ \text{S}) = 9.20\underline{/-90°}\ \text{A}$

$\qquad I_C = (230\ \text{V})j(0.0334\ \text{S}) = 7.68\underline{/90°}\ \text{A}$

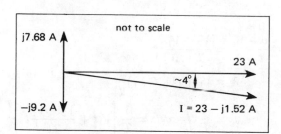

(d) $Y = G + jB_c + jB_L$

$\qquad = 0.1 + j0.0334 - j0.04$

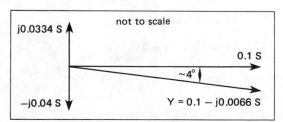

(e) $I = \sqrt{2}\sqrt{(23)^2 + (1.52)^2}\ \text{A}$

$\qquad \times \sin\left[377t - \tan^{-1}\left(\dfrac{1.52}{23}\right)\right]$

$\qquad = \boxed{32.6 \sin(377t - 3.8°)\ \text{A}}$

The circuit is inductive.

(f) $\text{PF} = \cos(-3.8°) = \boxed{0.998}$

(g) $S = VI^* = (230 \text{ V})(23 + j1.52 \text{ V})$
$\qquad = 5.29 \text{ kW} + j0.350 \text{ kVAR}$

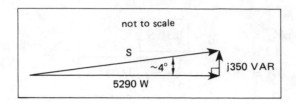

Concentrate 7

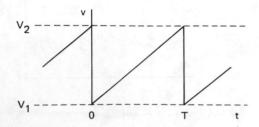

$$2 \text{ points} : (v, t) = (V_1, 0) \text{ and } (V_2, T)$$

$$\frac{v - V_1}{t - 0} = \frac{V_2 - V_1}{T - 0}$$

$$v = V_1 + (V_2 - V_1)\frac{t}{T}$$

$$v_{\text{avg}} = \frac{1}{T}\int_0^T v \, dt = \frac{1}{T}\left[V_1 t + \frac{V_2 - V_1}{2T}t^2\right]_0^T$$

$$= \frac{V_1 + V_2}{2} = 2 \text{ (given)}$$

$$V_2 = 4 - V_1$$

$$V_2 - V_1 = 4 - 2V_1$$

$$v = V_1 + (4 - 2V_1)\frac{t}{T} \qquad \text{find out } \frac{t}{T}$$

$$= 0 \text{ at } \frac{t_0}{T} = \frac{-V_1}{4 - 2V_1} \qquad \text{where } v = 0$$

The RMS calibrated full-wave rectifier DC meter reads

$$V_{\text{reading}} = \frac{\pi}{2\sqrt{2}}V_{\text{avg}}$$

If V_1 were positive, the average from the rectifier would also be 2 V, so the RMS meter would read

$$\left(\frac{\pi}{2\sqrt{2}}\right)(2 \text{ V}) = 2.22 \text{ V}$$

Because the RMS meter reads 6.85 V, the rectified average is

$$\left(\frac{6.85 \text{ V}}{\pi}\right)(2\sqrt{2}) = 6.17 \text{ V}$$

This requires V_1 to be negative.

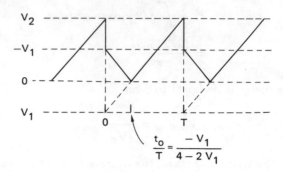

The rectified waveform shown has an average of

$$V_{\text{avg}} = \frac{1}{T}\left[\frac{1}{2}(-V_1 t_0) + \frac{1}{2}V_2(T - t_0)\right]$$

$$2V_{\text{avg}} = -V_1\frac{t_0}{T} + (4 - V_1)\left(1 - \frac{t_0}{T}\right)$$

$$\frac{t_0}{T} = \frac{-V_1}{4 - 2V_1}$$

$$2V_{\text{avg}} = \frac{V_1^2}{4 - 2V_1} + (4 - V_1)\left(\frac{4 - 2V_1 + V_1}{4 - 2V_1}\right)$$

$$= \frac{2V_1^2 - 8V_1 + 16}{4 - 2V_1}$$

For $V_{\text{avg}} = 6.17$ V,

$$V_1^2 + 8.32\,V_1 - 16.68 = 0$$

The negative solution is $V_1 = \boxed{-10 \text{ V}}$ so

$$V_2 = \boxed{+14 \text{ V}}$$

Concentrate 8

The RMS reading peak detector reads

$$V_{\text{reading}} = \frac{V_p}{\sqrt{2}}$$

$$V_p = \sqrt{2}\,V_{\text{reading}}$$

$$V_{\text{reading}} = 6.36 \text{ V}$$

$$V_p = 6.36\sqrt{2} = 9 \text{ V}$$

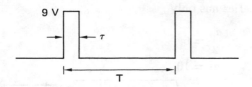

$$V_{\text{avg}} = \frac{1}{T}(9\text{ V})\tau = (9\text{ V})\frac{\tau}{T} = 0.5\text{ V}$$

$$\frac{\tau}{T} = \frac{0.5\text{ V}}{9\text{ V}} = 0.056$$

The duty cycle is then

$$100\frac{\tau}{T} = \boxed{5.6\%}$$

Concentrate 9

The load power is

$$\begin{aligned} P_{La} + P_{Lb} + P_{Lc} &= V_{an}I_a\cos\theta_{an} \\ &+ V_{bn}I_b\cos\theta_{bn} \\ &+ V_{cn}I_c\cos\theta_{cn} \end{aligned}$$

The measured power is

$$\begin{aligned} P_a + P_b + P_c &= V_{ax}I_a\cos\theta_{ax} \\ &+ V_{bx}I_b\cos\theta_{bx} \\ &+ V_{cx}I_c\cos\theta_{cx} \end{aligned}$$

$$V_{an} = V_{\text{ln}}\underline{/0°}$$
$$V_{bn} = V_{\text{ln}}\underline{/-120°}$$
$$V_{cn} = V_{\text{ln}}\underline{/+120°}$$
$$V_{nx} = V_{nx}\underline{/\theta_{nx}}$$

The P_a wattmeter reads

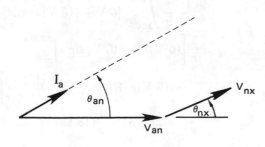

$$P_a = V_{an}I_a\cos\theta_{an} + V_{nx}I_a\cos(\theta_{an} - \theta_{nx})$$

The P_b wattmeter reads

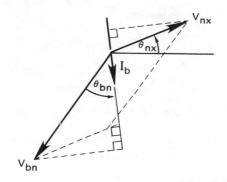

$$P_b = V_{bn}I_b\cos\theta_{bn} + V_{nx}I_b\cos(\theta_{nx} + 120 - \theta_{bn})$$

The P_c wattmeter reads

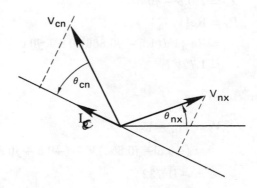

$$P_c = V_{cn}I_c\cos\theta_{cn} + V_nI_c\cos(120° + \theta_{cn} - \theta_{nx})$$

These are written in phasor form.

$$\begin{aligned} P_a + P_b + P_c &= V_{an}I_a\cos\theta_{an} + V_{bn}I_b\cos\theta_{bn} \\ &+ V_{cn}I_c\cos\theta_{cn} \\ &+ \text{Re}\left\{V_{nx}I_a\underline{/(\theta_{nx} - \theta_{an})}\right. \\ &+ V_{nx}I_b\underline{/(\theta_{nx} - \theta_{bn} + 120°)} \\ &+ \left. V_{nx}I_c\underline{/(\theta_{nx} - \theta_{cn} - 120°)}\right\} \end{aligned}$$

$$\begin{aligned} P_a + P_b + P_c &= P_{La} + P_{Lb} + P_{Lc} \\ &+ \text{Re}\left\{V_{nx}\underline{/\theta_{nx}}\left(I_a\underline{/\theta_{an}}\right.\right. \\ &+ I_b\underline{/\theta_{bn} + 120°} \\ &+ \left.\left. I_c\underline{/\theta_{cn} - 120°}\right)\right\} \end{aligned}$$

Because the circuit is connected in Y, $i_a + i_b + i_c \equiv 0$.

$$I_a\underline{/\theta_{an}} + I_b\underline{/(\theta_{bn} - 120)} + I_c\underline{/(\theta_{cn} + 120°)} = 0$$

Therefore,

$$\boxed{P_a + P_b + P_c = P_{La} + P_{Lb} + P_{Lc}}$$

Concentrate 10

Assume an *abc* sequence.

$$V_{an} = V\underline{/0}$$
$$V_{bn} = V\underline{/-120^\circ}$$
$$V_{cn} = V\underline{/+120^\circ}$$
$$\cos^{-1} 0.8 = -36.87^\circ$$
$$I_a = I\underline{/-36.87^\circ}$$
$$I_b = I\underline{/-156.87^\circ}$$

Wattmeter a has

$$V_a = V_{an} - V_{cn}$$
$$= V - V(-0.5 + j0.866)$$
$$= V(1.5 - j0.866)$$
$$I_a = I(0.8 - j0.6)$$
$$P_a = \text{Re}\{V_a I_a^*\}$$
$$= \text{Re}\{VI(1.5 - j0.866)(0.8 + j0.6)\}$$
$$= 1.72VI$$

Wattmeter b has

$$V_b = V_{bn} - V_{cn}$$
$$= (-0.5 - j0.866)V - (-0.5 + j0.866)V$$
$$= -j1.732\,V$$
$$I_b = (-0.9196 - j0.3928)I$$
$$\text{Re}\{V_b I_b^*\} = 0.6803\,VI$$
$$(3)(0.8)(VI) = 1000$$
$$VI = \frac{1000}{2.4}$$

$$P_a = \boxed{716.7 \text{ W}}$$

$$P_b = \boxed{283.5 \text{ W}}$$

$$P_a + P_b = 1000.2 \text{ W}$$
$$\uparrow$$
$$\text{rounding error}$$

Timed 1

(a) For a Fourier series, the RMS value is

$$f_{\text{RMS}}^2 = \left(\frac{a_0}{2}\right)^2 + \sum_{n=1}^{\infty} \frac{a_n^2}{2} + \sum_{n=1}^{\infty} \frac{b_n^2}{2}$$

The series has only

$$\frac{a_0}{2} = 6$$
$$a_1 = 10$$
$$V_{\text{RMS}} = \sqrt{(6)^2 + \left(\frac{1}{2}\right)(10)^2} = \boxed{9.27 \text{ V}}$$

(b)

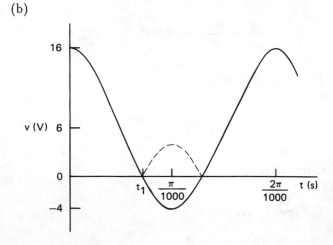

$$v_{\text{rectified}} = \boxed{6 + 10\cos\omega t \text{ V} \quad 0 < t < t_1}$$

$$= \boxed{-6 - 10\cos\omega t \text{ V} \quad t_1 < t < \frac{\pi}{1000}}$$

(c) The voltage polarity at

$$10\cos\omega t_1 \text{ V} = -6 \text{ V}$$
$$\omega t_1 = \cos^{-1} -0.6 = 126.9^\circ$$
$$= 0.705\,\pi \text{ rad}$$

$$V_{\text{rectified avg}} = \frac{1}{\pi}\int_0^\pi v_{\text{rectified}}\, d\omega t$$

$$= \frac{1}{\pi}\int^{126.9^\circ} [6 \text{ V} + (10 \text{ V})\cos\omega t]d\omega t$$

$$- \frac{1}{\pi}\int_{126.9^\circ}^{180^\circ} [6 \text{ V} + (10 \text{ V})\cos\omega t]d\omega t$$

$$V_{\text{rectified avg}} = \frac{1}{\pi}\left[(6 \text{ V})x + (10 \text{ V})\sin x\Big|_{x=0}^{0.705\pi}\right.$$

$$\left. - ((6 \text{ V})x + (10 \text{ V})\sin x)\Big|_{0.705\pi}^{\pi}\right]$$

$$= \frac{1}{\pi}(13.29 + 8) \quad \frac{1}{\pi}(18.85)$$

$$+ \frac{1}{\pi}(13.29 + 8)$$

$$= 7.55 \text{ V}$$

The RMS calibrated full-wave rectified meter reads

$$V_{\text{read}} = \frac{\pi}{2\sqrt{2}}V_{\text{avg}}$$

Here it reads

$$V_{\text{reading}} = \boxed{8.39 \text{ V}}$$

This is an error of

$$\left(\frac{8.39 \text{ V} - 9.27 \text{ V}}{9.27 \text{ V}}\right)(100) = -9.5\%$$

Timed 2

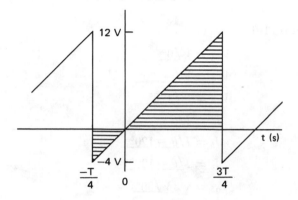

(a) The d'Arsonval average reading is

$$V_{\text{avg}} = \frac{1}{T}(\text{positive area} - \text{negative area})$$

$$= \left(\frac{1}{4}\right)\left[\left(\frac{1}{2}\right)(3)(12 \text{ V}) - \left(\frac{1}{2}\right)(1)(4 \text{ V})\right]$$

$$= \boxed{4 \text{ V}}$$

(b) Assuming the diode favors the 12 V polarity, and that it is calibrated for a half-wave rectified sinusoid,

$$V_{\text{reading}} = \frac{\pi}{\sqrt{2}}V_{\text{avg}} \text{ of half-wave}$$

The average of the positive voltage is

$$V_{\text{pos-avg}} = \left(\frac{1}{4}\right)\left(\frac{1}{2}\right)(3)(12 \text{ V}) = 4.5 \text{ V}$$

$$V_{\text{reading}} = \left(\frac{\pi}{\sqrt{2}}\right)(4.5 \text{ V}) = \boxed{10.0 \text{ V}}$$

(c) This meter reads the RMS value of a sinusoid by measuring peak-to-peak voltage.

$$V_{\text{p}} = \sqrt{2}\,V_{\text{RMS}}$$
$$V_{\text{p-p}} = 2\sqrt{2}\,V_{\text{RMS}}$$

$$V_{\text{reading}} = \frac{V_{\text{p-p}}}{2\sqrt{2}} = \frac{16}{2\sqrt{2}} = \boxed{5.7 \text{ V}}$$

(d) The electrodynomometer reads true RMS.

$$V_{\text{RMS}}^2 = \frac{1}{T}\int v^2 dt$$

$$= \frac{1}{4}\int_{-1}^{3}(4t)^2 dt$$

$$= 4\frac{t^3}{3}\Big|_{-1}^{3} = (4)\left[\frac{27}{3} - \left(-\frac{1}{3}\right)\right]$$

$$= \left(\frac{4}{3}\right)(28)$$

$$V_{\text{RMS}} = \boxed{6.11 \text{ V}}$$

Timed 3

On the 1.5-mA scale, the string of resistors will have 0.5 mA at full-scale, which is a voltage of $(0.5 \text{ mA})(1 \text{ k}\Omega) = 0.5$ V.

This is to result in a current of 1 mA flowing through the meter, so the combined $R_A + 50$ must be 0.5 V/jmA $= 500$ Ω so

$$R_a = \boxed{450 \ \Omega}$$

On the 15-mA position, 1 mA goes through $R_1 + R_A$ and 14 through $R_2 - R_5$ at full scale.

$$(14 \text{ mA})(R_2 + R_3 + R_4 + R_5) = (1 \text{ mA})(R_1 + 500 \ \Omega)$$

On the 150-mA position with full-scale current,

$$(149 \text{ mA})(R_3 + R_4 + R_5) = (1 \text{ mA})(R_1 + R_2 + 500 \ \Omega)$$

On the 1.5-A (1500-mA) scale,

$$(1499 \text{ mA})(R_4 + R_5) = (1 \text{ mA})(R_1 + R_2 + R_3 + 500 \ \Omega)$$

On the 15-A scale,

$$(14{,}999 \text{ mA})R_5 = (1 \text{ mA})(R_1 + R_2 + R_3 + R_4 + 500 \ \Omega)$$

By algebra,

$$\boxed{\begin{aligned} R_1 &= 900 \ \Omega \\ R_2 &= 90 \ \Omega \\ R_3 &= 9 \ \Omega \\ R_4 &= 0.9 \ \Omega \\ R_5 &= 0.1 \ \Omega \end{aligned}}$$

Timed 4

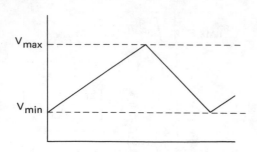

$$V_{avg} = 5 \text{ V (from d'Arsonval)}$$
$$= \frac{V_{max} + V_{min}}{2}$$
$$V_{max} + V_{min} = 10 \text{ V}$$

The RMS calibrated peak-to-peak meter reads

$$V_{read} = \frac{V_{\text{p-p}}}{2\sqrt{2}} = \frac{V_{max} - V_{min}}{2\sqrt{2}} = 7 \text{ V}$$
$$V_{max} - V_{min} = 14\sqrt{2} \text{ V}$$
$$2V_{max} = 14\sqrt{2} \text{ V} + 10 \text{ V}$$
$$V_{max} = 7\sqrt{2} + 5 = \boxed{14.9 \text{ V}}$$

$$V_{min} = -7\sqrt{2} + 5 = \boxed{-4.9 \text{ V}}$$

Timed 5

$$PF = 0.867 \text{ lagging}$$
$$\cos\theta = 0.867$$
$$\sin\theta = \sqrt{1 - \cos^2\theta} = 0.498$$
$$S = 100 \text{ kW} + j\left(\frac{0.498}{0.867}\right)(100 \text{ kW})$$
$$= 100 + j57.4 \text{ kVA}$$

(a) For PF = 0.895 lagging,

$$\sin\theta = \sqrt{1 - (0.895)^2} = 0.446$$
$$Q = \left(\frac{0.446}{0.895}\right)(100 \text{ kW}) = 49.8 \text{ kVAR}$$

Then $\Delta Q = 57.4 \text{ kVAR} - 49.8 \text{ kVAR} = 7.6 \text{ kVAR}$

$$Q_C = -7.6 \text{ kVAR} = \frac{V^2}{X_C}$$
$$X_C = \frac{(1320)^2}{7600} = -226 \text{ } \Omega$$

$$\boxed{7.6 \text{ kVAR at 1320 V}}$$

(b) For PF = 0.95 leading,

$$\sin\theta = \sqrt{1 - (0.95)^2} = 0.312$$
$$Q = \left(-\frac{0.312}{0.95}\right)(100 \text{ kW}) = -32.8 \text{ kVAR}$$

$$\Delta Q = 57.4 \text{ kVAR} - (-32.8 \text{ kVAR})$$
$$= 90.2 \text{ kVAR}$$

$$X_C = \frac{-(1320 \text{ V})^2}{90,200 \text{ VAR}} = -19.3 \text{ } \Omega$$

$$\boxed{90.2 \text{ kVAR at 1320 V}}$$

Timed 6

$$V_{an} = V\underline{/0°}$$
$$V_{bn} = V\underline{/-120°}$$
$$V_{cn} = V\underline{/120°}$$
$$I_a = I\underline{/\theta}$$
$$I_b = I\underline{/\theta - 120°}$$
$$I_c = I\underline{/\theta + 120°}$$
$$V_{ab} = \sqrt{3}\,V\underline{/30°}$$
$$V_{cb} = \sqrt{3}\,V\underline{/90°}$$
$$P_a = \text{Re}\,\{\sqrt{3}\,V\underline{/30°}\,I\underline{/-\theta}\}$$
$$= \sqrt{3}\,VI\cos(30° - \theta)$$

$$\cos(A \pm B) = \cos A \cos B \mp \sin A \sin B$$
$$P_a = \sqrt{3}\,VI(\cos 30° \cos\theta + \sin 30° \sin\theta)$$
$$= \frac{3}{2}VI\cos\theta + \frac{\sqrt{3}}{2}VI\sin\theta$$
$$P_c = \text{Re}\,\{\sqrt{3}\,V\underline{/90°}\,I\underline{/-(\theta + 120°)}\}$$
$$= \sqrt{3}\,VI\cos(-\theta - 30°)$$
$$= \sqrt{3}\,VI\cos(\theta + 30°)$$
$$= \sqrt{3}\,VI(\cos\theta \cos 30° - \sin\theta \sin 30°)$$
$$= \frac{3}{2}VI\cos\theta - \frac{\sqrt{3}}{2}VI\sin\theta$$
$$S = 3VI^* = 3VI\underline{/-\theta}$$
$$= 3VI\cos\theta - j3VI\sin\theta$$
$$= P + jQ$$

$$P_a = \boxed{\frac{1}{2}P + \frac{1}{2}\frac{1}{\sqrt{3}}Q}$$

$$P_c = \boxed{\frac{1}{2}P - \frac{1}{2}\frac{1}{\sqrt{3}}Q}$$

Timed 7

$$P_{\text{dBm}} = 10 \log_{10} \frac{10^3 V^2}{R}$$

$$= 30 - 10 \log R + 20 \log V$$

$$P_{\text{reading}} = 10 \log_{10} \frac{10^3 V^2}{600 \ \Omega}$$

$$= 30 - 10 \log 600 \ \Omega + 20 \log V$$

$$\text{reading error} = -10 \log 600 \ \Omega + 10 \log R$$

$$= \boxed{10 \log \left(\frac{R}{600 \ \Omega} \right)}$$

Correct the reading by subtracting the amount $10 \log(R/600 \ \Omega)$.

Timed 8

(a) A DC voltmeter reads the average.

$$\text{reading} = \frac{\text{area}}{\text{period}} = \frac{\left(\frac{1}{2} \right) (1 \ \text{ms})(5 \ \text{V})}{2 \ \text{ms}} = \boxed{1.25 \ \text{V}}$$

(b) A full-wave rectified RMS reading calibrated for sinusoids reads the average $\times \ \pi/(2\sqrt{2})$.

$$\text{reading} = \frac{\pi}{2\sqrt{2}} V_{\text{avg}} = 1.11 \ V_{\text{avg}} = \boxed{1.39 \ \text{V}}$$

(c) A half-wave rectifier calibrated to read RMS of a sinusoid reads the average $\times \ \pi/\sqrt{2}$.

$$\text{reading} = 2.22 V_{\text{avg}} = \boxed{2.78 \ \text{V}}$$

(d) A true RMS reads RMS value.

$$V_{\text{RMS}}^2 = \frac{1}{2} \int_0^1 (5t)^2 dt = \left(\frac{25}{2} \right) \frac{t^3}{3} \Big|_0^1$$

$$= \frac{25}{6}$$

$$\text{reading} = \sqrt{\frac{25}{6}} = \boxed{2.04 \ \text{V}}$$

(e) An RMS reading peak detector reads

$$\frac{V_p}{\sqrt{2}}$$

$$\text{reading} = \frac{5}{\sqrt{2}} = \boxed{3.54 \ \text{V}}$$

(f) An RMS reading peak-to-peak detector reads

$$\frac{V_{\text{max}} - V_{\text{min}}}{2\sqrt{2}}$$

$$\text{reading} = \frac{5 - 0}{2\sqrt{2}} = \boxed{1.77 \ \text{V}}$$

Timed 9

The average is calculated numerically.

$$V_{\text{avg}} = \left(\frac{1}{7} \right) (1 + 2 + 2 + 1 - 1 - 2 - 1)$$

$$= \frac{2}{7} = 0.286 \ \text{V}$$

Reading, $\boxed{\text{(b) is a DC meter.}}$

The RMS value is calculated.

$$V_{\text{RMS}}^2 = \left(\frac{1}{7} \right) [(1)^2 + (2)^2 + (2)^2 + (1)^2$$

$$+ (1)^2 + (2)^2 + (1)^2] = \frac{16}{7}$$

$$V_{\text{RMS}} = \sqrt{\frac{16}{7}} = 1.5 \ \text{V}$$

There does not appear to be a true RMS meter.

A full-wave rectified average is

$$V_{\text{f.w.,avg}} = \left(\frac{1}{7} \right) (1 + 2 + 2 + 1 + 1 + 2 + 1)$$

$$= \frac{10}{7} \ \text{V}$$

An RMS reading full-wave rectifier reads

$$\frac{\pi}{2\sqrt{2}} V_{\text{avg}}$$

$$\text{reading} = (1.11) \left(\frac{10}{7} \ \text{V} \right) = 1.6 \ \text{V}$$

There appears to be no full-wave rectifier meter.

The half-wave average could be of the positive or negative half-cycle.

For the positive,

$$V_{\text{h.c.,avg}}{}^+ = \left(\frac{1}{7} \right) (1 + 2 + 2 + 1) = \frac{6}{7} \ \text{V}$$

An RMS calibrated half-wave rectifier meter reads

$$V_{\mathrm{avg}}\left(\frac{\pi}{\sqrt{2}}\right) \text{ or } 2.22 V_{\mathrm{avg}}$$

$$\text{reading} = \left(\frac{6}{7}\ \mathrm{V}\right)(2.22) = 1.9\ \mathrm{V}$$

Then reading (c) could be this case. For the negative half cycle,

$$V_{\mathrm{h.c.,avg}^-} = \left(\frac{1}{7}\right)(1+2+1) = \frac{4}{7}\ \mathrm{V}$$

$$\text{reading} = \left(\frac{4}{7}\ \mathrm{V}\right)(2.22) = 1.3\ \mathrm{V}$$

Then reading (d) could come from this case.

The peak and peak-to-peak reading meters would both give a reading of $2/\sqrt{2} = 1.4$, so reading (a) could be either.

> (a) peak or peak-to-peak reading AC meter
> (b) DC meter
> (c) half-wave rectifier AC meter
> (d) half-wave rectifier AC meter

Timed 10

Full scale is 999_{10} for the first case. The noise is 0.5. At half scale the signal is 500_{10}, so the signal to noise ratio is $500/0.5 = 10^3$ or

$$S/N\bigg|_{\mathrm{dB}} = 20\log 10^3 = \boxed{60\ \mathrm{dB}}$$

For the octal, full scale in base 10 is

$$(7)(8)^3 + (7)(8)^2 + (7)(8)^1 + 7 = 4095$$

Half scale = 2048, and

$$S/N = 20\log\left(\frac{2048}{0.5}\right) = \boxed{72.2\ \mathrm{dB}}$$

For the binary, full scale in base 10 is

$$(2)^7 + (2)^6 + (2)^5 + (2)^4 + (2)^3 + (2)^2 + (2)^1 + 1 = 255$$

Half scale is 128.

$$S/N = 20\log\left(\frac{128}{0.5}\right) = \boxed{48.2\ \mathrm{dB}}$$

For the hexadecimal, the full scale is

$$(15)(16)^2 + (15)(16)^1 + 15 = 4095$$

The S/N ratio is the same as the octal.

$$S/N = 20\log\left(\frac{2048}{0.5}\right) = \boxed{72.2\ \mathrm{dB}}$$

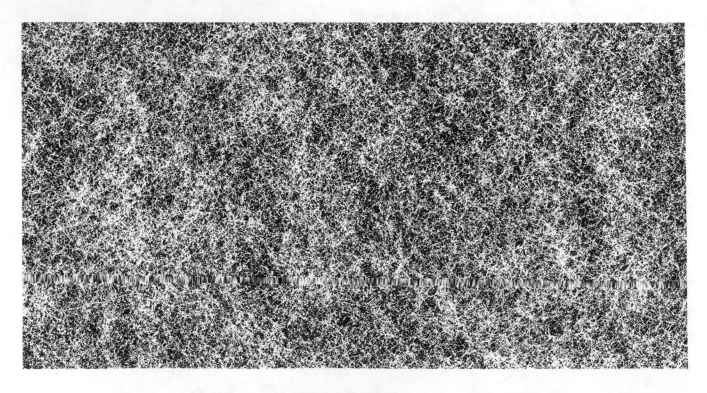

TIME AND FREQUENCY RESPONSE

Warmup 1

(a) With the switch closed, Kirchhoff's voltage law (KVL):

$$15 = 4i_s + v_L$$

$$v_L = L\frac{di}{dt} = 0 \text{ in steady state}$$

$$i_s = \frac{15}{4}$$

> The current through the 8-Ω resistor is $v_L/8 = 0$, therefore all of i_s flows through the inductance in steady state.

(b) In steady state, the currents eventually become zero.

Warmup 2

(a) With the switch closed,

$$i_C = C\frac{dv_C}{dt}$$

In steady state,

$$\frac{dv_C}{dt} = 0$$

Therefore, $i_C \rightarrow 0$. By voltage division,

$$v_C = \left(\frac{8\ \Omega}{12\ \Omega}\right)(15\text{ V}) = \boxed{10\text{ V}}$$

(b) With the switch open, the capacitance will discharge to 0 V.

Warmup 3

(a) A Thevenin equivalent circuit seen from the inductance is obtained.

$$v_{oc} = v_{Th} = \frac{8\ \Omega}{12\ \Omega}v_S = 10\cos(10t + 20°)\text{ V}$$

$$i_{sc} = \frac{15\cos(10t + 20°)\text{ V}}{4\ \Omega} = 3.75\ \cos(10t + 20°)\text{ A}$$

$$R_{Th} = \frac{v_{oc}}{i_{sc}} = \frac{10\text{ V}}{3.75\text{ A}} = \frac{8}{3}\ \Omega$$

Taking $\cos(10t + 20°)$ as the phasor reference,

$$V_{Th} = 10\underline{/0°}\text{ V}$$

$$Z_L = j\omega L = \left(j10\ \frac{\text{rad}}{\text{s}}\right)(0.1\text{ H}) = j1\ \Omega$$

$$I_L = \frac{V_{Th}}{R_{Th} + j1\ \Omega} = \left(\frac{10\text{ V}}{\frac{8}{3}\ \Omega + j1\ \Omega}\right)\left(\frac{\frac{8}{3}\ \Omega - j1\ \Omega}{\frac{8}{3}\ \Omega - j1\ \Omega}\right)$$

$$= \left(\frac{90}{73}\right)\left(\frac{8}{3} - j1\right) = \boxed{3.51\underline{/-20.6°}\text{ A}}$$

As a time function,

$$i_L(\infty) = 3.51\cos(10t + 20° - 20.6°)$$

$$= 3.51\cos(10t - 0.6°)\text{ A}$$

(b) $i_L(\infty)$ is zero with the switch open.

Warmup 4

With the switch closed for a long time, the capacitance voltage is 10 V (see Warmup 2). The initial voltage when the switch opens is therefore 10 V.

With the switch open, KVL is

$$v_C = 8i$$

$$i_C = 10^{-6}\frac{dv_C}{dt}$$

$$i_C = -i$$

$$v_C + (8 \times 10^{-6})\frac{dv_C}{dt} = 0$$

$$\frac{dv_C}{dt} + (1.25 \times 10^5)v_C = 0$$

For $\alpha = 1.25 \times 10^5$, the solution is of the form

$$v_C = V(t_1)e^{-\alpha(t-t_1)}$$

Taking $t_1 = 0$, $v_C(0) = 10$ V.

$$\frac{dv_C}{dt} = -\alpha v_C$$

$$\alpha = 1.25 \times 10^5$$

$$v_C(t) = \boxed{10e^{-(1.25\times10^5)t}\text{ V}}$$

Warmup 5

The initial capacitance voltage is zero.

Kirchhoff's current law (KCL) at the upper node, with the lower node as reference:

$$\frac{15\text{ V} - v_C}{4\ \Omega} = \frac{v_C}{8\ \Omega} + (10^{-6}\text{ F})\frac{dv_C}{dt}$$

This is manipulated to

$$\frac{8}{3} \times 10^{-6} \frac{dv_C}{dt} + v_C = 10$$

$$V_F = 10$$

$$\tau = \frac{8}{3} \times 10^{-6}$$

$$V_O = 0$$

$$v_C(t) = V_F + (V_O - V_F)e^{-\frac{t}{\tau}}$$

$$= \boxed{(10)(1 - e^{-(3.75\times10^5)t})u(t) \text{ V}}$$

Warmup 6

The homogeneous differential equation is

$$\frac{d^2v}{dt^2} + 5\frac{dv}{dt} + 4v = 0$$

This has solutions e^{st},

$$\frac{d^2v}{dt^2} \rightarrow s^2 V$$

$$\frac{dv}{dt} \rightarrow sV$$

$$s^2 + 5s + 4 = 0$$

$$(s+4)(s+1) = 0$$

Transient solutions are of the form

$$Ae^{-4t} + Be^{-t}$$

The steady-state sinusoidal solution must be found before A and B can be evaluated.

The phasor solution is

$$12\sin 2t \Rightarrow 12\underline{/0^\circ}$$

$$\omega = 2$$

$$\frac{d}{dt} \rightarrow j\omega = j2$$

$$\frac{d^2}{dt^2} \rightarrow -\omega^2 = -4$$

The phasor equation is

$$12 \text{ V} = -4V_{ss} + (5)(j2)V_{ss} + 4V_{ss}$$

$$= j10V_{ss}$$

$$V_{ss} = \frac{1.2}{j} = 1.2\underline{/-90^\circ} \text{ V}$$

$$v_{ss} = 1.2\sin(2t - 90^\circ) \text{ V}$$

$$= -1.2\cos 2t \text{ V}$$

$$v(t) = Ae^{-4t} + Be^{-t} - 1.2\cos 2t$$

$$v(0) = A + B - 1.2 \text{ V} = -5 \text{ V}$$

$$A + B = -3.8 \text{ V}$$

$$\frac{dv}{dt} = -4Ae^{-4t} - Be^{-t} + 2.4\sin 2t$$

$$\frac{dv}{dt}(0) = -4A - B = 2$$

$$A = 0.6 \text{ V}$$

$$B = -4.4 \text{ V}$$

$$v(t) = \boxed{(0.6e^{-4t} - 4.4e^{-t} - 1.2\cos 2t)u(t) \text{ V}}$$

Warmup 7

The impedance of the inductance branch is

$$Z_{LR} = 10 + 0.25s \ \Omega$$

KCL applied to the upper node is

$$I_s = \frac{V_c}{30 \ \Omega} + (0.001 \text{ F})sV_c + \frac{V_c}{10 \ \Omega + (0.25 \text{ H})s}$$

Solving,

$$G = \frac{V_c}{I_s} = \frac{3 \times 10^4 + 750s}{0.75s^2 + 55s + 4000} \text{ S}$$

$$= \boxed{(1000)\left(\frac{s + 40}{s^2 + 73.33s + 5333}\right) \text{ S}}$$

Warmup 8

$$Z = 10 + 0.5s + \frac{10^4}{s} \ \Omega$$

$$= \left(\frac{1}{2}\right)\left(\frac{s^2 + 20s + 2 \times 10^4}{s}\right) \ \Omega$$

$$= \left(\frac{1}{2s}\right)\left(s^2 + \frac{\omega_o}{Q}s + \omega_o^2\right) \ \Omega$$

$$\omega_o = \boxed{\sqrt{2} \times 10^2 \text{ rad/s}}$$

$$Q = \frac{\omega_o}{20} = \boxed{5\sqrt{2}}$$

$$BW = \frac{\omega_o}{Q} = \boxed{20 \text{ rad/s}}$$

Warmup 9

$$Y = 0.1 + \frac{1}{0.5s} + 10^{-4}s$$

$$= \frac{10^{-4}}{s}(s^2 + 10^3 s + 2 \times 10^4)$$

$$= \frac{10^{-4}}{s}\left(s^2 + \frac{\omega_o}{Q}s + \omega_o^2\right)$$

$$\omega_o = \sqrt{2 \times 10^4} = \boxed{100\sqrt{2} \text{ rad/s}}$$

$$\text{BW} = \frac{\omega_o}{Q} = \boxed{10^3 \text{ rad/s}}$$

$$Q = \frac{\omega_o}{\text{BW}} = \frac{\sqrt{2}}{10} = \boxed{0.1\sqrt{2}}$$

Warmup 10

With the switch open for a long time, the upper-right capacitor is charged to 10 V and the lower (center) capacitor is discharged to 0 V.

At the instant of switching, the capacitors can be modeled as ideal voltage sources with their initial voltages.

The resulting equivalent circuit is shown.

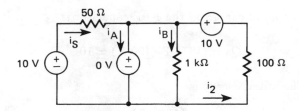

Kirchhoff's voltage law on the left loop is

$$10 \text{ V} - (50 \text{ } \Omega)i_S + 0.0 = 0$$

$$i_S = \frac{1}{5} \text{ A}$$

Kirchhoff's voltage law on the right loop is

$$0.0 + 10 \text{ V} - (100 \text{ } \Omega)i_2 = 0$$

$$i_2 = \frac{1}{10} \text{ A}$$

> The current in the right (upper) capacitor is i_2, 0.1 A flowing left.

As the voltage across the 1-kΩ resistor is zero, $i_B = 0$. By Kirchhoff's current law, the other capacitor current is

$$i_A = i_S + i_2 = \frac{1}{5} \text{ A} + \frac{1}{10} \text{ A} = \boxed{0.3 \text{ A}}$$

Concentrate 1

The homogeneous equation is

$$s^2 + 4s + 4 = 0$$

The roots are $(s+2)^2$. The homogeneous solution is

$$Ae^{-2t} + Bte^{-2t}$$

The steady-state solution is

$$s \to j\omega$$
$$\omega = 4$$
$$\frac{d}{dt} \Rightarrow j\omega$$
$$\frac{d^2}{dt^2} \Rightarrow -\omega^2 = -16$$

The sine reference is used,

$$20 \text{ V} = (-16 \text{ } \Omega + 16j \text{ } \Omega + 4 \text{ } \Omega)I_{ss}$$

$$I_{ss} = \frac{20}{-12 + j16} = -0.6 + j(-0.8) \text{ A}$$

$$i_{ss} = -0.6 \sin 4t - 0.8 \sin(4t + 90°) \text{ A}$$

$$= -0.6 \sin 4t - 0.8 \cos 4t \text{ A}$$

$$i = i_{ss} + Ae^{-2t} + Bte^{-2t}$$

$$i(0) = -0.8 + A = 0$$

$$A = 0.8 \text{ A}$$

$$\frac{di}{dt} = -2.4 \cos 4t + 3.2 \sin 4t$$
$$- 2Ae^{-2t} + Be^{-2t} - 2Bte^{-2t}$$

$$\frac{di}{dt}(0) = -2.4 - 2A + B = 4$$

$$B = 2.4 + 2A + 4 = 8 \text{ A}$$

$$i(t) = 0.8e^{-2t} + 8te^{-2t} - 0.6 \sin 4t - 0.8 \cos 4t \text{ A}$$

$$= \boxed{0.8e^{-2t} + 8te^{-2t} - \sin(4t + 53.1) \text{ A}}$$

Concentrate 2

A phasor analysis prior to switching gives the steady-state inductance current (positive down).

$$i_L = 5.15 \cos(377t - 57.5°) \text{ A}$$

At $t = 0$, the inductance current is

$$i_L(0) = 5.15 \cos 57.5° = 2.77 \text{ A}$$

No information was given so the capacitance voltage is assumed to be initally zero.

At $t = 0^+$, the inductance is replaced by a current source of 2.77 A and the capacitance is replaced by a voltage source of 0 V.

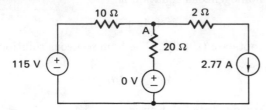

Kirchhoff's current law at node A is

$$\frac{115 \text{ V} - v_A}{10 \text{ } \Omega} = \frac{v_A}{20 \text{ } \Omega} + 2.77 \text{ A}$$

$$v_A = 58.2 \text{ V}$$

$$i_C(0^+) = \frac{v_A}{20 \text{ } \Omega} = \boxed{2.91 \text{ A}}$$

$$v_L(0^+) = v_A - (2 \text{ } \Omega)(2.77 \text{ A}) = \boxed{52.7 \text{ V}}$$

Concentrate 3

Circuit equations are obtained in terms of the state variables i_L and v_C.

Kirchhoff's voltage law for the left-hand loop is

$$100 \text{ V} = (100 \text{ } \Omega)\left[i_L + (10^{-4} \text{ F})\frac{dv_C}{dt}\right] + v_C$$

For the right-hand loop,

$$v_C = (10 \text{ } \Omega)i_L + (1.0 \text{ H})\frac{di_L}{dt}$$

The Laplace transformation of these equations gives

$$\frac{100}{s} = 100I_L + 10^{-2}(sV_c - v_C(0^+)) + V_C \qquad [1]$$

$$V_c = 10I_L + sI_L - i_L(0^+) \qquad [2]$$

With $i_L(0^+) = 1$ A and $v_C(0^+) = 20$ V, Eq. 2 becomes

$$V_c = (s + 10)I_L - 1 \text{ V}$$

Eq. 1 becomes

$$\frac{100}{s} + 0.2 = 100I_L + \left(\frac{s}{100} + 1\right)V_c$$

Substituting for I_L,

$$V_c = \frac{20s^2 + 200s + 10^5}{s(s^2 + 110s + 1.1 \times 10^4)} \text{ V}$$

This has complex poles at $s = 55 \perp j80.3$.

A partial fraction expansion will involve the terms

$$\frac{A}{s} + B\frac{s + 55}{(s + 55)^2 + (89.3)^2} + C\frac{89.3}{(s + 55)^2 + (89.3)^2}$$

Cross multiplying the last expression to put it over a common denominator and equating the result with V_c,

$$A = 9.09$$
$$B = 10.91$$
$$C = -15.68$$

The inverse transform yields

$$v_C(t) = 9.09 + 10.91e^{-55t}\cos 89.3t - 15.68e^{-55t}\sin 89.3t$$

$$v_C(t) = \boxed{9.09 + 19.10e^{-55t}\cos(89.3t - 55.2°) \text{ V}}$$

Concentrate 4

The initial charge on the 1-μF capacitor is

$$Q_0 = (10^{-6} \text{ F})(100 \text{ V}) = 10^{-4} \text{ C}$$

The initial energy is

(a) $W_0 = \frac{1}{2}C_1V_0^2 = \left(\frac{10^{-6} \text{ F}}{2}\right) \times (100 \text{ V})^2 = 0.005 \text{ J}$

In the final condition, the voltage across the two capacitors is the same.

$$V_f = \frac{Q_1}{C_1} = \frac{Q_2}{C_2} \text{ or } Q_2 = 2Q_1$$

As $Q_1 + Q_2 = Q_0$,

$$Q_1 = \frac{1}{3} \times 10^{-4} \text{ C}$$

$$Q_2 = \frac{2}{3} \times 10^{-4} \text{ C}$$

$$W_{\text{final}} = \left(\frac{1}{2}\right)\left(\frac{Q_1^2}{C_1}\right) + \left(\frac{1}{2}\right)\left(\frac{Q_2^2}{C_2}\right) \text{ J}$$

$$= \boxed{\begin{array}{l}\left(\frac{1}{2}\right)(10^6 \text{ F}^{-1})\left(\frac{1}{9} \times 10^{-8} \text{ C}^2\right) \\ + \left(\frac{10^6 \text{ F}^{-1}}{2}\right)\left(\frac{4}{9} \times 10^{-8} \text{ C}^2\right)\end{array} \text{ J}}$$

(b) $\quad W_{\text{final}} = \frac{3}{18} \times 10^{-2} = \boxed{0.00167 \text{ J}}$

(c) $\quad W_{\text{loss}} = 0.005 - 0.00167 = \boxed{0.00333 \text{ J}}$

Concentrate 5

By voltage division,

$$\frac{V_{out}}{V_{in}}(s) = \frac{0.01s}{0.01s + 50 + \dfrac{10^6}{s}}$$

$$= \boxed{\frac{s^2}{s^2 + 5000s + 10^8}}$$

The denominator requires an underdamped response, so it is put into the form to take advantage of the Laplace transform pairs table.

$$\frac{V_{out}}{V_{in}}(s) = \frac{s^2}{(s+2500)^2 + (9682)^2}$$

For the frequency response $s \to j\omega$,

$$\frac{V_{out}}{V_{in}}(j\omega) = \frac{-\omega^2}{10^8 - \omega^2 + j5000\omega}$$

At low frequency,

$$\frac{V_{out}}{V_{in}} \to \frac{-\omega^2}{10^8}$$

This has a slope of 40 dB/dec and a phase of 180° on a Bode diagram.

At high frequency,

$$\frac{V_{out}}{V_{in}} \to 1$$

At $\omega = 10^4$ rad/s,

$$\frac{V_{out}}{V_{in}} = 2\underline{/90°}$$

The value is 6 dB.

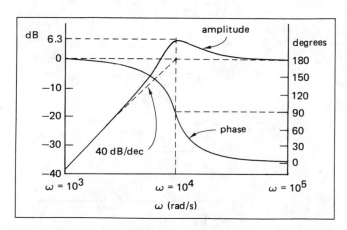

The step response is, with $V_{in} = 1/s$,

$$V_{out} = \frac{s}{(s+2500)^2 + (9682)^2} \text{ V-s}$$

$$= \frac{s + 2500}{(s+2500)^2 + (9682)^2}$$

$$- \left(\frac{2500}{9862}\right)\left[\frac{9862}{(s+5000)^2 + (9682)^2}\right]$$

$$v_{out}(t) = e^{-2500t}\cos 9682t - 0.258e^{-2500t}\sin 9682t$$

$$= \boxed{1.03e^{-2500t}\cos(9682t + 14°) \text{ V}}$$

Concentrate 6

By voltage division,

$$\frac{V_{out}}{V_{in}} = \frac{\dfrac{10^6}{s}}{10^{-2}s + 50 + \dfrac{10^6}{s}} = \boxed{\frac{10^8}{s^2 + 5000s + 10^8}}$$

$$\frac{V_{out}}{V_{in}}(j\omega) = \frac{10^8}{10^8 - \omega^2 + j5000\omega}$$

At low frequency,

$$\frac{V_{out}}{V_{in}} \to 1\underline{/0°}$$

At high frequency,

$$\frac{V_{out}}{V_{in}} \to \frac{10^8}{-\omega^2}$$

On the Bode diagram, this has a slope of -40 dB/dec and an angle of $-180°$. At $\omega = 10^4$ rad/s,

$$\frac{V_{out}}{V_{in}} = 2\underline{/-90°}$$

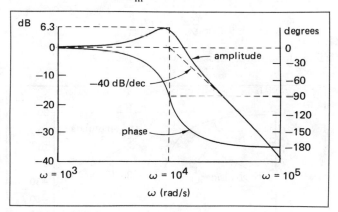

The step response is, with $V_{in} = 1/s$,

$$V_{out} = \frac{10^8}{s(s^2 + 5000s + 10^8)} \text{ V-s}$$

This is expanded in partial fractions to

$$V_{out} = \frac{1}{s} - \frac{s + 5000}{(s+2500)^2 + (9682)^2}$$

This is recast to fit the Laplace transform pairs table.

$$V_{out} = \frac{1}{s} - \frac{s + 2500}{(2 + 2500)^2 + (9682)^2}$$

$$+ \frac{\left(\dfrac{2500}{9682}\right)(9682)}{(s+2500)^2 + (9682)^2}$$

$$v_{\text{out}}(t) = 1 - e^{-2500t}(\cos 9682t + 0.258 \sin 9682t) \text{ V}$$

$$\boxed{v_{\text{out}}(t) = 1 - 1.033e^{-2500t} \cos(9682t - 14.5°) \text{ V}}$$

Concentrate 7

By voltage division,

$$\frac{V_{\text{out}}}{V_{\text{in}}} = \frac{50}{10^{-2}s + 50 + \dfrac{10^6}{s}} = \boxed{\frac{5000s}{s^2 + 5000s + 10^8}}$$

$$\frac{V_{\text{out}}}{V_{\text{in}}}(j\omega) = \frac{j5000\omega}{10^8 - \omega^2 + j5000\omega}$$

At low frequency,

$$\frac{V_{\text{out}}}{V_{\text{in}}} \to 0.5 \times 10^{-4}\omega\underline{/90°}$$

This has a slope of 20 dB/dec.

At high frequency,

$$\frac{V_{\text{out}}}{V_{\text{in}}} \to \frac{5000}{\omega}\underline{/-90°}$$

This has a slope of -20 dB/dec.

The asymptotes intersect at $\omega = 10^4$ rad/s and -6 dB.

At $\omega = 10^4$ rad/s,

$$\frac{V_{\text{out}}}{V_{\text{in}}} \to 1\underline{/0°}$$

The Bode diagram is shown.

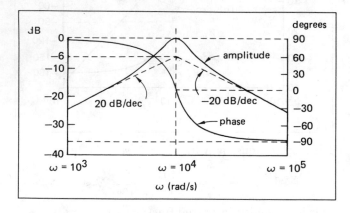

The step response is, with $V_{\text{in}} = 1/s$,

$$V_{\text{out}} = \frac{5000}{(s + 2500)^2 + (9682)^2} \text{ V-s}$$

To fit the Laplace transform pairs table,

$$V_{\text{out}} = \left(\frac{5000}{9682}\right)\left[\frac{9682}{(s + 2500)^2 + (9682)^2}\right] \text{ V-s}$$

$$\boxed{v_{\text{out}}(t) = 0.516e^{-2500t} \sin 9682t \text{ V}}$$

Concentrate 8

$$G = \frac{k}{\left(\dfrac{s}{\omega_o}\right)^2 + \dfrac{1}{Q}\left(\dfrac{s}{\omega_o}\right) + 1}$$

Let $S = s/\omega_o$ and $k = 1$.

$$G = \frac{1}{S^2 + \dfrac{1}{Q}S + 1}$$

Let $s \to j\omega$ and $S \to j\dfrac{\omega}{\omega_o}$.

$$G\left(j\frac{\omega}{\omega_o}\right) = \frac{1}{1 - \left(\dfrac{\omega}{\omega_o}\right)^2 + j\dfrac{\frac{\omega}{\omega_o}}{Q}}$$

$$\left|G\left(j\frac{\omega}{\omega_o}\right)\right|^2 = \frac{1}{1 - (2)\left(\dfrac{\omega}{\omega_o}\right)^2 + \left(\dfrac{\omega}{\omega_o}\right)^4 + \dfrac{\left(\dfrac{\omega}{\omega_o}\right)^2}{Q^2}}$$

The minimax of $|G|^2$ is at

$$-4\frac{\omega}{\omega_o} + (4)\left(\frac{\omega}{\omega_o}\right)^3 + \frac{(2)\left(\dfrac{\omega}{\omega_o}\right)}{Q^2} = 0$$

$\dfrac{\omega}{\omega_o} = 0$ is the minima, and the maxima is at

$$\left(\frac{\omega}{\omega_o}\right)^2 = 1 - \frac{1}{2Q^2}$$

At this value,

$$|G|_{\max} = \frac{Q}{\sqrt{1 - \dfrac{1}{4Q^2}}}$$

For step response, the form is changed.

$$G = \frac{\omega_o^2}{s^2 + \dfrac{\omega_o}{Q}s + \omega_o^2}$$

$$= \frac{\omega_o^2}{\left(s + \dfrac{\omega_o}{2Q}\right)^2 + \omega_o^2\left(1 - \dfrac{1}{4Q^2}\right)}$$

$$\frac{\omega_o}{2Q} = \alpha$$

$$\omega_o^2\left(1 - \frac{1}{4Q^2}\right) = \beta^2$$

$$G = \frac{\omega_o^2}{(s + \alpha)^2 + \beta^2} = \frac{\alpha^2 + \beta^2}{(s + \alpha)^2 + \beta^2}$$

The step response is

$$G\frac{1}{s} = \frac{1}{s} - \frac{s+2\alpha}{(s+\alpha)^2 + \beta^2}$$

$$= \frac{1}{s} - \frac{s+\alpha}{(s+\alpha)^2 + \beta^2} - \frac{\frac{\alpha}{\beta}\beta}{(s+\alpha)^2 + \beta^2}$$

$$v(t) = 1 - e^{-\alpha t}\cos\beta t - \frac{\alpha}{\beta}e^{-\alpha t}\sin\beta t \text{ V}$$

This reaches its peak at

$$\beta t = \pi$$

$$V_p = 1 + e^{-\frac{\alpha}{\beta}\pi}$$

In terms of Q and ω_o,

$$V_p = 1 + e^{-\left\{\frac{\pi}{\sqrt{4Q^2-1}}\right\}} \text{ V}$$

Q	$|G|_{max}$	V_p (V)
0.707	1.000	1.043
1.00	1.115	1.163
1.414	1.512	1.305
2.0	2.066	1.444
4.0	4.032	1.673

For large Q,

$$|G|_{max} \to Q$$
$$V_p \to 2$$

Concentrate 9

A third-order Butterworth low-pass is

$$G = \frac{10\omega_o^3}{(s+\omega_o)(s^2 + \omega_o s + \omega_o^2)}$$

For a unit step input, the output becomes

$$V_{out} = \frac{10}{s} - \frac{10}{s+\omega_o} - \frac{10\omega_o}{\left(s + \frac{w_o}{2}\right)^2 + \frac{3}{4}\omega_o^2}$$

$$v_{out}(t)$$

$$= \left\{10 - 10e^{-\omega_o t} - 10\sqrt{\frac{4}{3}}e^{-\frac{\omega_o}{2}t}\sin\sqrt{\frac{3}{4}}\omega_o t\right\} \text{ V}$$

$$\text{(for } t > 0\text{)}$$

Concentrate 10

$$s^2 + \frac{\omega_o}{Q}s + \omega_o^2 \to s^2 + 5s + 100$$

$$Q = \boxed{2}$$

The unit step response is

$$V_{out} = \frac{s^2 + 100}{s(s^2 + 5s + 100)} \text{ V}$$

$$= \frac{1}{s} - \frac{5}{(s+2.5)^2 + 93.75}$$

$$= \frac{1}{s} - \left(\frac{5}{\sqrt{93.75}}\right)\left(\frac{\sqrt{93.75}}{(s+2.5)^2 + 93.75}\right)$$

$$v_{out}(t) = \boxed{\begin{array}{c} 1 - \frac{5}{\sqrt{93.75}}e^{-2.5t}\sin\sqrt{93.75}\,t \text{ V} \\ \text{(for } t > 0\text{)} \end{array}}$$

Timed 1

The transfer function is obtained by voltage division.

$$\frac{V_{out}}{V_{in}} = \left(\frac{KR_2}{R_1 + R_2}\right)\left(\frac{sCR_1 + 1}{sC\frac{R_1 R_2}{R_1 + R_2} + 1}\right)$$

$$z = \frac{1}{CR_1}$$

$$p = \frac{R_1 + R_2}{CR_1 R_2}$$

The phase angle is found from

$$\frac{j\omega + z}{j\omega + p}$$

$$\phi = \arctan\frac{\omega}{z} - \arctan\frac{\omega}{p}$$

The minimax is found by

$$\frac{d\phi}{d\omega} = 0 \text{ at } \omega^2 = zp$$

This is a maximum for phase lead, and minimum for phase lag. This is phase lead, and at the maximum angle

$$\phi_{max} = \arctan\sqrt{\frac{p}{z}} - \arctan\sqrt{\frac{z}{p}}$$

$$\tan\phi_{max} = \left(\frac{1}{2}\right)\left(\sqrt{\frac{p}{z}} - \sqrt{\frac{z}{p}}\right)$$

from

$$\tan(A - B) = \frac{\tan A - \tan B}{1 + \tan A \tan B}$$

The specifications call for a phase lead of ϕ_d at frequency ω_d. Set

$$\omega_d = \sqrt{pz} = \frac{1}{CR_1}\sqrt{1 + \frac{R_1}{R_2}}$$

and

$$\tan\phi_d = \left(\frac{1}{2}\right)\left(\sqrt{\frac{p}{z}} - \sqrt{\frac{z}{p}}\right) = \frac{\omega_d}{2}\left(\frac{1}{z} - \frac{1}{p}\right)$$

$$\frac{1}{z} - \frac{1}{p} = \frac{p-z}{pz} = \frac{p-z}{\omega_d^2}$$

$$2\omega_d\tan\phi_d = p - z = \frac{1}{CR_2}$$

Substituting ω_d,

$$2\tan\phi_d = \frac{\dfrac{R_1}{R_2}}{\sqrt{1 + \dfrac{R_1}{R_2}}}$$

This is solved for

$$\frac{R_1}{R_2} = \boxed{\frac{2\sin\phi_d}{1 - \sin\phi_d}}$$

Also,

$$\frac{1}{CR_2} = \boxed{2\omega_d\tan\phi_d}$$

To set the gain = 1 at $\omega = \omega_d$,

$$1 = \left(\frac{KR_2}{R_1 + R_2}\right)\left[\frac{\left(\dfrac{\omega_d}{z}\right)^2 + 1}{\left(\dfrac{\omega_d}{p}\right)^2 + 1}\right]^{\frac{1}{2}}$$

$$\frac{\omega_d^2}{z^2} = \frac{p}{z}$$

$$\frac{\omega_d^2}{p^2} = \frac{z}{p}$$

This requires

$$\frac{R_1}{R_2} = \boxed{K^2 - 1}$$

> The angle cannot reach 90°. For stability and noise considerations, the ratio of the pole to the zero is normally limited to 10, for a maximum angle of about 55°.

Timed 2

(a) By voltage division,

$$\frac{V_{\text{out}}}{V_{\text{in}}} = \frac{\dfrac{100}{10^{-3}s + 1}}{1000 + \dfrac{100}{10^{-3}s + 1}} = \boxed{\frac{100}{s + 1100}}$$

(b) For a unit step input $1/s$,

$$V_{\text{out}} = \frac{1}{s}\left(\frac{100}{s + 1100}\right) = \frac{1}{11s} - \frac{\frac{1}{11}}{s + 1100} \text{ V}$$

$$v_{\text{out}}(t) = \boxed{\left(\frac{1}{11}\right)\left(1 - e^{-1100t}\right)u(t) \text{ V}}$$

(c) For a 1-ms pulse, $v_{\text{in}}(t)$ is

$$v_{\text{in}}(t) = u(t) - u(t - 10^{-3}) \text{ V}$$

$$V_{\text{in}}(s) = \frac{1}{s} - \frac{e^{-0.001s}}{s} \text{ V}$$

The output is

$$V_{\text{out}} = (100)\left[\frac{1 - e^{-0.001s}}{s(s + 1100)}\right] \text{ V}$$

$$v_{\text{out}}(t) = \boxed{\begin{array}{l}\left(\dfrac{1}{11}\right)\left(1 - e^{-1100t}\right)u(t) \\[2mm] - \left(\dfrac{1}{11}\right)\left(1 - e^{-1100(t-0.001)}\right) \\[2mm] \times\, u(t - 0.001) \text{ V}\end{array}}$$

Timed 3

For $t < 0$ (before switch opens), the circuit has reached a steady state, so all time derivatives are zero.

$$v_L = 0$$
$$i_C = 0$$

Inductors are replaced by short circuits and capacitors by open circuits.

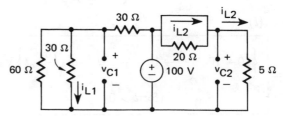

Because of L_2, the 20-Ω resistor has no current, so

$$v_{C2} = 100 \text{ V}$$

$$i_{L2} = \frac{100 \text{ V}}{5\ \Omega} = 20 \text{ A}$$

The 30- and 60-Ω parallel paths combine to 20 Ω, so

$$v_{C1} = \left(\frac{20\ \Omega}{20\ \Omega + 30\ \Omega} \right)(100\ \text{V}) = 40\ \text{V}$$

$$i_{L1} = \frac{40\ \text{V}}{30\ \Omega} = \frac{4}{3}\ \text{A}$$

The initial conditions on the state variables are

$$i_{L1}(0^-) = i_{L1}(0^+) = \frac{4}{3}\ \text{A}$$

$$i_{L2}(0^-) = i_{L2}(0^+) = 20\ \text{A}$$

$$v_{C1}(0^-) = v_{C1}(0^+) = 40\ \text{V}$$

$$v_{C2}(0^-) = v_{C2}(0^+) = 100\ \text{V}$$

At the instant the switch opens, these branches are replaced (for that instant only) by corresponding sources.

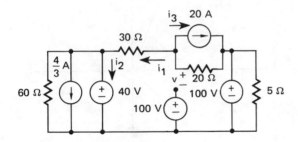

A loop including the two capacitors, according to Kirchhoff's voltage law, is

$$40\ \text{V} + i_1(30\ \Omega) + (20\ \Omega)(i_1 + 20\ \text{A}) = 100\ \text{V}$$

$$i_1 = \boxed{-6.8\ \text{A}}$$

At the 40-V node,

$$i_1 = \frac{4}{3}\ \text{A} + \frac{40\ \text{V}}{60\ \Omega} + i_2 = -6.8\ \text{A}$$

$$i_2 = \boxed{-8.8\ \text{A}}$$

The voltage v is found.

$$40\ \text{V} + (30\ \Omega)i_1 = v + 100\ \text{V}$$

$$v = 40\ \text{V} - 204\ \text{V} - 100\ \text{V}$$

$$= \boxed{-264\ \text{V}}$$

The voltage across the 2-H coil is the same as v, so

$$2\frac{di_3}{dt} = -264\ \text{A/s}$$

$$\frac{di_3}{dt} = \boxed{-132\ \text{A/s}}$$

Timed 4

By voltage division,

$$V_{c1} = \frac{\dfrac{1}{sC_1}V_{\text{in}}}{\dfrac{1}{sC_1} + 10^4\ \Omega} = \frac{V_{\text{in}}}{10^4 C_1 s + 1}\ \text{V-s}$$

$$V_{c2} = \frac{\dfrac{1}{sC_2}V_{c1}}{\dfrac{1}{sC_2} + (R_2 + 5\ \Omega) + (10^{-2}\ \text{H})s}$$

$$= \frac{V_{c1}}{10^{-2}C_2 s^2 + (5 + R_2)C_2 s + 1}\ \text{V-s}$$

The transfer function is

$$\frac{V_{\text{out}}}{V_{\text{in}}} = \left(\frac{1}{10^4 C_1 s + 1} \right)$$

$$\times \left(\frac{1}{10^{-2}C_2 s^2 + (5 + R_2)C_2 s + 1} \right)$$

For Butterworth,

$$\frac{V_{\text{out}}}{V_{\text{in}}} = \left(\frac{1}{\dfrac{s}{\omega_o} + 1} \right) \left(\frac{1}{\left(\dfrac{s}{\omega_o}\right)^2 + \dfrac{s}{\omega_o} + 1} \right)$$

$$\omega_o = (2\pi)(150) = 300\pi\ \text{rad/s}$$

$$10^4 C_1 = \frac{1}{\omega_o}$$

$$C_1 = \frac{10^{-4}}{300\pi}\ \text{F}$$

$$10^{-2}C_2 = \frac{1}{\omega_o^2}$$

$$C_2 = \frac{100}{(300\ \pi)^2}\ \text{F}$$

$$(5 + R_2)C_2 = \frac{1}{\omega_o} = \frac{1}{300\ \pi}$$

$$5 + R_2 = 3\pi$$

$$R_2 = 3\pi - 5\ \Omega$$

$$C_1 = \boxed{106\ \text{nF}}$$

$$C_2 = \boxed{113\ \mu\text{F}}$$

$$R = \boxed{4.43\ \Omega}$$

Timed 5

By voltage division, the A1 output circuit transfer function is

$$\cfrac{\dfrac{10^6}{s}}{\dfrac{10^6}{s} + 50 + \left(3 \times 10^{-3}\right) s}$$

$$= \frac{1}{\left(3 \times 10^{-9}\right) s^2 + \left(5 \times 10^{-5}\right) s + 1}$$

The output of A2 is

$$\cfrac{\left(3 \times 10^{-3}\right) s}{\dfrac{10^6}{s} + 50 + \left(3 \times 10^{-3}\right) s}$$

$$= \frac{\left(3 \times 10^{-9}\right) s^2}{\left(3 \times 10^{-9}\right) s^2 + \left(5 \times 10^{-5}\right) s + 1}$$

The overall transfer function becomes

$$\frac{V_{\text{out}}}{V_{\text{in}}} = \frac{\left(3 \times 10^{-9}\right) s^2 + 1}{\left(3 \times 10^{-9}\right) s^2 + \left(5 \times 10^{-5}\right) s + 1}$$

$$= \frac{\left(\dfrac{s}{18{,}260}\right)^2 + 1}{\left(\dfrac{s}{18{,}260}\right)^2 + (0.913)\left(\dfrac{s}{18{,}260}\right) + 1}$$

This is a notch filter at 18,260 rad/s or 2.9 kHz.

It has -3 dB points where

$$\pm(0.913)\left(\frac{\omega}{18{,}260}\right) = 1 - \left(\frac{\omega}{18{,}260}\right)^2$$

$$\frac{\omega}{13{,}260} = 1.099 \pm \frac{0.913}{2}$$

$$\omega_{3\text{dB}} = \boxed{28{,}400 \text{ and } 11{,}730 \text{ rad/s}}$$

The bandwidth is

$$\text{BW} = (0.913)(1826) = \boxed{16.67 \text{ krad/s}}$$

Timed 6

Dividing the numerator and denominator by 10^4,

$$G = \frac{10}{\left\{ \left(\dfrac{s}{10}\right)^4 + (2.613)\left(\dfrac{s}{10}\right)^3 + (3.414)\left(\dfrac{s}{10}\right)^2 + 2.613\dfrac{s}{10} + 1 \right\}}$$

This is a Butterworth fourth-order with roots of the denominator as shown, with

$$\omega_o = \boxed{10 \text{ rad/s}}$$

The roots are

$$\frac{s}{\omega_o} = \sin 22.5° \pm j \cos 22.5°$$

and

$$\frac{s}{\omega_o} = \sin 67.5° \pm j \cos 67.5°$$

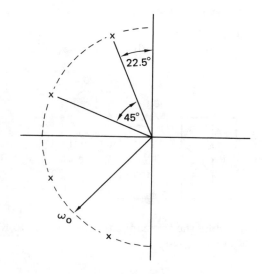

The factors are found,

$$G(s) = \frac{10}{\left\{ \left[\left(\dfrac{s}{10}\right)^2 + 0.765\dfrac{s}{10} + 1 \right] \times \left[\left(\dfrac{s}{10}\right)^2 + 1.848\dfrac{s}{10} + 1 \right] \right\}}$$

$$= \frac{100{,}000}{(s^2 + 7.65s + 100)(s^2 + 18.48s + 100)}$$

The unit step response is

$$G(s)\frac{1}{s} = \frac{A}{s} + \frac{Bs + C}{s^2 + 7.65s + 100} + \frac{Ds + E}{s^2 + 18.48s + 100}$$

Solving,

$$A = 10 \text{ V}$$
$$B = 7.064 \text{ V}$$
$$C = -38.32 \text{ V}$$
$$D = -17.064 \text{ V}$$
$$E = -223 \text{ V}$$

$$\frac{1}{s}G(s) = \frac{10}{s} + \frac{7.064s - 38.32}{(s+3.825)^2 + (9.25)^2}$$

$$- \frac{17.064s + 223}{(s+9.24)^2 + (3.825)^2}$$

$$= \frac{10}{s} + \frac{(7.064)[(s+3.825) - 9.25]}{(s+3.825)^2 + (9.25)^2}$$

$$- \frac{(17.064)[(s+9.24) + 3.825]}{(s+9.24)^2 + (3.825)^2}$$

The inverse transform is

$$v_{\text{out}}(t) = \Big[10 + 7.06e^{-3.825t}(\cos 9.25t - \sin 9.25t)$$

$$- 17.06e^{-9.25t}(\cos 3.83t + \sin 3.83t) \text{ V} \Big]$$

For $t > 0$,

$$v_{\text{out}}(t) = \boxed{\begin{array}{l} 10 + 9.99e^{-3.83t}\cos(9.25t + 45°) \\ - 24.1e^{-9.25t}\cos(3.83t - 45°) \text{ V} \end{array}}$$

Timed 7

The order of the filter is obtained using Eq. 4.125.

$$n = \frac{\log_{10}[(10)^{3.9} - 1]}{2\log_{10}\dfrac{(2\pi)(150)}{(2\pi)(60)}} = 4.9$$

The order must be 5. A fifth-order Butterworth has poles at

$$\frac{90}{5} = 18° \text{ and } \frac{(3)(90)}{5} = 54° \text{ and } \frac{(5)(90)}{5} = 90°$$

From the positive j-axis, the poles are

$$\frac{s}{\omega_o} + \sin 18° \pm j\cos 18°$$

$$\frac{s}{\omega_o} + \sin 54° \pm j\cos 54°$$

$$\frac{s}{\omega_o} + 1$$

The high-pass filter at $\omega_o = (2\pi)(150) = 300\pi$ is

$$\frac{V_{\text{out}}}{V_{\text{in}}} = \boxed{\begin{array}{l} \left(\dfrac{s}{s+300\pi}\right)\left(\dfrac{s^2}{s^2 + 582.5s + (300\pi)^2}\right) \\ \times \left(\dfrac{s^2}{s^2 + 1525s + (300\pi)^2}\right) \end{array}}$$

Timed 8

The band-reject is

$$G = \frac{s^2 + \omega_r^2}{s^2 + bs + \omega_r^2}$$

$$G(j\omega) = \frac{\omega_r^2 - \omega^2}{\omega_r^2 - \omega^2 + jb\omega} = \frac{1}{1 + j\dfrac{b\omega}{\omega_r^2 - \omega^2}}$$

This has its 3-dB frequency at

$$\frac{b\omega_{3\text{dB}}}{\omega_r^2 - \omega_{3\text{dB}}^2} = \pm 1$$

$$b = \pm\frac{\omega_r^2 - \omega_{3\text{dB}}^2}{\omega_{3\text{dB}}}$$

$$\omega_r = (2\pi)(120)$$

$$\omega_{3\text{dB}} = (2\pi)(150)$$

$$b = (2\pi)\left(\frac{(150)^2 - (120)^2}{150}\right)$$

$$= 108\pi$$

$$G(s) = \boxed{\dfrac{s^2 + (240\pi)^2}{s^2 + 108\pi s + (240\pi)^2}}$$

Timed 9

For a third-order Butterworth, the poles are 30° and 90° from the imaginary axis. The poles are

$$\frac{s}{\omega_o} + \sin 30° \pm j\cos 30°$$

$$\frac{s}{\omega_o} + 1 = 0$$

$$G(s) = \frac{\omega_o^3}{(s + \omega_o)(s^2 + \omega_o s + \omega_o^2)}$$

The step response is

$$\frac{1}{s}G(s) = \frac{\omega_o^3}{s(s + \omega_o)(s^2 + \omega_o s + \omega_o^2)}$$

$$= \frac{1}{s} - \frac{1}{s + \omega_o} - \frac{\omega_o}{s^2 + \omega_o s + \omega_o^2}$$

$$v_{\text{out}}(t) = 1 - e^{-\omega_o t} - \frac{2}{\sqrt{3}}e^{-0.5\omega_o t}\sin\frac{\sqrt{3}}{2}\omega_o t$$

For $t > 0$ with $\omega_o = 100$ rad/s,

$$v_{\text{out}}(t) = \boxed{1 - e^{-100t} - \dfrac{2}{\sqrt{3}}e^{-50t}\sin 86.6t \text{ V}}$$

Timed 10

For Butterworth filters, following Eq. 4.110, where ω_1 and ω_2 are the 3-dB frequencies,

$$\text{BW} = \omega_2 - \omega_1 = \frac{\omega_o}{Q} \text{ rad/s}$$

$$\omega_1 \omega_2 = \omega_o^2$$

For an octave bandwidth $\omega_2 = 2\omega_1$, and $\text{BW} = 2\omega_1 - \omega_1 = \omega_1$ and $\omega_o^2 = 2\omega_1^2$,

$$Q = \frac{\omega_o}{\omega_1} = 1.414$$

The specifications call for 39-dB attenuation at $\omega_1/10$, which is $\omega_o/10\sqrt{2}$, so the order is found from Eq. 4.138.

$$n = \frac{\log(10^{3.9} - 1)}{2\log\left[\sqrt{2}\left(10\sqrt{2} - \frac{1}{10\sqrt{2}}\right)\right]}$$

$$= 1.50 \rightarrow 2$$

The low-pass second order is

$$G_L = \frac{1}{s^2 + \sqrt{2}s + 1} \quad (\sqrt{2} = k)$$

Transforming to bandpass with

$$s \rightarrow Q_o\left(\frac{s}{\omega_o} + \frac{\omega_o}{s}\right) = \left(\frac{0.707}{\omega_o s}\right)(s^2 + \omega_o^2)$$

$$G_L = \frac{\dfrac{1}{Q^2}\omega_o^2 s^2}{\left\{\begin{array}{l} s^4 + k\dfrac{\omega_o}{Q_o}s^3 + \left(2 + \dfrac{1}{Q_o^2}\right)\omega_o^2 s^2 \\ + k\dfrac{\omega_o^3}{Q_o}s + \omega_o^4 \end{array}\right\}}$$

The denominator is factored into two quadradic terms.

$$\left(s^2 + \frac{\omega_1}{Q_1}s + \omega_1^2\right)\left(s^2 + \frac{\omega_2}{Q_2}s + \omega_2^2\right)$$

By matching coefficents of s, obtain from multiplying,

$$\omega_1^2 \omega_2^2 = \omega_o^4$$

$$\omega_1 \omega_2 = \omega_o^2 \quad\quad [1]$$

$$\frac{k\omega_o}{Q_o} = \frac{\omega_1}{Q_1} + \frac{\omega_2}{Q_2} \quad\quad [2]$$

$$\left(2 + \frac{1}{Q_o^2}\right)\omega_o^2 = \left(\frac{\omega_1 \omega_2}{Q_1 Q_2} + \omega_1^2 + \omega_2^2\right) \quad\quad [3]$$

$$\frac{k\omega_o^3}{Q_o} = \frac{\omega_1 \omega_2^2}{Q_1} + \frac{\omega_1^2 \omega_2}{Q_2}$$

$$= \omega_1 \omega_2 \left(\frac{\omega_2}{Q_1} + \frac{\omega_1}{Q_2}\right) \quad\quad [4]$$

From Eqs. 1, 2, and 4,

$$\frac{\omega_1}{Q_1} + \frac{\omega_2}{Q_2} = \frac{\omega_2}{Q_1} + \frac{\omega_1}{Q_2}$$

This gives three possibilities,

$$\omega_1 = \omega_2$$

$$Q_1 = Q_2$$

$$Q_1 = Q_2 \text{ and } \omega_1 = \omega_2$$

The latter is easily shown to be inconsistent. For $\omega_1 = \omega_2 = \omega_o$ ($Q_1 \neq Q_2$), this can arise only for $k > 2$, which does not occur for Butterworth filters of any order. By elimination,

$$Q_1 = Q_2$$

Through a complicated set of manipulations,

$$Q_1^2 = \frac{4Q_o^2 + 1}{2k^2}\left\{1 + \sqrt{1 - \frac{4k^2 Q_o^2}{(4Q_o^2 + 1)^2}}\right\}$$

Having calculated Q_1, further manipulation gives

$$\frac{\omega_{1,2}}{\omega_o} = \frac{kQ_1}{2Q_o} \mp \sqrt{\frac{k^2 Q_1^2}{4Q_o^2} - 1}$$

Note: These last two equations can be used for any Butterworth bandpass.

For this problem, $k = \sqrt{2}$ and $Q_o = \sqrt{2}$, so for all filters,

$$Q_1 = 2.0653$$

$$\frac{\omega_1}{\omega_o} = 0.7750$$

$$\frac{\omega_2}{\omega_o} = 1.2903$$

The only differences will be in ω_o. The form of all the transfer functions is

$$G(s) = \boxed{\frac{2\omega_o^2 s^2}{(s^2 + 0.3753\omega_o s + \omega_o^2)(s^2 + 0.6247\omega_o s + \omega_o^2)}}$$

Band (Hz)	ω_o (rad/s)
200–400	1777
400–800	3554
800–1600	7109
1600–3200	14,220
3200–6400	28,430
6400–12,800	56,870

POWER SYSTEMS

Warmup 1

IF Δ connected

$$I_{\text{phase}} = \frac{\dfrac{|S|}{3}}{V} = \frac{2 \times 10^8 \text{ VA}}{(3)(230 \times 10^3 \text{ V})}$$
$$= 289.9 \text{ A}$$

The line current is $\sqrt{3}$ times the phase current.

$$\boxed{|I_{\text{line}}| = (\sqrt{3})(289.9 \text{ A}) = \boxed{502 \text{ A}}}$$

The power factor correction is on a phase basis. For unity power factor, the lagging part of the current is cancelled.

$$I_{\text{phase}} = I_p + jI_q : I_p = |I_{\text{phase}}| \cos \theta$$

$$I_q = |I_{\text{phase}}| \sin \theta$$

$$\cos \theta = 0.9$$

$$I_q = 289.9 \sin(-25.8°) = -126.4 \text{ A}$$

$$I_{\text{comp}} = j(126.4 \text{ A}) = \frac{230 \times 10^3}{jX_c}$$

$$X_c = \frac{230 \times 10^3}{j^2 126.4} = \boxed{-1820 \ \Omega}$$

Warmup 2

The open-circuit test obtains the core parameters G and B.

$$G = \frac{P_{\text{oc}}}{V_{\text{oc}}^2} = \frac{900 \text{ W}}{(13,800 \text{ V})^2} = \boxed{4.73 \times 10^{-6} \text{ S}}$$

$$Q^2 = S^2 - P^2 = [(13,800 \text{ VA})(0.2)]^2 - (900 \text{ W})^2$$

$$Q = 2609 \text{ VAR}$$

$$B = \frac{Q}{V^2} = \frac{2609 \text{ VAR}}{(13,800 \text{ V})^2} = \boxed{13.7 \times 10^{-6} \text{ S}}$$

The turns ratio is

$$\frac{V_p}{N_p} = \frac{V_s}{N_s} : \frac{N_p}{N_s} = \frac{V_p}{V_s}$$

$$\frac{N_p}{N_s} = \frac{13,800 \text{ V}}{460 \text{ V}} = \boxed{30}$$

Warmup 3

$$N_p I_p = N_s I_s$$

$$a = \frac{N_p}{N_s} = \frac{I_s}{I_p}$$

$$= \frac{100 \text{ A}}{20 \text{ A}} = 5$$

$$P_{\text{sc}} = I_p^2 R_{\text{wp}} + I_s^2 R_{\text{ws}} = 1000 \text{ W}$$

$$I_P^2(R_{\text{wp}} + a^2 R_{\text{ws}}) = 1000 \text{ W}$$

$$R_{\text{wp}} + a^2 R_{\text{ws}} = \frac{1000 \text{ W}}{(20 \text{ A})^2} = 2.5 \ \Omega$$

Assume $R_{\text{wp}} = a^2 R_{\text{ws}} = \boxed{1.25 \ \Omega}$

$$R_{\text{ws}} = \frac{1.25}{(5)^2} = \boxed{0.05 \ \Omega}$$

$$|S| = V_p I_p = (80 \text{ V})(20 \text{ A}) = 1600 \text{ VA}$$

$$S = P + jQ$$

$$Q^2 = S^2 - P^2$$

$$|Q| = 1249 \text{ VAR}$$

$$|Q| = I_1^2(X_p + a^2 X_s)$$

$$X_p + a^2 X_s = \frac{1249 \text{ VAR}}{(20 \text{ A})^2} = 3.12 \ \Omega$$

Assume $X_p = a^2 X_s$.

$$X_p = \frac{3.12}{2} = 1.56 \ \Omega = 377 L_p$$

$$X_s = \frac{1.56}{a^2} = 0.0624 \ \Omega = 377 L_s$$

$$L_p = \boxed{4.14 \text{ mH}}$$

$$L_s = \boxed{0.166 \text{ mH}}$$

Warmup 4

$$Z_{\text{base}} = \frac{V_{\text{base}}}{I_{\text{base}}} = \frac{V_{ll}^2}{VA} = \frac{(440 \text{ V})^2}{10,000 \text{ VA}}$$

$$= 19.36 \ \Omega$$

$$Z = Z_{\text{P.U.}} \times Z_{\text{base}} = (j0.8)(19.36)$$

$$= \boxed{15.49 \ \Omega}$$

The system base is

$$Z_{\text{base-2}} = \frac{(440 \text{ V})^2}{100 \text{ kVA}} = 1.936 \ \Omega$$

$$Z_{\text{P.U.-2}} = \frac{Z}{Z_{\text{base-2}}} = \frac{15.49}{1.936} = \boxed{8 \text{ P.U.}}$$

Warmup 5

The short-circuit test is done at rated current.

$$I_{\text{rated}} = \frac{500 \text{ kVA}}{115 \text{ kV}} = 4.35 \text{ A}$$

$$|S_{\text{sc}}| = (4.35 \text{ A})(2.5 \text{ kV}) = 10.88 \text{ kVA}$$

$$= P + jQ = 435 + jQ$$

$$|Q| = \sqrt{(10{,}880 \text{ VA})^2 - (435 \text{ W})^2} = 10{,}870 \text{ VAR}$$

$$P = I^2 R$$

$$R = \frac{435 \text{ W}}{(4.35 \text{ A})^2} = 23 \ \Omega$$

$$|Q| = I^2 X$$

$$X = \frac{10{,}870 \text{ VAR}}{(4.35 \text{ A})^2} = 574 \ \Omega$$

$$Z_{\text{base}} = \frac{115 \text{ kV}}{4.35 \text{ A}} = 26{,}440 \ \Omega$$

$$Z_{\text{P.U.}} = \frac{23 + j574}{26{,}440} = 0.0009 + j0.022 \text{ P.U.}$$

$$\approx \boxed{0.001 + j0.022 \text{ P.U.}}$$

Warmup 6

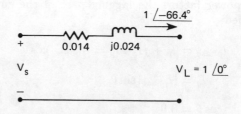

$$V_s = 1 + IZ = 1 + 0.014 + j0.024 \text{ P.U.}$$

$$= 1.014 + j0.024 = 1.014\underline{/1.4°} \text{ P.U.}$$

It is assumed that V_s does not change amplitude. At half-load,

$$V_s = V_L + IZ$$

$$I = 0.5\underline{/0°} \text{ P.U.}$$

$$V_L = |V_L|\underline{/0°}$$

$$V_s = V_L + (0.5)(0.014 + j0.024)$$

$$= V_L + 0.007 + j0.012$$

But $|V_s|^2 = (1.014)^2$, so

$$(1.014)^2 = (V_L + 0.007)^2 + (0.012)^2$$

Solving for V_L,

$$V_{\text{half-load}} = 1.007 \text{ P.U.}$$

$$V_{\text{no-load}} = 1.014 \text{ P.U.}$$

$$V_{\text{full-load}} = 1.000 \text{ P.U.}$$

The regulations are

half-load to full-load:	$1.007 - 1.000 = 0.007$ (0.7%)
no-load to full-load:	$1.014 - 1.000 = 0.014$ (1.4%)

Warmup 7

$$\text{arccos } 0.4 = 66.4°$$

$$Z = 0.014 + j0.024 = 0.0278\underline{/59.7°} \text{ P.U.}$$

$$ZI = (0.0278\underline{/59.7°})(1\underline{/-66.4°}) \text{ P.U.}$$

$$= 0.0278\underline{/-6.7°} = 0.0276 - j0.0032 \text{ P.U.}$$

$$V_s = 1 + ZI = 1.0276 - j0.0032 \text{ P.U.}$$

$$|V_s| = 1.0276 \text{ P.U.}$$

At half-load,

$$V_s = V_L + 0.0138 - j0.0016$$

$$|V_s| = 1.0276 \text{ P.U.}$$

$$V_L = 1.014 \text{ P.U.}$$

The regulations are

half-load to full-load:	$1.014 - 1.000 = 0.014$ (1.4%)
no-load to full-load:	$1.028 - 1.000 = 0.028$ (2.8%)

Warmup 8

$$V_L = 1 \text{ P.U.}$$

$$I_L = 1\underline{/-36.9°} \text{ P.U.}$$

$$Z_{\text{line}} = 0.03 + j0.04 = 0.05\underline{/53.1°} \text{ P.U.}$$

$$V_s = 1 + 0.05\underline{/(53.1° - 36.9°)} \text{ P.U.}$$

$$= 1.048 + j0.014 \text{ P.U.}$$

$|V_s| = 1.048$ P.U., so the regulation is 0.048 (4.8%).

For unity power factor,

$$I_L = 1\underline{/0°} \text{ P.U.}$$
$$V_s = 1 + 0.03 + j0.04 = 1.03 + j0.04 \text{ P.U.}$$
$$|V_s| = 1.03 \text{ P.U.}$$

The regulation is 0.03 (3%). The regulation is improved from 4.8% to 3%, a percentage change of

$$\left(\frac{4.8\% - 3\%}{4.8\%}\right)(100\%) = \boxed{37.5\%}$$

Warmup 9

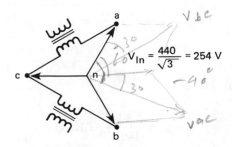

$$V_{an} = 254\underline{/0°} \text{ V}$$
$$V_{bn} = 254\underline{/-120°} \text{ V}$$
$$V_{cn} = 254\underline{/+120°} \text{ V}$$
$$I_{an} = 65.6\underline{/0°} \text{ A}$$
$$I_{bn} = 65.6\underline{/-120°} \text{ A}$$
$$V_{ac} = V_{an} - V_{cn} = 440\underline{/-30°} \text{ A}$$
$$S_{ac} = V_{ac}I_{an}^* = (440\underline{/-30°})(65.6) \text{ VA}$$
$$= \boxed{28.9 \text{ kVA at } -30°}$$
$$V_{bc} = V_{bn} - V_{cn} = 440\underline{/-90°} \text{ V}$$
$$S_{bc} = V_{bc}I_{bn}^* = (440\underline{/-90°})(65.6\underline{/120°}) \text{ VA}$$
$$= \boxed{28.9 \text{ kVA at } +30°}$$

Warmup 10

One transformer has a voltage of 1 P.U. and the other 1.025 P.U. They are connected in parallel.

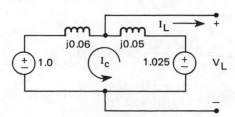

Ignoring the effect of the load current (which has a differential effect on the circulation current),

$$I_c = \frac{1.025 - 1.0}{j0.06 + j0.05} = \frac{0.025}{j0.11} = -j0.227 \text{ P.U.}$$

The circulating current is 22.7% of the rated current.

Concentrate 1

(a) $$I_{\text{line}} = \frac{\dfrac{500 \text{ kW}}{3 \text{ phases}}}{\left(\dfrac{11.5 \text{ kV}}{\sqrt{3}}\right)(0.866)} = \boxed{29 \text{ A}}$$

(b) $$|S| = \frac{500 \text{ kW}}{0.866} = \boxed{577 \text{ kVA}}$$

(c) $$|I_q| = (29 \text{ A})\sqrt{1 - (0.866)^2} = 14.5 \text{ A}$$

$$X_{\text{comp}} = -\frac{\dfrac{11.5 \text{ kV}}{\sqrt{3}}}{14.5 \text{ A}} = \boxed{-458 \text{ }\Omega}$$

Concentrate 2

The turns ratio, $a(N_p/N_s)$, is found so the low-voltage secondary measurements can be referred to the primary.

$$a = \frac{115 \text{ kV}}{13.8 \text{ kV}} = 8.33$$

Assume that the open-circuit measurements are made at rated voltage.

$$I_{p\text{-oc}}\big|_{\text{equiv}} = \frac{I_{s\text{-oc}}}{a} = \frac{350 \text{ A}}{8.33} = 42.0 \text{ A}$$
$$|S_{\text{oc}}| = |V_s I_s| = (13.8 \text{ kV})(350 \text{ A}) = 4.83 \text{ MVA}$$
$$|Q_{\text{oc}}| = \sqrt{S_{\text{oc}}^2 - P_{\text{oc}}^2} = 4.82 \text{ MVAR}$$
$$G = \frac{P}{V^2} = \frac{250 \text{ kW}}{(115 \text{ kV})^2} = 18.9 \times 10^{-6} \text{ S}$$
$$B = \frac{Q}{V^2} = \frac{4.82 \text{ MVAR}}{(115 \text{ kV})^2} = 364 \times 10^{-6} \text{ S}$$

Assume that the short-circuit test is at rated current.

$$I_{p\text{-rated}} = \frac{50 \text{ MVA}}{115 \text{ kV}} = 435 \text{ A}$$
$$V_{p\text{-oc}}\big|_{\text{equiv}} = a(1.5 \text{ kV}) = 12.5 \text{ kV}$$
$$|S_{\text{sc}}| = (12.5 \text{ kV})(435 \text{ A}) = 5.44 \text{ MVA}$$

$$R_p + a^2 R_s = \frac{P}{I^2} = \frac{300 \text{ kW}}{(435 \text{ A})^2} = 1.585 \ \Omega$$

$$|Q_{oc}| = \sqrt{S_{sc}^2 - P_{sc}^2} = 5.43 \text{ MVAR}$$

$$X_p + a^2 X_s = \frac{Q_{oc}}{I^2} = 28.7 \ \Omega$$

Assume $R_p = a^2 R_s$, $X_p = a^2 X_s$.

$$R_p = a^2 R_s = 0.79 \ \Omega$$
$$X_p = a^2 X_s = 14.35 \ \Omega$$

(a) The equivalent circuit is

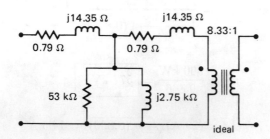

(b) $Z_1 = a^2 Z_2 = 0.79 + j14.35 \ \Omega$
$Y = Y_c = (18.9 - j364) \times 10^{-6} \text{ S}$
$YZ = 5.24 \times 10^{-3} \underline{/-0.3^\circ} = 0.0052$

From the Tee network of Fig. 5.10 with $Z_2 = Z_1$,

$$A = D = 1 + YZ \approx \boxed{1.0}$$

$$B = 2Z_1 + YZ_1^2 = \boxed{28.7 \underline{/86.9^\circ} \ \Omega}$$

$$C = Y = \boxed{364 \times 10^{-6} \underline{/-87^\circ} \text{ S}}$$

From Eqs. 5.61 and 5.62,

(c) $$\frac{V_1}{I_1} = \frac{Aa^2 Z_L + B}{Ca^2 Z_L + D}$$
$$a^2 Z_L = 0.5$$

$$Z_{in} = \frac{0.5 + 28.7 \underline{/86.9^\circ}}{(0.5)(364 \times 10^{-6}) \underline{/-87^\circ} + 1}$$

$$= \boxed{28.7 \underline{/85.9} \ \Omega}$$

Concentrate 3

For the transformers separately,

$$A = D = 1$$
$$B = 2Z_1$$
$$C = Y_c$$

Refer to Eqs. 5.65 through 5.68.

$$Y_c Z_1 = (0.0002 - j0.001)(0.01 + j0.02)$$
$$= 22.8 \times 10^{-6} \underline{/-15.3^\circ}$$
$$= (22.0 - j6.0) \times 10^{-6}$$

For the combined transformers,

$$A = 1 \times 1 + 2Z_1 Y_c = 1.00$$

$$B = 2Z_1 + 2Z_2 = 0.04 + j0.08 \ \Omega$$

$$C = Y_c + Y_c = 0.0004 - j0.002 \text{ S}$$

$$D = 2Z_1 Y_c + 1 = 1.00$$

$$a^4 Z_L = 0.1$$

$$\frac{V_1}{I_1} = Z_{in} = \frac{Aa^4 Z_L + B}{Ca^4 Z_L + D} = \boxed{0.14 + j0.08 \ \Omega}$$

Concentrate 4

$$a_{ps} = \frac{6.8 \text{ kV}}{440 \text{ V}} = 15.45$$

$$a_{pt} = \frac{6.8 \text{ kV}}{1.38 \text{ kV}} = 4.93$$

For the secondary base,

$$Z_{s\text{-base}} = \frac{(440 \text{ V})^2}{30 \text{ kVA}} = 6.453 \ \Omega$$

Referring to the secondary,

$$Z_p \rightarrow \frac{49.5 + j110}{(15.45)^2}$$

$$Z_p(\text{P.U.})|_{s\text{-base}} = \frac{49.5 + j110 \ \Omega}{(15.45)^2 (6.453 \ \Omega)}$$
$$= 0.032 + j0.071 \text{ P.U.}$$

$$Z_s(\text{P.U.})|_{s\text{-base}} = \frac{70.5 + j90 \ \Omega}{(15.45)^2 (6.453 \ \Omega)}$$
$$= 0.046 + j0.058 \text{ P.U.}$$

$$Z_t(\text{P.U.})|_{s\text{-base}} = \frac{50.5 + j70 \ \Omega}{(1545)^2 (6.453 \ \Omega)}$$
$$= 0.033 + j0.045 \text{ P.U.}$$

For the tertiary,

$$Z_{t\text{-base}} = \frac{(1380 \text{ V})^2}{20,000 \text{ VA}} = 95.22 \ \Omega$$

$$Z_p|_{t\text{-base}} = \frac{45 + j110 \ \Omega}{(4.93)^2 (95.22 \ \Omega)} = 0.019 + j0.048 \text{ P.U.}$$

$$Z_s|_{t\text{-base}} = \frac{70.5 + j90 \ \Omega}{(4.93)^2(95.22 \ \Omega)} = 0.030 + j0.039 \ \text{P.U.}$$

$$Z_t|_{t\text{-base}} = \frac{50.5 + j70 \ \Omega}{(4.93)^2(95.22 \ \Omega)} = 0.022 + j0.030 \ \text{P.U.}$$

Using a percentage basis, in a secondary base,

$$\boxed{\begin{aligned} Z_p &= 3.2 + j7.1\% \\ Z_s &= 4.6 + j5.8\% \\ Z_t &= 3.3 + j4.5\% \end{aligned}}$$

In a tertiary base,

$$\boxed{\begin{aligned} Z_p &= 1.9 + j4.8\% \\ Z_s &= 3.0 + j3.9\% \\ Z_t &= 2.2 + j3.0\% \end{aligned}}$$

Concentrate 5

Using the transformer base,

$$V_{\text{base}} = \frac{440 \ \text{V}}{\sqrt{3}} = 254 \ \text{V}$$

$$I_{\text{base}} = \frac{\dfrac{250 \ \text{kVA}}{3}}{V_{\text{base}}} = 328 \ \text{A}$$

$$Z_{\text{base}} = \frac{254 \ \text{V}}{328 \ \text{A}} = 0.774 \ \Omega$$

The wire resistance (P.U.) is

$$\left(\frac{0.053 \ \Omega}{1000 \ \text{ft}}\right)\left(\frac{500 \ \text{ft}}{0.774 \ \Omega}\right) = 0.0342 \ \text{P.U.}$$

$$Z_{\text{trans}} + R = 0.0442 + j0.05 \ \text{P.U.}$$

V_{in} is the transformer input; V_L is assumed to be 1 P.U. in all cases.

$$V_{\text{in}} = V_L + (0.0442 + j0.05)I_L$$

Operating without compensation, the motor will have

$$\text{PF} = 0.6 \ (\text{lagging})$$

$$|I| = \left[\frac{\dfrac{120 \ \text{kW}}{3}}{(254)(0.6)}\right]\left(\frac{1}{328}\right) = 0.8 \ \text{P.U.}$$

I (P.U) = $\dfrac{\text{factual}}{I_{base}}$

$$V_{\text{in}} = V_L + (Z + R)(0.8\underline{/-\cos^{-1}0.6})$$
$$= 1 + (0.067\underline{/48.5°})(0.8\underline{/-53.1°})$$
$$= 1.053\underline{/-0.2°}$$

The rated wire current is

$I_{PU} = \dfrac{I_{rated}}{I_{base}}$ $\dfrac{225}{328} = 0.686 \ \text{P.U.}$

The compensation must be just sufficient to deliver the same load power at a current of 0.686 P.U.

$$0.686\cos\theta = 0.8\cos(\cos^{-1}0.6)$$
$$\cos\theta = \frac{0.48}{0.686} = 0.7$$
$$I_{\text{line}} = 0.686\underline{/-45.6°} \ \text{P.U.}$$
$$V_{\text{in}} = 1 + (0.067\underline{/48.5°})I_{\text{line}}$$
$$= 1.046 \ \text{P.U.}$$

The input voltage decreases from 1.053 to 1.046. Keeping the primary voltage at 1.053, the load voltage increases by the same percentage.

$$V_L = \frac{1.053}{1.046} = 1.007 \ \text{P.U.}$$

an increase of $\boxed{0.7\%}$

Concentrate 6

(a)
$$I_L = 0.855\underline{/0°} \ \text{P.U.}$$
$$Z = 0.716\underline{/65.2°} \ \text{P.U.}$$
$$E_{g''m} = 0.935 - 0.855(j0.25) \ \text{P.U.}$$
$$= 0.959\underline{/-12.9°} \ \text{P.U.}$$
$$I_m = \frac{E_{g''m}}{j0.25} = 3.84\underline{/-102.9°} \ \text{P.U.}$$
$$E_{g''g} = 0.935 + 0.855Z = 1.315\underline{/25°} \ \text{P.U.}$$
$$I_g = \frac{E_{g''g}}{Z} = 1.84\underline{/-40.2°} \ \text{P.U.}$$

The breaker ratings are

$$\boxed{\begin{aligned} &\text{generator: } (1.84 \ \text{P.U.})(15 \ \text{MVA}) = 27.6 \ \text{MVA} \\ &\hspace{4cm} \text{at } 13.9 \ \text{kV} \\ &\text{motor: } (3.84 \ \text{P.U.})(15 \ \text{MVA}) = 57.5 \ \text{MVA} \\ &\hspace{4cm} \text{at } 13.9 \ \text{kV} \end{aligned}}$$

(b)
$$I_L = 0.855\underline{/36.9°} \ \text{P.U.}$$
$$I_m = \frac{0.935 - j0.25I_L}{j0.25} = 4.308\underline{/-99.1°} \ \text{P.U.}$$
$$I_g = \frac{0.935 - ZI_L}{Z} = 1.403\underline{/-28.6°} \ \text{P.U.}$$

The breaker ratings are

> generator: 21 MVA at 13.9 kV
>
> motor: 64.6 MVA at 13.9 kV

(c)   PF = 1, $I_{\text{fault}} = 4.96\underline{/-83.66°}$ P.U.

PF = 0.8 load, $I_{\text{fault}} = 4.96\underline{/-83.6°}$ P.U.

> The total fault current is not affected by the power factor.

Concentrate 7

As in Ex. 5.20, the pre-fault current is $0.76\underline{/2.3°}$ P.U.
At point A,

$0.76\underline{/2.3°}\,(j0.1 + 0.02 + j0.05 + j0.1)$

$$V_{\text{Th}} = 0.9 + (0.76\underline{/2.3°})(0.02 + j0.25)$$
$$= 0.927\underline{/11.85°} \text{ P.U.}$$

The impedance seen from point A is

$j0.1 + 0.02 + j0.05 + j0.1 + j0.2$

$$Z_{\text{Th}} = (j0.09) \parallel (0.02 + j0.25) + j0.2) \parallel (1.6 + j1.2)$$
$$= 0.075\underline{/89.2°} \text{ P.U.}$$

$$I_{a1} = \frac{V_{\text{Th}}}{Z_{\text{Th}}} = 12.4\underline{/-77.3°} \text{ P.U.}$$

For a balanced fault,

$$I_{a0} = I_{a2} = 0$$
$$I_{\text{fault}} = I_{a1}$$

$$|I_{\text{fault}}| = \boxed{12.4 \text{ P.U.}}$$

Concentrate 8

From Prob. 7,

$$E_{\text{Th},a} = 0.927\underline{/11.85°} \text{ P.U.}$$
$$Z_{\text{Th},1} = 0.075\underline{/89.2°} \text{ P.U.} = Z_1$$
$$Z_2 = j0.085 \parallel [0.02 + j0.25$$
$$+ \{j0.195 \parallel (1.6 + j1.2)\}]$$
$$= 0.071\underline{/89.3°} \text{ P.U.}$$
$$Z_0 = j0.6 + j0.03 = j0.63 \text{ P.U.}$$

$$I_{a1} = \frac{E_{\text{Th},a}}{Z_0 + Z_1 + Z_2} = \frac{0.927\underline{/11.85°} \text{ P.U.}}{0.776\underline{/89.85°} \text{ P.U.}}$$

$$= 1.1946\underline{/-78.0°} \text{ P.U.}$$
$$I_a = I_{a1} + I_{a2} + I_{a0}$$
$$I_{a1} = I_{a2} = I_{a0}$$

$$I_a = \boxed{3.58\underline{/-78.0°} \text{ P.U.}}$$

Concentrate 9

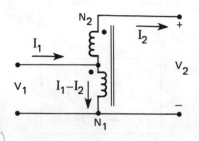

$$\frac{V_1}{N_1} = \frac{V_2}{N_2 + N_1}$$
$$N_1(I_1 - I_2) = N_2 I_2$$

The requirement is

$$V_1 I_1 = V_2 I_2 = \frac{750 \text{ MVA}}{3}$$

For the common winding,

$$V_1(I_1 - I_2) = \text{rating}$$

For the series winding,

$$(V_2 - V_1)I_2 = \text{rating}$$
$$V_1 = 345 \text{ kV}$$
$$I_1 = \frac{250 \text{ MVA}}{345 \text{ kV}}$$
$$V_2 = 500 \text{ kV}$$
$$I_2 = \frac{250 \text{ MVA}}{500 \text{ kV}}$$

The common rating is

$$(345 \text{ kV})\left(\frac{250}{345} - \frac{250}{500}\right)\frac{\text{MVA}}{\text{kV}} = \boxed{77.5 \text{ MVA}}$$

The series rating is

$$(500 - 345 \text{ kV})\left(\frac{250}{500}\right)\frac{\text{MVA}}{\text{kV}} = \boxed{77.5 \text{ MVA}}$$

Concentrate 10

Using a motor base, assume 90% efficiency and PF = 0.85 lagging.

$$P_{out} = 0.9 P_{in}$$

$$VA_{in} = \frac{P_{in}}{0.85} = \frac{(500 \text{ hp})\left(0.746 \dfrac{\text{kW}}{\text{hp}}\right)}{(0.9)(0.85)}$$

$$= 488 \text{ kVA}$$

Converting system impedance to the motor's base,

$$Z_s = (0.05 + j0.2 \ \Omega)\left(\frac{488 \text{ kVA}}{100 \text{ MVA}}\right)\left(\frac{13.8 \text{ kV}}{2.4 \text{ kV}}\right)^2$$

$$= 0.0081 + j0.0323 \text{ P.U.}$$

Converting transformer impedance to the motor's base,

$$Z_t = (0.05 \ \Omega)(\cos 81.9° + j \sin 81.9°)\left(\frac{488 \text{ kVA}}{2500 \text{ kVA}}\right)$$

$$= 0.0014 + j0.0097 \text{ P.U.}$$

Estimating the motor starting reactance,

$$I_{starting} = (6 \text{ P.U.})(PF) = 5.1 \text{ P.U.}$$

$$X_{starting} = \frac{1}{5.1} = 0.1961 \text{ P.U.}$$

Assuming that at full-load steady state, the motor voltage is 1 P.U. and the current is 1 P.U., then the source voltage is found.

$$V_s = V_L + I(Z_t + Z_s)$$

$$I = 1\underline{/-31.8°} \text{ P.U.}$$

$$V_s = 1 + (1\underline{/-31.8°} \text{ P.U.})(0.0095 + j0.0420 \text{ P.U.})$$

$$= 1.031\underline{/1.7°} \text{ P.U.}$$

By line starting the motor, initially the voltage is determined by voltage division.

$$V_m = V_s \frac{Z_{starting}}{Z_{starting} + Z_t + Z_s}$$

$$= (1.031)\left(\frac{j0.1961}{0.0095 + j0.2381}\right)$$

$$= 0.848\underline{/2.2°} \text{ P.U.}$$

The voltage is 85% of the running voltage for a dip of 15%.

Timed 1

The transformer base is used.

(a)
$$hp_{rated} = \frac{(0.9)(0.85)\text{kVA}_{rated}}{0.746 \dfrac{\text{kVA}}{\text{hp}}}$$

$$= 1.025 \text{ kVA}_{rated}$$

$$\text{kVA}_{rated} = \left[(3)\left(\frac{0.44}{\sqrt{3}}\right)\right] I_{rated}$$

$$= 0.762 \ I_{rated}$$

To find the maximum voltage drop, take the starting current as $(6)(PF)(I_{rated})$.

$$I_{starting} = 5.1 \ I_{rated}$$

For a 3% maximum voltage drop,

$$0.03 \text{ (P.U.)} = (0.04)(5.1)I_{rated} \text{ (P.U.)}$$

$$I_{rated} \text{ (P.U.)} = \frac{0.03}{(0.04)(5.1)} = 0.147 \text{ P.U.}$$

The base current is

$$I_{base} = \frac{\dfrac{250 \text{ kVA}}{3}}{\dfrac{440 \text{ V}}{\sqrt{3}}} = 328 \text{ A}$$

$$I_{rated} = (0.147)(328) = 48.2 \text{ A}$$

$$\text{kVA}_{rated} = (0.762)(48.2) = 36.75 \text{ kVA}$$

$$hp_{rated} = (1.025)(36.75) = \boxed{37.7 \text{ hp}}$$

(b) Switching from delta to wye results in three times the starting impedance, reducing the current by one-third. Thus, a motor with three times the starting current and three times the hp could be used.

$$hp_{rated} \rightarrow (3)(37.7 \text{ hp}) = \boxed{113.1 \text{ hp}}$$

(c) A 40% tap corresponds to a turns ratio of $1:0.4$, so the impedance seen by the transformer primary would be

$$\frac{1}{(0.4)^2}Z_L = \frac{Z_L}{0.16}$$

The starting current would then be $I_{rated}/0.16$, so

$$hp_{rated} = \frac{37.7 \text{ hp}}{0.16} = \boxed{235.6 \text{ hp}}$$

Timed 2

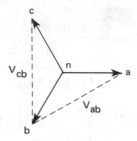

$$V_{an} = 254\underline{/0°}\ \text{V}$$

$$V_{ab} = 440\underline{/30°}\ \text{V}$$

$$V_{cb} = 440\underline{/90°}\ \text{V}$$

The balanced load is

$$I_{an} = \frac{\dfrac{50\ \text{kVA}}{3}}{254}\underline{/-\cos^{-1}0.8}$$

$$= 65.6\underline{/-36.9°}\ \text{A}$$

$$I_{cn} = 65.6\underline{/83.1°}\ \text{A}$$

(a)

$$\frac{|V_{ab}^2|}{10\ \text{kW}} = 19.36\ \Omega$$

$$I_{1\phi} = \frac{440}{19.36} = 22.7\ \text{A}$$

$I_{1\phi}$ is in phase with V_{ab}.

$$I_a = I_{an} + 22.7\underline{/30°}$$

$$= 77.4\underline{/-21.2°}\ \text{A}$$

$$S_{ab} = (440\underline{/30°}\ \text{V})(77.4\underline{/+21.2°}\ \text{A})$$

$$= 34.05\underline{/51.23°}\ \text{kVA}$$

$$S_{cb} = (440\underline{/90°}\ \text{V})(65.62\underline{/-83.13°}\ \text{A})$$

$$= 28.87\underline{/6.87°}\ \text{kVA}$$

$$=\ \boxed{\begin{array}{l}\text{a-b transformer rating 35 kVA}\\ \text{c-b transformer rating 29 kVA}\end{array}}$$

(b) $$I_c = 65.6\underline{/83.1°}\ \text{A} + 22.7\underline{/90°}\ \text{A}$$

$$= 88.2\underline{/84.9°}\ \text{A}$$

$$S_{cb} = (440\underline{/90°}\ \text{V})(88.2\underline{/-84.9°}\ \text{A})$$

$$= 38.81\underline{/5.1°}\ \text{kVA}$$

$$S_{ab} = (440\underline{/30°}\ \text{V})(65.6\underline{/36.9°}\ \text{A})$$

$$= 28.87\underline{/66.9°}\ \text{kVA}$$

$$=\ \boxed{\begin{array}{l}\text{a-b transformer rating 29 kVA}\\ \text{c-b transformer rating 39 kVA}\end{array}}$$

Timed 3

The 25-MVA base is used. Converting 15-MVA imped-ance to 25-MVA base,

$$Z_{15} = (j0.06)\left(\frac{25}{15}\right) = j0.10$$

Both windings have the same impedance.

(a) $\boxed{\begin{array}{l}\text{With equal reactances and equal voltages, the}\\ \text{two transformers carry equal currents—50\% of}\\ \text{the load current.}\end{array}}$

(b) The load voltage is taken as 1 P.U., and on the 25-MVA base,

$$I_L = \frac{30\ \text{MVA}}{25\ \text{MVA}}\underline{/\cos^{-1}0.8} = 1.2\underline{/-36.87°}\ \text{P.U.}$$

$$I_{base} = \frac{\dfrac{25\ \dfrac{\text{MVA}}{3}}{35\ \dfrac{\text{kV}}{\sqrt{3}}}}{} = 412\ \text{A}$$

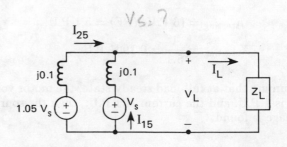

The Thevenin equivalent of the transformers is

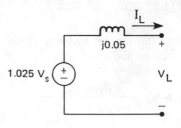

$$1.025\,V_s = V_L + j0.05\,I_L$$

$$= 1 + 0.036 + j0.048$$

$$V_s = 1.012\underline{/2.65°}$$

$$I_{25} = \frac{1.05\,V_s - 1}{j0.1}$$

$$= 0.787\underline{/-51.4^\circ}\ \text{P.U.}$$

$$= (412\ \text{A})(0.787\underline{/-51.4^\circ})$$

$$= \boxed{324\underline{/-51.4^\circ}\ \text{A}}$$

$$I_{15} = \frac{V_s - 1}{j0.1} = 0.481\underline{/-13.1^\circ}\ \text{P.U.}$$

$$= (412\ \text{A})(0.481\underline{/-13.1^\circ})$$

$$= \boxed{198\underline{/-13.1^\circ}\ \text{A}}$$

$$I_L = I_{25} + I_{15} = 0.959 - j0.724$$

$$= 1.202\underline{/-37.0^\circ}\ \text{P.U.}$$

This checks within rounding errors.

$$I_{\text{circ}} : I_{25} = I_{\text{circ}} + \frac{I_L}{2}$$

$$I_{15} = \frac{I_L}{2} - I_{\text{circ}}$$

Therefore,

$$I_{\text{circ}} = \frac{I_{25} - I_{15}}{2} = \frac{0.023 - j0.505}{2}$$

$$= 0.253\underline{/-87.4^\circ}\ \text{P.U.} = (412\ \text{A})(0.253\underline{/-87.4^\circ})$$

$$= \boxed{104\underline{/-87.4^\circ}\ \text{A}}$$

Timed 4

Using the calculations of Concentrate 8,

$$E_{\text{Th},a} = 0.927\underline{/11.5^\circ}$$

$$Z_1 = 0.075\underline{/89.2^\circ}$$

$$Z_2 = 0.071\underline{/89.3^\circ}$$

From Fig. 5.18,

$$-I_{a2} = I_{a1} = \frac{E_{\text{Th},a}}{Z_1 + Z_2} = 6.35\ \text{P.U.}\underline{/-77.4^\circ}$$

Using Eq. 5.150,

$$I_{\text{fault}} = \sqrt{3}\,j I_{a1} = \boxed{11.0\underline{/12.7^\circ}\ \text{P.U.}}$$

Using Eq. 5.144 with $V_{a0} = 0$,

$$V_a = -2V_b$$

Using Eq. 5.145,

$$3V_{a1} = V_a + (a + a^2)V_b = -3V_b$$

From Fig. 5.18,

$$V_{a1} = \frac{Z_2}{Z_1 + Z_2} E_{\text{Th},a} = 0.464\underline{/11.9^\circ}\ \text{P.U.}$$

$$V_b = \boxed{-0.464\underline{/11.9^\circ}\ \text{P.U.}}$$

$$V_a = \boxed{0.928\underline{/11.9^\circ}\ \text{P.U.}}$$

Timed 5

Since no current flows when bus number 3 is open, $e_{\text{Th},a} = 1\underline{/0^\circ}$. The Thevenin equivalent impedance seen from bus number 3 is found by shorting the sources to obtain a bridge circuit.

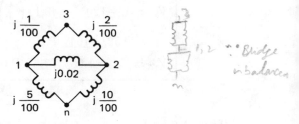

Notice that the bridge is balanced, so that no current flows in the branch from bus 1 to bus 2. So busses 1 and 2 constitute a single node, and

$$Z_{\text{Th}} = \left(\frac{j}{100}\,\Big\|\,\frac{j2}{100}\right) + \left(\frac{j10}{100}\,\Big\|\,\frac{j5}{100}\right)$$

$$= j0.04\ \text{P.U.}$$

From Fig. 5.18, with $Z_1 = Z_2 = Z_{\text{Th}}$,

$$-I_{a2} = I_{a1} = \frac{E_{\text{Th},a}}{Z_1 + Z_2} = 12.5\underline{/-90^\circ}\ \text{P.U.}$$

From Eq. 5.150,

$$I_{\text{fault}} = -j\sqrt{3} I_{a1} = -21.65\underline{/0^\circ}\ \text{P.U.}$$

Because the voltages at busses 1 and 2 are equal, the current delivered by each is inversely proportional to the impedance to bus 3.

$$I_{13} = \frac{2}{3} I_{\text{fault}}$$

$$I_{23} = \frac{1}{3} I_{\text{fault}}$$

At bus 1,

$$
\boxed{
\begin{aligned}
V_{a1} &= 1\underline{/0^\circ}\ \text{P.U. (no fault current;} \\
&\quad \text{fault between } b \text{ and } c) \\[4pt]
V_{b1} &= 1\underline{/-120^\circ} - (j0.05)\left(\frac{2}{3}\right) I_{\text{fault}} \\
&= 0.52\underline{/-164^\circ}\ \text{P.U.} \\[4pt]
V_{c1} &= 1\underline{/+120^\circ} - (j0.05)\left(\frac{2}{3}\right) I_{\text{fault}} \\
&= 1.66\underline{/107.5^\circ}\ \text{P.U.}
\end{aligned}
}
$$

At bus 2,

$$
\boxed{
\begin{aligned}
V_{a2} &= 1\underline{/0^\circ}\ \text{P.U.} \\[4pt]
V_{b2} &= 1\underline{/-120^\circ} - (j0.1)\left(\frac{1}{3}\right) I_{\text{fault}} \\
&= 0.52\underline{/-164^\circ}\ \text{P.U.} \\[4pt]
V_{c2} &= V_{c1} = 1.66\underline{/107.5^\circ}\ \text{P.U.}
\end{aligned}
}
$$

Timed 6

The transformer primary is rated at 60 MVA for the secondary and 21 MVA for the tertiary, so its total rating is 81 MVA.

Assuming all impedances are referred to the primary, and given in the primary base,

$$
Z_{\text{base}} = \frac{(138\ \text{kV})^2}{81\ \text{MVA}} = 235\ \Omega
$$

$$
Z_l = \frac{j3.1\ \Omega}{235\ \Omega} = j0.0132\ \text{P.U.}
$$

(a) For a three-phase fault on the X winding, ignoring any tertiary current (which would be quite small),

∴ Tertiary wdg
in Δ connection

$$
\begin{aligned}
Z_l + Z_{\text{H-X}} &= j0132 + j0.0977\ \text{P.U.} \\
&= 0.111j\ \text{P.U.}
\end{aligned}
$$

The primary fault current is

$$
I_{\text{H-fault}} = \frac{1}{0.111j} = -j9.02\ \text{P.U.}
$$

The actual fault current is amplified by the turns ratio, 138 kV/34.5 kV = 4.0. The primary current base is

$$
I_{\text{base}} = \frac{\dfrac{81\ \text{MVA}}{3}}{\dfrac{138\ \text{kV}}{\sqrt{3}}} = 339\ \text{A}
$$

The fault current is   (on secondary side)

$$
(339\ \text{A})(4)(-j9.02\ \text{P.U.}) = \boxed{12{,}231\underline{/-90^\circ}\ \text{A}}
$$

(b) For a single-phase fault to ground (see Fig. 5.15(e)) with both H and X in grounded neutral configurations,

$$
Z_0 = Z_1 = Z_2 = j0.111
$$

Then, from Fig. 5.17(b),

$$
I_{a1} = \frac{E_{\text{Th},a}}{Z_1 + Z_2 + Z_0} = \frac{1}{(3)(j0.111)} = -j3
$$

From Eq. 5.136,

$$
I_a = 3I_{a1} = -j9\ \text{P.U.}
$$

$$
I_{\text{fault}} = (4)(339\ \text{A})(-j9\ \text{P.U.})
$$

$$
= \boxed{-j12{,}204\ \text{A}}
$$

Timed 7

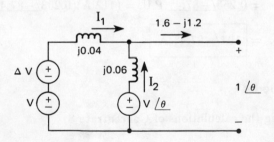

The transformer base is used.

$$
I_1 = \frac{V(1+\Delta) - 1}{j0.04}
$$

$$
I_2 = \frac{V\cos\theta + jV\sin\theta - 1}{j0.06}
$$

Because $I_1 + I_2 = 1.6 - j1.2$ P.U. and $|I_1| = |I_2| = 1$ P.U., it is necessary that $I_1 = I_2 = 0.8 - j0.6$ P.U.

$$
\begin{aligned}
V(1+\Delta) &= (j0.04)(0.8 - j0.6) + 1 \\
&= 1.024\underline{/1.8^\circ}\ \text{P.U.} \\
V\underline{/\theta} &= (j0.06)(0.8 - j0.6) + 1 \\
&= 1.037\underline{/2.7^\circ}\ \text{P.U.} \\
|V| &= 1.037 \\
\underline{/\theta} &= 2.7^\circ - 1.8^\circ = 0.9^\circ
\end{aligned}
$$

$$V = 1.037\underline{/1.8°}\ \text{P.U.}$$

$$1 + \Delta = \frac{1.024}{1.037} = 0.9875$$

$$\Delta = -0.0125 = \frac{0.1}{\frac{32}{2}}n$$

$$n = \boxed{-2}$$

$$\theta = \boxed{0.09°}$$

Timed 8

The load is 34 MW/0.85 PF = 40 MVA, so the transformer must be on the 50 MVA setting.

$$Z_{\text{base}} = \frac{(12\ \text{kV})^2}{50\ \text{k}^2\text{VA}} = 2.88\ \Omega$$

This uses the transformer secondary base.

On the same base,

$$Z_l = \left(\frac{1.555}{2.88}\right)(0.02 + j0.1)$$

$$= 0.011 + j0.054\ \text{P.U.}$$

$$Z_{\text{tr}} = R(1 + j15)$$

$$R = \frac{0.075}{|1 + j15|} = 0.005$$

$$Z_{\text{tr}} = 0.005 + j0.075\ \text{P.U.}$$

$$V_{\text{load}} = \frac{12.16}{12} = 1.013\ \text{P.U.}$$

$$I_{\text{load}} = \frac{\frac{40\ \text{MVA}}{50\ \text{MVA}}}{1.013}\underline{/\cos^{-1}0.85}$$

$$= 0.789\underline{/-31.8°}\ \text{P.U.}$$

$$Z = Z_{\text{tr}} + Z_l = 0.13\underline{/82.9°}\ \text{P.U.}$$

$$V_s = IZ + 1.013 = 1.077\underline{/4.2°}\ \text{P.U.}$$

The regulation is

$$1.077 - 1.013 = \boxed{0.064\ (6.4\%)}$$

Timed 9

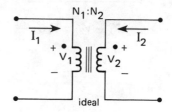

$1.03\underline{/5°}$ $j0.08$ I $0.98\underline{/-2.5°}$

$$I = \frac{1.03\underline{/5°} - 0.98\underline{/-2.5°}}{j0.08} = 1.758\underline{/-19.5°}$$

$$S = VI^* = (1.03\underline{/5°})(1.758\underline{/19.5°})$$

$$= 1.811\underline{/24.5°}$$

$$= 1.648 + j0.751$$

$$P = (1.648)(200\ \text{MW}) = \boxed{330\ \text{MW}}$$

$$Q = (0.751)(200\ \text{MVAR}) = \boxed{150\ \text{MVAR}}$$

Timed 10

For these purposes, the transformer can be treated as ideal. Winding no. 1 is rated at 500 V and winding no. 2 is rated at 100 V. The current rating on winding no. 2 is five times that of winding no. 1.

Ideal:
$$N_1 I_1 + N_2 I_2 = 0$$
$$\frac{V_1}{N_1} = \frac{V_2}{N_2}$$

For this example,

$$\frac{N_1}{N_2} = 5$$

$$V_1 = 5V_2$$

$$I_2 = -5I_1$$

For the correct configuration (see (c) below),

$$V_{\text{in}} = V_1 + V_2 = 6V_2 = 600\ \text{V}$$

$$V_{\text{out}} = V_1 = 5V_2 = 500\ \text{V}$$

$$\frac{V_{\text{out}}}{V_{\text{in}}} = \frac{5}{6}$$

$$I_{\text{in}} = I_2$$

$$I_{\text{out}} = I_2 - I_1 = -6I_1$$

With I_2 at its rated value, I, will also be at its rated value. Notice that I_1 is negative in this situation. The input V-A product is

$$V_{\text{in}}I_{\text{in}} = \left|\frac{6}{5}V_{\text{out}}\right|\left\|5I_1\right|$$

$$= 6|V_1 I_1|$$

This is six times the rated value of either winding. The output V-A product is

$$V_{out}I_{out} = V_1| - 6I_1|$$
$$= 6|V_1I_1|$$

If the transformer is operating at rated V-A, it can accommodate six times its rated value.

(a) For a wrong connection,

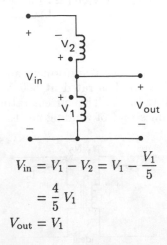

$$V_{in} = V_1 - V_2 = V_1 - \frac{V_1}{5}$$
$$= \frac{4}{5} V_1$$
$$V_{out} = V_1$$

With $V_{in} = 600$ V, the output voltage will be

$$V_{out} = \left(\frac{5}{4}\right)(600) = \boxed{750 \text{ V}}$$

This will exceed the rated voltage on the winding by 50%.

(b) | The wrong connection results (1) in the wrong output voltage, and (2) in the voltage ratings on the windings being exceeded by 50%.

(c)

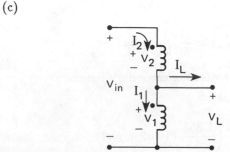

TRANSMISSION LINES

Warmup 1

From Eq. 6.4,

$$\delta = \sqrt{\frac{\rho}{\pi f \mu}}$$
$$\rho = 1.8 \times 10^{-8} \ \Omega \cdot m$$
$$f = 10^7 \ Hz$$
$$\mu = \mu_o = 4\pi \times 10^{-7}$$
$$\delta = 21.35 \times 10^{-6} \ m$$

For the inner conductor, the conducting area $\sim 2\pi r \times \delta$ in m^2. The approximate width is $2\pi r$.

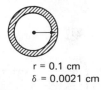

r = 0.1 cm
δ = 0.0021 cm

For the outer conductor, the conducting area is $2\pi R \times \delta$. From Eq. 6.5, the impedance per unit length is

$$Z = Z_{inner} + Z_{outer}$$
$$= \frac{\rho}{\delta 2\pi r}(1+j) + \frac{\rho}{\delta 2\pi R}(1+j)$$
$$= \left[\frac{(1.8 \times 10^{-8}\Omega \cdot m)\left(100 \ \frac{cm}{m}\right)}{(2\pi)(21.35 \times 10^{-6} \ m)} \right]$$
$$\times \left(\frac{1}{0.1 \ cm} + \frac{1}{0.5 \ cm} \right)(1+j)$$
$$= \boxed{(0.161)(1+j) \ \Omega}$$

Warmup 2

From App. A, AWG #1 wire has a diameter of 289 mils (1 mil = 0.001 in).

From Ex. 6.1, it was shown that the skin depth for copper at 10 kHz is 26 mils. The ratio is

$$\frac{r}{\delta} = \frac{\frac{289}{2}}{26} = 5.56$$

Using Eq. 6.8,

$$\frac{R}{R_0} = 0.25 + 0.5\frac{r}{\delta} = 3.03$$

Using Eq. 6.9,

$$\frac{X}{R_0} = 0.5025 \frac{r}{\delta} = 2.79$$

From Ex. 6.3,

$$R_0 = 0.124 \ \Omega/1000 \ ft$$
$$Z_{int} = (0.124)(3.03 + j2.79)$$
$$= \boxed{0.376 + j0.346 \ \Omega/1000 \ ft}$$

Warmup 3

From App. A, $r = 16$ mils. From Ex 6.2, $\delta = 2.6$ mils. From App. A, $R_0 = 10.15 \ \Omega/1000$ ft.

$$\frac{r}{\delta} = 6.15$$

From Eq. 6.9,

$$\frac{X_{int}}{R_0} = 0.5025 \frac{r}{\delta} = 3.09$$

Then, for each conductor,

$$X_{int} = (3.09)(10.15) = 31.36 \ \Omega/1000 \ ft$$
$$X_{int,total} = 2X_{int} = 62.72 \ \Omega/1000 \ ft$$
$$\frac{D}{r} = \left(\frac{1 \ cm}{16 \ mils} \right) \left(\frac{10^3 \ mils}{in} \right) \left(\frac{in}{2.54 \ cm} \right)$$
$$= 24.61$$

From Eq. 6.10,

$$L_{ext} = 4 \times 10^{-7} \ln \frac{D}{r} = 1.281 \times 10^{-6} \ H/m$$
$$X_{ext} = 2\pi f L_{ext} = 8.05 \ \Omega/m$$
$$= \left(8.05 \ \frac{\Omega}{m} \right) \left(\frac{1 \ m}{100 \ cm} \right) \left(\frac{2.54 \ cm}{in} \right) \left(\frac{12 \ in}{ft} \right)$$
$$= 2.454 \ \frac{\Omega}{ft} = 2454 \ \Omega/1000 \ ft$$
$$X_{total} = X_{int} + X_{ext} = \boxed{2517 \ \Omega/1000 \ ft}$$

Warmup 4

From Eq. 6.16,

$$C_l = \frac{2\pi\epsilon}{\ln \dfrac{D}{d}}$$

D is the I.D. of the outer conductor and d is the diameter of the inner conductor.

$$\epsilon = \epsilon_o = \frac{1}{36\pi \times 10^9} \text{ F/m}$$

$$C_l = \frac{\dfrac{2\pi}{36\pi} \times 10^{-9} \dfrac{\text{F}}{\text{m}}}{\ln \left(\dfrac{2}{0.2}\right)} = \boxed{24.1 \text{ pF/m}}$$

Warmup 5

From Table 6.2,

$$\text{GMR} = 0.0586$$

$$X_L(1 \text{ ft}) = 0.344 \ \Omega/\text{mi}$$

From Eq. 6.19,

$$K_L = 1 + \frac{\ln D}{\ln \dfrac{1}{\text{GMR}}} = 1 + \frac{\ln 10}{\ln \dfrac{1}{\text{GMR}}} = 1.812$$

$$X_L = (1.812)(0.344) = \boxed{0.623 \ \Omega/\text{mi}}$$

Warmup 6

From Table 6.2,

$$X_C = 0.0776 \text{ M}\Omega\text{-mi}$$

The correction factor K_C is

$$K_C = 1 + \frac{\ln (\text{separation in feet})}{\ln \dfrac{1}{\text{wire radius in feet}}}$$

$$= 1 + \frac{\ln 20}{\ln \left(\dfrac{24}{1.762}\right)} = 2.147$$

$$X_C = (2.147)(0.0776) \text{ M}\Omega\text{-mi/conductor}$$

For 2 miles and 2 conductors,

$$X_C = \frac{(2.147)(0.0776) \text{ M}\Omega\text{-mi}}{2 \text{ mi}}(2 \text{ conductors})$$

$$= \boxed{0.167 \text{ M}\Omega \ (167 \text{ k}\Omega)}$$

Warmup 7

As outside diameter (O.D.) is in inches and the spacing is 1.0 foot,

$$\ln \frac{d}{r} = \ln \frac{d \text{ (ft)}}{\left(\dfrac{\text{O.D.}}{2}\right)\left(\dfrac{1}{12}\right)} = \ln \frac{24d \text{ (ft)}}{\text{O.D. (in)}}$$

From Eq. 6.43,

$$X_C = 29{,}668 \ln \left(\frac{d}{r}\right) \Omega\text{-mi}$$

$$= 29{,}668 \ln \left[\frac{24d \text{ (ft)}}{\text{O.D. (in)}}\right] \Omega\text{-mi}$$

conductor	calculated X_C(MΩ-mi)	Table 6.2 X_C(MΩ-mi)
Waxwing	0.1090	0.1090
Partridge	0.1074	0.1074
Bluebird	0.0775	0.0776

Warmup 8

From Chap. 2, Fig. 2.21,

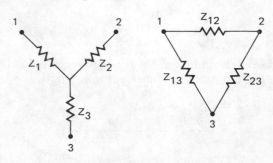

Let $a \to 1$, $b \to 2$, $c \to 3$.

Using Eqs. 2.37, 2.38, and 2.39,

$$Z_1 = \frac{Z_{12}Z_{13}}{Z_{12} + Z_{23} + Z_{13}}$$

$$Z_2 = \frac{Z_{12}Z_{23}}{Z_{12} + Z_{23} + Z_{13}}$$

$$Z_3 = \frac{Z_{13}Z_{23}}{Z_{12} + Z_{13} + Z_{23}}$$

$$Z_{an} = \frac{(2)(1.8)}{2 + 2.5 + 1.8} = \frac{3.6}{6.3} = \boxed{0.571 \ \Omega}$$

$$Z_{bn} = \frac{(2)(2.5)}{6.3} = \boxed{0.794 \ \Omega}$$

$$Z_{cn} = \frac{(2.5)(1.8)}{6.3} = \boxed{0.714 \ \Omega}$$

Warmup 9

> The volt-ampere ratings are the same. The voltage rating for the delta connection must be $\sqrt{3}$ times that for the wye connection. The current rating for the wye connection must be $\sqrt{3}$ times that for the delta connection.

Warmup 10

The radiation resistance is obtained from Eq. 6.142.

$$R_{\mathrm{rad}} = \frac{\beta^2 (dz)^2}{6\pi} \sqrt{\frac{\mu_o}{\epsilon_o}}$$

$$\beta = \frac{\omega}{C} = \frac{\omega_o}{3 \times 10^8}$$

$$\sqrt{\frac{\mu_o}{\epsilon_o}} = 120\pi \ \Omega$$

$$\omega = (2\pi)(60) = 120\pi \ \mathrm{rad/s}$$

$$R_{\mathrm{rad}} = 3.2 \times 10^{-11} \ \Omega$$

From App. A,

$$R_0 = 10.15 \ \Omega/1000 \ \mathrm{ft}$$

$$= \left(\frac{10.15 \ \Omega}{1000 \ \mathrm{ft}}\right)\left(\frac{1 \ \mathrm{ft}}{12 \ \mathrm{in}}\right)\left(\frac{1 \ \mathrm{in}}{2.54 \ \mathrm{cm}}\right)\left(\frac{100 \ \mathrm{cm}}{\mathrm{m}}\right)$$

$$= 0.0333 \ \Omega/\mathrm{m}$$

$$\epsilon = \left(\frac{3.2 \times 10^{-11} \ \Omega}{0.0333 \ \Omega}\right)(100\%)$$

$$= \boxed{9.6 \times 10^{-8}\% \ (\text{i.e., not very efficient})}$$

Concentrate 1

From Table 6.2, GMR = 0.0217.

$$d_s = \sqrt[3]{(10)(10)(10\sqrt{2})} = 11.22 \ \mathrm{ft}$$

From Eq. 6.33,

$$L = 2 \times 10^{-7} \ln \frac{d_s}{\mathrm{GMR}} = 1.25 \ \mu\mathrm{H/m}$$

$$X_L = 120\pi L = 4.71 \times 10^{-4} \ \Omega/\mathrm{m}$$

From Eq. 6.34,

$$M_{bc} = 2 \times 10^{-7} \ln \frac{r_{ab} r_{ac}}{d_s^2} \ \mathrm{H/m}$$

$$M_{ab} = M_{ac} = 2 \times 10^{-7} \ln \frac{(10)(10\sqrt{2})}{d_s^2} \ \mathrm{H/m}$$

$$= 2.33 \times 10^{-8} \ \mathrm{H/m}$$

$$M_{bc} = 2 \times 10^{-7} \ln \frac{(10)(10)}{d_s^2} \ \mathrm{H/m}$$

$$= -4.60 \times 10^{-8} \ \mathrm{H/m}$$

Since there are 1609 meters per mile,

$$X_L = \left(1609 \ \frac{\mathrm{m}}{\mathrm{mi}}\right)\left(4.7 \times 10^{-4} \ \frac{\Omega}{\mathrm{m}}\right)$$

$$= \boxed{0.758 \ \Omega/\mathrm{mi}}$$

$$X_{ab} = X_{ac} = \left(1609 \ \frac{\mathrm{m}}{\mathrm{mi}}\right)\left(120\pi \ \frac{\mathrm{rad}}{\mathrm{s}}\right) M_{ab}$$

$$= \boxed{0.014 \ \Omega/\mathrm{mi}}$$

$$X_{bc} = \left(1609 \ \frac{\mathrm{m}}{\mathrm{mi}}\right)\left(120\pi \ \frac{\mathrm{rad}}{\mathrm{s}}\right) M_{bc}$$

$$= \boxed{-0.028 \ \Omega/\mathrm{mi}}$$

Concentrate 2

For a balanced three-phase load, the wye-delta transformation is a factor of 3.

$$Z_{ln} = \frac{Z_{ll} \times Z_{ll}}{Z_{ll} + Z_{ll} + Z_{ll}} = \frac{Z_{ll}}{3}$$

Converting to an equivalent wye configuration,

$$Z_{\mathrm{phase}} = 3 + j4 + \frac{20 + j15}{3} = \frac{29 + j27}{3}$$

$$P_{\mathrm{load}} = \frac{30 \ \mathrm{kW}}{3 \ \mathrm{phases}} = I_{\mathrm{line}}^2 \left(\frac{20}{3}\right)$$

$$|I_{\mathrm{line}}| = \sqrt{1500}$$

Selecting the a-phase current as a reference,

$$V_s = \left(\sqrt{1500}\right)\left(\frac{29 + j27}{3}\right) \ \mathrm{V}$$

Note!→
$$= 511.5 \underline{/42.95^\circ} \ \mathrm{V}$$

$$\boxed{S_{\mathrm{phase}} = V_s I_{\mathrm{line}}^* = (14.5 + j13.5)\mathrm{kVA}}$$

(a)
$$|V_s| = 511.5 \ \mathrm{V}$$

$$P = 14.5 \ \mathrm{kW/phase}$$

$$Q = 13.5 \ \mathrm{kVAR/phase}$$

$$|V_{s,ll}| = (511.5 \text{ V})(\sqrt{3}) = \boxed{886 \text{ V}}$$

$$P = \boxed{43.5 \text{ kW}}$$

$$Q = \boxed{40.5 \text{ kVAR}}$$

(b) Compensation is by means of a parallel capacitance, so the load impedance is converted to admittance.

$$Y_L = \frac{3}{20 + j15 \ \Omega} = \frac{60 - j45}{625} \text{ S}$$

Compensation requires a parallel capacitor with

$$B_C = \frac{45}{625} \text{ S or } X_C = -13.89 \ \Omega$$

The compensated load impedance is then

$$Z_{L,\text{comp}} = \frac{625}{60} = 10.42 \ \Omega$$

Assuming the load voltage remains the same, the previous value is calculated

$$V_{L,\text{uncomp}} = \left(\sqrt{1500} \text{ A}\right)\left(\frac{20 + j15}{3} \ \Omega\right)$$

$$= 322.7\underline{/36.87°} \text{ V}$$

The current is then

$$|I_{\text{line}}| = \frac{322.7 \text{ V}}{10.42 \ \Omega} = 30.97 \text{ A}$$

$$V_s = (30.97 \text{ A})(13.42 + j4 \ \Omega)$$

$$= 433.7\underline{/16.60°} \text{ V}$$

$$P_{\text{phase}} = 12.87 \text{ kW}$$

$$Q_{\text{phase}} = 3.84 \text{ kVAR}$$

$$|V_{ll}| = \left(\sqrt{3}\right)(433.7 \text{ V}) = \boxed{751 \text{ V}}$$

$$\text{Total } P = \boxed{38.6 \text{ kW}}$$

$$\text{Total } Q = \boxed{11.5 \text{ kVAR}}$$

Concentrate 3

From Table 6.2, the resistance per mile is 0.1943 Ω at 20°C and 0.2134 Ω at 50°C. Example 6.9 found a current of 225 A, which is a current density of about

370 A/in², so the temperature should rise. The 50°C value of 0.2134 Ω is used.

$$R_l = (25)(0.2134) = 5.335 \ \Omega$$

From Table 6.2, the inductive reactance at 1-ft spacing is 0.432 Ω/mile. With GMR = 0.0284, the correction factor is

$$K_L = 1 + \frac{\ln 7}{\ln\left(\dfrac{1}{0.0284}\right)} = 1.5464$$

$$X_L = (1.5464)\left(0.432 \ \frac{\Omega}{\text{mi}}\right)(25 \text{ mi})$$

$$= 16.70 \ \Omega$$

The line impedance is then

$$Z_l = 5.335 + j16.70 \ \Omega$$

The unknown voltage at the receiving end is taken as the reference. The current then leads this voltage by 25.8° ($\cos^{-1} 0.9$). Then,

$$V_s = V_L + (225\underline{/25.84°} \text{ A})(Z_l)$$

$$= V_L + 3.945\underline{/98.1°} \text{ kV}$$

$$= V_L - 0.556 + j3.906 \text{ kV}$$

$$= 11\cos\theta + j11\sin\theta \text{ kV}$$

$$V_L = |V_L| + j0$$

$$11\sin\theta = 3.906$$

$$\sin\theta = 0.355$$

$$\theta = 20.8°$$

$$V_L = 11\cos 20.8° + 0.556 \text{ kV}$$

$$= 10.84 \text{ kV}$$

$$V_s = 11\cos 20.8° + j11\sin 20.8° \text{ kV}$$

$$|V_s| = 11 \text{ kV}$$

The regulation is

$$\left(\frac{V_{\text{no load}} - V_{\text{full load}}}{V_{\text{full load}}}\right)(100\%) = \left(\frac{11 \text{ kV} - 10.84 \text{ kV}}{10.84 \text{ kV}}\right) \times (100\%)$$

The regulation is $\boxed{1.48\%.}$

Concentrate 4

The table parameters for Falcon are

O.D. inches	R/mi 60 Hz 50°C	GMR feet	1-ft spacing	
			X_L Ω/mi	X_C MΩ-mi
1.545	0.0667	0.0523	0.358	0.0814

The correction factors for 20-ft spacing are

$$K_L = 1 + \frac{\ln 20}{\ln\left(\dfrac{1}{0.0523}\right)} = 2.015$$

$$K_C = 1 + \frac{\ln 20}{\ln\left(\dfrac{24}{1.545}\right)} = 2.092$$

$$X_L = \left(0.358\frac{\Omega}{\text{mi}}\right)(2.015) = 0.7214\ \Omega/\text{mi}$$

$$X_C = (0.0814\ \text{M}\Omega\text{-mi})(2.092) = 0.1703 \times 10^6\ \Omega\text{-mi}$$

$$Z = 0.0667 + j0.7214\ \Omega/\text{mi}$$

$$Y = j\frac{1}{0.1703 \times 10^6} = j5.8724 \times 10^{-6}\ \text{S/mi}$$

These parameters are converted to a per meter basis. There are 1609.3 meters per mile.

$$Z = 41.45 \times 10^{-6} + j448.3 \times 10^{-6}\frac{\Omega}{\text{m}}$$

$$= 450.2 \times 10^{-6}\underline{/84.72°}\ \Omega/\text{m}$$

$$Y = j3.649 \times 10^{-9}\ \text{S/m}$$

$$YZ = 1.643 \times 10^{-12}\underline{/174.7°}\ \text{m}^{-2}$$

$$\sqrt{YZ} = 1.282\ \underline{/87.36°}\ \text{m}^{-1} = \gamma$$

(a) $\gamma = \boxed{59.06 \times 10^{-9} + j1.280 \times 10^{-6}\ \text{m}^{-1}}$

(b) $\gamma = \alpha + j\beta$

$$\alpha = \boxed{59.06 \times 10^{-9}\ \text{m}^{-1}}$$

(c) $\beta = \boxed{1.280 \times 10^{-6}\ \text{m}^{-1}}$

(d) $z_o = \sqrt{\dfrac{Z}{Y}} = \sqrt{\dfrac{450.2 \times 10^{-6}\underline{/84.72°}\ \Omega}{3.649 \times 10^{-9}\underline{/90°}\ \text{S}}}$

$$= 351.2\underline{/\left(\tfrac{1}{2}\right)(84.72 - 90)°}\ \Omega$$

$$= 351.2\underline{/-2.64°}\ \Omega$$

$$= \boxed{350.8 - j16.2\ \Omega}$$

(e) $\rho = \dfrac{Z_L - z_o}{Z_L + z_o} = \dfrac{-250.8 + j16.2}{450.8 - j16.2}$

$$= -0.557\underline{/-1.6°}$$

$$= \boxed{0.557\underline{/178.4°}}$$

$Z_L = 100\ \Omega$

$$\frac{100 - (350.8 - j16.2)}{100 + 350.8 - j16.2}$$

Concentrate 5

(a) $\rho = \dfrac{Z_L - z_o}{Z_L + z_o} = \dfrac{70 - 50}{70 + 50} = \boxed{\dfrac{1}{6}}$

(b) $Z_i = z_o\dfrac{Z_L \cos \beta l + jz_o \sin \beta l}{z_o \cos \beta l + jZ_L \sin \beta l}$

$$= (50\ \Omega)\left(\frac{70 \cos \dfrac{\pi}{2} + j50 \sin \dfrac{\pi}{2}}{50 \cos \dfrac{\pi}{2} + j70 \sin \dfrac{\pi}{2}}\right)$$

$$= \boxed{35.71\ \Omega}$$

(c) $\text{VSWR} = \dfrac{1 + |\rho|}{1 - |\rho|} = \dfrac{1 + \dfrac{1}{6}}{1 - \dfrac{1}{6}} = \boxed{1.40}$

Concentrate 6

$$\frac{Z_L}{z_o} = \frac{25 - j25\ \Omega}{50\ \Omega} = \frac{1}{2} - j\frac{1}{2}\ \text{P.U.}$$

The load point is shown on the Smith chart shown. Impedance locus is shown as a dashed circle.

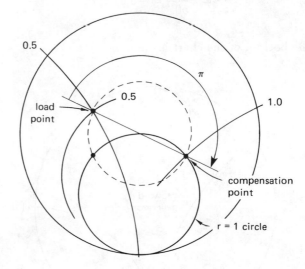

The compensation point for series capacitance is where the impedance locus intersects the $r = 1$ circle on the right-hand side of the chart.

For this particular load, the compensation point is 180° (on the chart) from the load point, at

$$\frac{Z_i}{z_o} = 1 + j1\ \text{P.U.}$$

180°on the Smith chart is $\lambda/4$ or

$$\beta l = \boxed{\pi/2 \text{ rad}}$$

$$\frac{Z_i}{z_o} = \frac{\dfrac{Z_l}{z_o}\cos\beta l + j\sin\beta l}{\cos\beta l + j\dfrac{Z_L}{z_o}\sin\beta l}$$

$$= \frac{\dfrac{1}{2}\cos\beta l + j\left(\sin\beta l - \dfrac{1}{2}\cos\beta l\right)}{\cos\beta l + \dfrac{1}{2}\sin\beta l + j\dfrac{1}{2}\sin\beta l}$$

At $\beta l = \pi/2$,

$$\sin\beta l = 1$$

$$\cos\beta l = 0$$

$$\frac{Z_i}{z_o} = \frac{j}{\dfrac{1}{2}+j\dfrac{1}{2}} = \frac{2}{\dfrac{1}{j}+1} = 1+j1$$

The compensating reactance must be $-j1$ or

$$X_C = -z_o = \boxed{-50\,\Omega}$$

Concentrate 7

(a) $\qquad \dfrac{Z}{z_o} = \dfrac{-j25}{50} = -0.5j$ P.U.

The bottom of the chart is open.

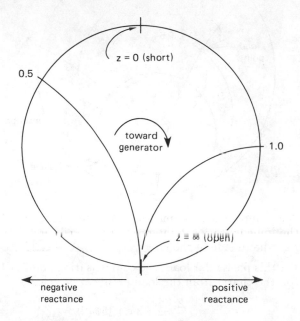

The shortest length to obtain $-j0.5 \times 50$ is to start with an open line, going clockwise 126.5° to the intersection with $x = 0.5$ on the left half of the Smith chart. This corresponds to

$$\beta l = \left(\frac{126}{2}\right)\left(\frac{\pi}{180}\right) \text{ rad}$$

$$\beta l = 1.1 \text{ rad} = \boxed{0.175\lambda}$$

(b) $\qquad \dfrac{Z}{z_o} = \dfrac{j50}{50} = j1$ P.U.

The shortest line is found for a shorted line (short point at the top of the Smith chart) going clockwise to intersect the $x = 1$ circle (on the right). This is 90° on the chart corresponding to

$$\beta l = (45)\left(\frac{\pi}{180}\right) \text{ rad}$$

$$\beta l = \boxed{0.785 \text{ rad or } \lambda/8}$$

Concentrate 8

Assume $c = 3 \times 10^8$ m/s.

$$\beta = \frac{2\pi f}{c} = \frac{2\pi \times 10^8}{3 \times 10^8} = \frac{2\pi}{3} \text{ rad/m}$$

$$\beta l = \frac{2\pi}{3}\text{rad, as } l = 1 \text{ m}$$

$$\tan\beta l = -1.732 = -\sqrt{3}$$

From Eq. 6.131,

$$\frac{Z_u}{z_o} = \frac{1 - j\,\text{VSWR}\tan\beta l}{\text{VSWR} - j\tan\beta l}$$

$$\text{VSWR} = 2$$

$$\frac{Z_u}{z_o} = \frac{1 + 2\sqrt{3}\,j}{2 + j\sqrt{3}} = 1.143 + j0.742 \text{ P.U.}$$

$$z_o = 50\,\Omega$$

$$Z_u = 57.14 + j37.12\,\Omega$$

$$R = \boxed{57.14\,\Omega}$$

$$X = \boxed{37.12\,\Omega}$$

Concentrate 9

Following Eq. 6.158, the radiated power from a half-wave dipole antenna is

$$P_r = 73.08\, I_m^2$$

The radiation resistance corresponds,

$$P_r = I_m^2 R_r$$
$$R_r = 73.08\,\Omega$$

At a frequency of 100 MHz, the wavelength is 3 m and $h = \lambda/4 = 0.75$ m.

The skin depth for copper at 100 MHz is 0.26 mils (see Ex. 6.1).

AWG #20 wire has a diameter of 32 mils, and a DC resistance of 10.14 Ω/1000 ft, so

$$R_0 = \left(\frac{10.15\,\Omega}{1000\,\text{ft}}\right)\left(\frac{\text{ft}}{12\,\text{in}}\right)$$
$$\times \left(\frac{\text{in}}{2.54\,\text{cm}}\right)\left(\frac{100\,\text{cm}}{\text{m}}\right)(0.75\,\text{m})$$
$$= 0.025\,\Omega$$

At high frequencies (see Eq. 6.8),

$$R = (0.025\,\Omega)\left(0.25 + 0.5\frac{r}{\delta}\right)$$
$$= (0.025\,\Omega)\left(0.25 + \frac{8}{0.26}\right) = 0.775\,\Omega$$

The radiation efficiency is

$$e = \left(\frac{R_r}{R_r + R}\right)(100\%)$$
$$= \frac{(73.08\,\Omega)(100\%)}{73.08\,\Omega + 0.775\,\Omega}$$
$$= \boxed{99.0\%}$$

Concentrate 10

From Eq. 6.145,

$$g = e \times g_D$$
$$e = \text{efficiency} = 0.90$$
$$g_D = \text{directivity} = 20$$
$$g = (20)(0.9) = 18$$
$$g_{\text{dB}} = 10\log_{10} 18 = \boxed{12.55\,\text{dB}}$$

From Eq. 6.183,

$$\Omega_A = \frac{4\pi}{g_D} = \boxed{\frac{\pi}{5}}\ \text{steradians}$$

Timed 1

O.D. inches	R_{ac} 60 Hz 50°C	GMR feet	1-ft spacing reactance/conductor	
			X_L Ω/mi	X_C MΩ-mi
0.846	0.2134	0.0284	0.432	0.0992

The correction factors are

$$K_L = 1 + \frac{\ln 7}{\ln\left(\dfrac{1}{0.0284}\right)} = 1.5464$$

$$K_C = 1 + \frac{\ln 7}{\ln\left(\dfrac{24}{0.846}\right)} = 1.5817$$

$$X_L = \left(0.432\,\frac{\Omega}{\text{mi}}\right) K_L = 0.6680\,\Omega/\text{mi}$$

$$X_C = (0.0992\,\Omega\text{-mi}) K_C = -156.90 \times 10^3\,\Omega\text{-mi}$$

$$Z = \left(0.2134 + j0.6680\frac{\Omega}{\text{mi}}\right)(100\,\text{mi})$$
$$= 21.34 + j66.8 = 70.126\,\underline{/72.28°}\ \Omega$$

$$\boxed{X_C = \frac{-157 \times 10^3\,\Omega\text{-mi}}{100\,\text{mi}} = -1.57\,\text{k}\Omega}$$

Note $X_C = \dfrac{X_C \times K_C}{\text{miles of line}}$

$$Y = -\frac{j}{X_C} = 637 \times 10^{-6}\,\underline{/90°}\ \text{S}$$

$$YZ = 44.67 \times 10^{-3}\,\underline{/162.28°}$$

From Eq. 6.59,

$$V_s = \left(1 + \frac{YZ}{2}\right)V_r + ZI_r$$

From Eq. 6.60,

$$I_s = Y\left(1 + \frac{YZ}{4}\right)V_r + \left(1 + \frac{YZ}{2}\right)I_r$$

$$1 + \frac{YZ}{2} = 0.9787 + j0.0068 = 0.9787\underline{/0.4°}$$

$$1 + \frac{YZ}{4} = 0.9894 + j0.0034 = 0.9894\underline{/0.2°}$$

$$V_{ln} = V_r = \frac{86.6}{\sqrt{3}}\,\text{kV} = 50\,\text{kV}$$

$$|I_r| = \frac{\left(\dfrac{8500}{3}\right) \text{kVA}}{50 \text{ kV}} = 56.67 \text{ A}$$

$$\underline{/I_r} = -\cos^{-1}\left(\frac{75}{85}\right) = -28.07°$$

$$I_r = 56.67 \underline{/-28.07°}$$

From Eq. 6.59,

$$V_s = (0.9787 \underline{/0.4°})(50 \text{ kV})$$
$$+ (70.126 \underline{/72.28°})(56.67 \underline{/-28.07°})$$
$$= 51.88 \underline{/3.44°} \text{ kV}$$

When $I_r = 0$, from Eq. 6.59,

$$51.88 \underline{/3.44°} \text{ kV} = (0.9788 \underline{/0.4°})V_r$$
$$V_r = 53.00 \underline{/3.04°} \text{ kV}$$

Then, the regulation is

$$\left(\frac{53 \text{ kV} - 50 \text{ kV}}{50 \text{ kV}}\right)(100\%) = \boxed{6.0\%}$$

Timed 2

$$z_o = 72 \ \Omega$$
$$Z_L = 50 \ \Omega$$
$$\beta = 0.5$$
$$l = 7.5 \text{ m}$$
$$\frac{Z_L}{z_o} = z_L = \frac{50}{72} = 0.6944 \text{ P.U.}$$

$$\beta l = 3.75 \text{ rad} = 214.86°$$

$$2\beta l = 429.72° = 360° + 69.72°$$

The load point and source point are shown.

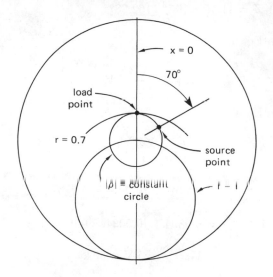

Reading from the enlarged chart of App. C, the value is

$$\frac{Z_i}{z_o} \approx 0.84 + j0.29 \text{ P.U.}$$

$$Z_i \approx 60 + j21 \ \Omega$$

Using Eq. 6.117,

$$\frac{Z_i}{z_o} = \frac{50 + j72 \tan 3.75 \text{ (rad)}}{72 + j50 \tan 3.75}$$

$$= 0.8358 + j0.2923 \text{ P.U.}$$

$$Z_i = \boxed{60.18 + j21.05 \ \Omega}$$

Timed 3

$$z_o = 100 \ \Omega$$
$$Z_L = 25 + j25 \ \Omega$$
$$z_L = 0.25 + j0.25$$
$$y_L = 2 - j2$$

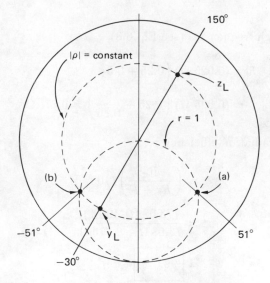

(a) The z_L point, $0.25 + j0.25$, is at $150°$. Following a constant $|\rho|$ circle toward the generator, the compensation point is at $51°$, where $z_i = 1 + j1.6$. A series compensation of $-j1.6$ can be added. The line length from the load is

$$\frac{150° - 51°}{720°}\lambda = \boxed{0.1375\lambda}$$

$$Z_C = (-j100)(1.6) = -j160 \ \Omega$$

Using a 72-Ω line for the compensator, its reactance is

$$x_C = -\frac{160}{72} = -2.22 \text{ P.U.}$$

Starting from the open position (bottom of the Smith chart), the location of $-j2.22$ is at about $-48°$, for a compensator length of

$$l_{\text{comp}} = \frac{48°}{720°}\lambda \approx \frac{\lambda}{15}$$

Using Eq. 6.117 with $Z_L = \infty$,

$$\frac{Z_i}{z_o} = \frac{\cos\beta l}{j\sin\beta l} = \frac{-j}{\tan\beta l}$$

$$\tan\beta l = \frac{1}{2.22}$$

$$\beta l = \frac{2\pi}{\lambda}l_{\text{comp}} = 0.423$$

$$l_{\text{comp}} = \frac{0.423}{2\pi}\lambda = \boxed{\frac{\lambda}{14.85}}$$

(b) The y_L point is $180°$ from the z_L point on the same $|\rho| = $ constant circle.

The parallel compensation point is at $-51°$, so the distance from the load for compensation is at

$$\frac{51° - 30°}{720°}\lambda = \boxed{0.0292\lambda}$$

At that point,

$$y_L = 1 - j1.6 \text{ P.U.}$$

$$y = \frac{z_o}{Z} = z_o Y$$

$$Y_{\text{comp}} = \frac{y}{z_o} = j\frac{1.6}{100} \text{ S}$$

For the 72-Ω line,

$$y_{\text{comp}} = \left(j\frac{1.6}{100\,\Omega}\right)(72\,\Omega) = j1.152 \text{ P.U.}$$

1.152 is on the right side of the chart at $82°$. The shortest line is from the top of the chart ($y = 0$: open) at $180°$.

$$l = \frac{180° - 82°}{720°}\lambda = 0.136\lambda$$

More exactly, using Eq. 6.117 with $Z_L = \infty$,

$$y_{\text{comp}} = j\tan\beta l = j1.152 \text{ P.U.}$$

$$\beta l = \tan^{-1} 1.152 = 0.8559$$

$$l_{\text{comp}} = \frac{0.8559\lambda}{2\pi} = \boxed{0.1362\lambda}$$

Timed 4

$$y_i = Yz_o = \frac{50\,\Omega}{25 - j25\,\Omega} = 1 + j1 \text{ P.U.}$$

Compensating with a shunt capacitance,

$$y_{\text{comp}} = jb_C$$

$$B_C z_o = b_C$$

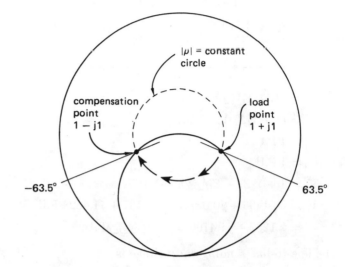

The load point is at $63.5°$. Traverse the $|\rho| = $ constant circle clockwise to $1 - j1$ at $-63.5°$. The distance from the load is

$$d = \frac{63.5° - (-63.5°)}{720°}\lambda = \boxed{0.1764\lambda}$$

$$B_C = \frac{b_C}{z_o} = \omega C$$

$$C = \frac{1}{50\,\omega} = \boxed{\frac{0.02}{\omega} \text{ F}}$$

Timed 5

The line-to-neutral voltage is $220/\sqrt{3}$ kV; the load current is

$$I_r = \frac{\dfrac{500 \text{ MW}}{(3)(0.9)}}{\dfrac{220 \text{ kV}}{\sqrt{3}}}\underline{/-\cos^{-1} 0.9}$$

$$V_r = V_{\text{base}}$$

$$|I_r| = I_{\text{base}}$$

$$Z_{\text{base}} = \frac{V_{\text{base}}}{I_{\text{base}}} = \frac{\left(\dfrac{220 \text{ kV}}{\sqrt{3}}\right)^2}{\dfrac{500 \text{ MW}}{3 \times 0.9}}$$

$$= 87.12\,\Omega$$

$$Z_l = \frac{40 + j160 \ \Omega}{87.12 \ \Omega} = 0.4591 + j1.8365 \ \text{P.U.}$$

$$Y_l = \frac{Y Z_{\text{base}}}{2} = j0.04630 \ \text{P.U.}$$

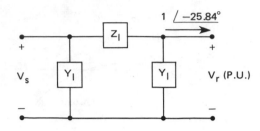

$$V_s = (I_r + Y_l V_r) Z_l + V_r$$
$$= (1 + Y_l Z_l) V_r + I_r Z_l$$

$$|V_r| = 1 \ \text{P.U.}$$

$$|I_r| = 1 \ \text{P.U.}$$

$$V_s = 1 + Y_l Z_l + Z_l \underline{/-25.84°} \ \text{P.U.}$$

$$V_s = 0.91496 + j0.02126 + 1.2137 + j1.4528 \ \text{P.U.}$$

$$= 2.1287 + j1.4706 = 2.59\underline{/34.7°} \ \text{P.U.}$$

The line-to-line sending-end voltage is

$$\boxed{|V_s| = (220 \ \text{kV})(2.59 \ \text{P.U.}) = \boxed{569.8 \ \text{kV}}}$$

Timed 6

Taking V_r and $|I_r|$ as 1 P.U.,

$$Z_{\text{base}} = \frac{(132 \ \text{kV})^2}{\dfrac{75 \ \text{MVA}}{0.92}} = 213.73 \ \Omega$$

$$Z_l = \left(0.1 + j0.6 \ \frac{\Omega}{\text{mi}}\right)(100 \ \text{mi})$$

$$Z = \frac{Z_l}{Z_{\text{base}}} = 0.2846 \ \underline{/80.54°} \ \text{P.U.}$$

$$-X_C = \frac{0.15 \times 10^6 \ \Omega\text{-mi}}{100 \ \text{mi}} = 1.5 \times 10^3 \ \Omega$$

$$Y = \frac{Z_{\text{base}}}{-jX_C} = j0.1425 \ \text{P.U.}$$

$$1 + \frac{YZ}{2} = 0.980 + j0.0033 \ \text{P.U.}$$

As in Timed 5,

$$V_s = 1 + \frac{YZ}{2} + Z\underline{/-\cos^{-1} 0.92} \ \text{P.U.}$$

$$= 1 + \frac{YZ}{2} + 0.1531 + j0.2399 \ \text{P.U.}$$

$$= 1.133 + j0.243 \ \text{P.U.}$$

$$= 1.16\underline{/12.1°} \ \text{P.U.}$$

The base voltage is 132 kV, so

$$|V_s| = (132 \ \text{kV})(1.16 \ \text{P.U.}) = \boxed{153.1 \ \text{kV}}$$

Timed 7

The power density from an isotropic antenna at a distance r will be

$$p_r = \frac{e_t P_t}{4\pi r^2} \ \text{(isotropic)}$$

e_t is the transmitting antenna efficiency.

For a directional antenna with a beam solid angle of Ω_T, the maximum power density will be increased over the isotropic case by the directivity.

$$g_D = \frac{4\pi}{\Omega_t}$$

$$p_r = \frac{e_t P_t}{\Omega_t r^2} \ \text{(anisotropic)}$$

The receiving antenna will have a power P_r.

$$P_r = e_r p_r A_{\text{eff}}$$

$$A_{\text{eff}} = \frac{\lambda^2}{4\pi} g_D = \frac{\lambda^2}{\Omega_r}$$

$$P_r = \frac{e_r e_t \lambda^2 P_t}{\Omega_t \Omega_r r^2}$$

For a conical beam with half-angle n,

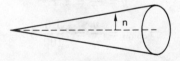

$$\Omega = 2\pi(1 - \cos n) \ \text{steradians}$$

Both antennas have $n = 1.50°$.

$$\Omega_t = \Omega_r = 2\pi(1 - \cos 1.5°) \ \text{steradians}$$

$$= 2.153 \times 10^{-3} \ \text{steradians}$$

For $f = 10 \ \text{gHz}$,

$$\lambda = \frac{3 \times 10^8 \ \dfrac{\text{m}}{\text{s}}}{10 \times 10^9 \ \dfrac{\text{cycle}}{\text{s}}} = 0.030 \ \text{m/cycle}$$

$$P_r = 10^{-9} \ \text{mW}$$

$$P_t = \frac{(2.153 \times 10^{-3})^2 (4 \times 10^7 \ \text{m})^2 (10^{-9} \ \text{mW})}{e_r e_t (0.03 \ \text{m})^2}$$

$$= \boxed{\frac{8.241}{e_r e_t} \ \text{mW} \approx 8 \ \text{mW}}$$

Timed 8

For a half-wave dipole,

$$P_r = 73.08\, I_m^2$$

For an isotropic antenna,

$$P = 120\pi\, I_m^2$$

$$g_D = \frac{120\text{ W}}{73.08\text{ W}}$$

For $f = 50$ MHz, $\lambda = 6$ m, so the ohmic resistance will be small. It is therefore neglected, so assume $e = 1$.

$$p_{\max} = \frac{e g_D P_t}{4\pi r^2} = \frac{E^2}{120\pi}$$

$$r^2 = \frac{120\pi e g_D P_t}{4\pi E^2}$$

$$= (30\ \Omega)\left(\frac{120\text{ W}}{73.08\text{ W}}\right)(1)\left[\frac{100\text{ W}}{\left(10^{-4}\dfrac{\text{V}}{\text{m}}\right)^2}\right]$$

$$r = \boxed{702\text{ km}}$$

Timed 9

$$P_{\text{amp}} = \left(\frac{\lambda}{4\pi r}\right)^2 g_{Dt} g_{Dr} P_t$$

$$g_D = \frac{4\pi}{\lambda^2} A_{\text{eff}}$$

$$P_{\text{amp}} = \left[\frac{\lambda^2}{(4)^2 \pi^2 r^2}\right]\left(\frac{4\pi}{\lambda^2}\right)^2 A_{\text{eff}}^2 P_t$$

$$= \frac{A_{\text{eff}}^2}{r^2 \lambda^2} P_t$$

$$r = \frac{A_{\text{eff}}}{\lambda}\sqrt{\frac{P_t}{P_{\text{amp}}}}$$

Assume $A_{\text{eff}} = 50\%$ of the physical aperture of 0.2 m^2.

$$\lambda = \frac{3 \times 10^8}{3 \times 10^9} = 0.1$$

$$\frac{A_{\text{eff}}}{\lambda} = 1$$

$$r = \sqrt{\frac{1}{10^{-9}}} = \boxed{31.62\text{ km}}$$

Timed 10

At the first null of the shorted line, the half wavelength is $\beta l = \pi$, so

$$\beta = \frac{\pi}{3}\frac{\text{rad}}{\text{m}} = 60°/\text{m}$$

With the antenna connected to the line, the first minimum of the voltage standing wave occurs at the minimum impedance, which is purely real.

It is given that $R = 73\ \Omega$ and X is small.

$$\frac{Z_i}{z_o} = \frac{\dfrac{R+jX}{z_o} + j\tan\left(\dfrac{1.6\pi}{3}\right)}{1 + j\dfrac{R+jX}{z_o}\tan\left(\dfrac{1.6\pi}{3}\right)}$$

$$\frac{1.6\pi}{3}\text{ rad} \rightarrow (1.6)(60°) = 96°$$

Z_i/z_o is a real number, so the angles of the numerator and denominator must be equal.

$$\frac{\tan 96° + \dfrac{X}{z_o}}{\dfrac{R}{z_o}} = \frac{\dfrac{R}{z_o}\tan 96°}{1 - \dfrac{X}{z_o}\tan 96°}$$

$$\left(\frac{X}{z_o}\right)^2 + \left(\frac{\tan^2 96° - 1}{\tan 96°}\right)\left(\frac{X}{z_o}\right) - \left[1 - \left(\frac{R}{z_o}\right)^2\right] = 0$$

$$\frac{R}{z_o} = \frac{73}{75}\text{ P.U.}$$

This is solved using the quadradic formula

$$\frac{X}{z_o} = 4.7046 \pm \sqrt{(4.7046)^2 + 1 - \left(\frac{73}{75}\right)^2}\text{ P.U.}$$

As X is made small by tuning, the minus sign is appropriate and

$$\frac{X}{z_o} = -5.5893 \times 10^{-3}\text{ P.U.}$$

In order that the amplifier appear as the complex conjugate of the antenna impedance,

$$\frac{Z_{\text{ant}}}{z_o} = \frac{73}{75} - j5.5893 \times 10^{-3}\text{ P.U.}$$

The amplifier must have the same impedance as the minimum seen from the transmission line.

$$\frac{Z_{\min}}{z_o} = \frac{\dfrac{R}{z_o}}{1 - \dfrac{X}{z_o}\tan 96°} = 1.028 \text{ P.U.}$$

With a transmission line of 1.6 m, this impedance seen from the antenna will be

$$\frac{Z}{z_o} = \frac{1.028 + j\tan 96°}{1 + j1.028\tan 96°} \text{ P.U.}$$

$$= 0.9733 + j5.589 \times 10^{-3} \text{ P.U.}$$

$$Z = \boxed{\begin{array}{l}73.00 + j0.4192\,\Omega, \text{ which is the desired} \\ \text{complex conjugate.}\end{array}}$$

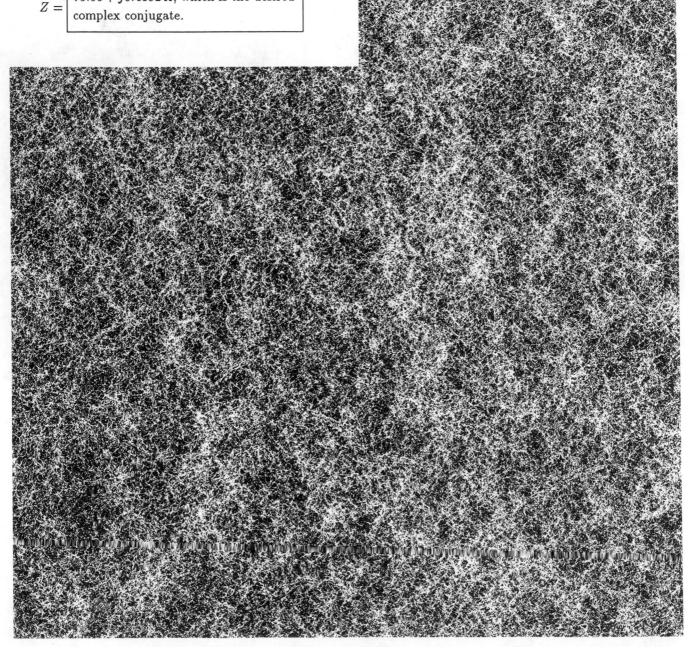

ROTATING MACHINES

Warmup 1

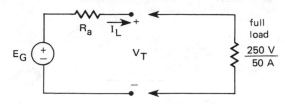

$$V_T = E_G - R_a I_L$$

At no-load,

$$V_T = E_G = 260 \text{ V}$$

At full-load,

$$V_T = E_G - (50 \text{ A})R_a$$
$$250 \text{ V} = E_G - (50 \text{ A})R_a$$
$$R_a = \frac{260 \text{ V} - 250 \text{ V}}{50 \text{ A}} = \boxed{0.2 \ \Omega}$$

Warmup 2

$$I_{\text{full load}} = \frac{10 \text{ kW}}{240 \text{ V}} = 41.67 \text{ A}$$

$$R_a = \frac{V_{\text{no load}} - V_{\text{full load}}}{I_{\text{full load}}} \quad \text{(see Warmup 1)}$$

$$= \frac{260 \text{ V} - 240 \text{ V}}{41.67 \text{ A}} = 0.48 \ \Omega$$

$$P_{\text{in}} = P_{\text{mech. loss}} + I_A^2 R_a + P_{\text{out}}$$

$$= (15 \text{ hp})\left(\frac{746 \text{ W}}{\text{hp}}\right) = 11.190 \text{ kW}$$

$$I_A^2 R_a = (41.67 \text{ A})^2 (0.48 \ \Omega) = \boxed{0.833 \text{ kW}}$$

$$P_{\text{out}} = 10 \text{ kW}$$

$$P_{\text{mech. loss}} = 11.190 \text{ kW} - 10.833 \text{ kW} = \boxed{357 \text{ W}}$$

Warmup 3

For field flux, Φ is proportional to line voltage.

$$\Phi = aV$$
$$\Omega_R = \text{rotor speed (rad/s)}$$
$$E_G = k\Phi\Omega_R$$
$$= kaV\Omega_R$$
$$T = k\Phi I_A = kaV I_A \text{ (torque in N·m)}$$
$$V = E_G + R_a I_A$$
$$P_{\text{in}} \approx V I_A$$
$$P_{\text{out}} \approx T\Omega_R$$

(a) For T = constant, if V is decreased by 10%, to keep T constant, I_A is increased by approximately 10% and E_G is decreased by 10% with V.

$$P_{\text{in}} = \boxed{V I_A \approx \text{constant}}$$
$$P_{\text{out}} = P_{\text{in}} - I_A^2 R_a - \text{mech. loss}$$

Since I_A has increased by 10%, I_A^2 is increased by 20%, but $I_A^2 R_a$ is on the order of 5% of the load power, so it only causes a 1% drop in P_{out}.

E_G drops 10% with V, but

$$\boxed{\Omega_R \text{ drops only 1\%}}$$

(b) For $T \propto \Omega_R$, in a first approximation,

$$E_G \approx V$$
$$E_G = kaV\Omega_R$$

$ka\Omega_R \approx 1$, and there is no change in speed.

In a second approximation,

$$I_A = \frac{V - E_G}{R_a}$$
$$T = kaV I_A$$

The air-gap power is

$$P_{\text{air gap}} = E_G I_A = T\Omega_R$$
$$T = m\Omega_R$$
$$T\Omega_R = m\Omega_R^2$$
$$E_G = kaV\Omega_R$$
$$E_G I_A = \frac{kaV^2 \Omega_R (1 - ka\Omega_R)}{R_a} = m\Omega_R^2$$
$$\frac{kaV^2}{R_a} = \frac{m\Omega_R}{1 - ka\Omega_R} = \frac{m}{\dfrac{1}{\Omega_R} - ka}$$

When V goes down 10%, $1/\Omega_R - ka$ must go up by 21%, so Ω_R must decrease some amount. If under normal conditions $I_A R_a = 0.05V$,

$$I_A R_a = V - E_{G0} = V(1 - ka\Omega_{R0})$$
$$1 - ka\Omega_{R0} = 0.05$$
$$ka = \frac{0.95}{\Omega_{R0}}$$

PROFESSIONAL PUBLICATIONS, INC. • Belmont, CA

When V goes down 10%,

$$\frac{m\Omega_R}{1 - ka\Omega_R} \rightarrow (0.81)\frac{m\Omega_{R0}}{1 - ka\Omega_{R0}}$$

$$\frac{\Omega_R}{1 - 0.95\frac{\Omega_R}{\Omega_{R0}}} = \left(\frac{0.81}{0.05}\right)\Omega_{R0} = 16.2\Omega_{R0}$$

$$\frac{\Omega_R}{\Omega_{R0}} = (16.2)\left(1 - 0.95\frac{\Omega_R}{\Omega_{R0}}\right)$$

$$= \frac{16.2}{(1 + 0.95)(16.2)} = 0.99$$

$\boxed{\Omega_R \text{ drops by about 1%.}}$

$$I_A R_a = V - E_G = V - ka\Omega_R$$
$$T = m\Omega_R = kaVIA$$

Eliminating Ω_R,

$$I_A R_a = \frac{V}{1 + \frac{(kaV)^2}{mR_a}}$$

The original value of $I_A R_a$ is

$$I_{A0} R_a \approx 0.05V_0$$

V_0 is the initial voltage. Then,

$$1 + \frac{(kaV_0)^2}{mR_a} \approx 20$$

When the voltage drops 10%,

$$1 + \frac{[ka(0.9)V_0]^2}{mR_a} = 16.39$$

The resulting armature IR drop is

$$I_A R_a = \frac{0.9V_0}{16.39} = 0.0549V_0$$

The current changes by

$$\frac{0.0549 - 0.05}{0.05} = 1.098 \text{ P.U.}$$

The input power changes also.

$$P_{\text{in}} = (0.9V_0)(1.098I_{A0}) = 0.988P_0$$

$\boxed{\text{The power drops by about 1%.}}$

Warmup 4

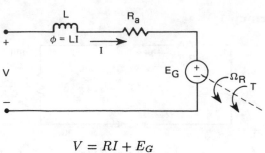

$$V = RI + E_G$$

$$E_G = k\Phi\Omega_R = kLI\Omega_R$$

$$T = k\Phi I = kLI^2$$

If T is up 25%, so is I^2, and $\sqrt{1.25} = 1.11$, so

$\boxed{I \text{ is up 11%}}$

Using subscript zero for the initial values,

$$E_{G0} = V = I_0 R_a$$

When I increases by 11%,

$\boxed{E_G \text{ decreases by about 1%}}$

$$E_{G1} = 0.99\,E_{G0}$$

$$E_{G0} = kLI_0\Omega_{R0}$$

$$E_{G1} = 0.99\,kLI_0\Omega_{R0}$$

$$= kLI_1\Omega_{R1}$$

$$\Omega_{R1} = \frac{0.99\,I_0}{I_1}\Omega_{R0}$$

$$= \frac{0.99}{1.11}\Omega_{R0} = 0.89\,\Omega_{R0}$$

$\boxed{\text{The speed also drops by about 11%.}}$

The output power is

$$P_d = (1.25\,T_0)(0.89\,\Omega_{R0}) = 1.11\,P_0$$

$\boxed{\text{The air-gap power increases by 11%.}}$

Warmup 5

$$\frac{P}{q} = V_{an}^2 g_c + I_r^2 \left(r_s + \frac{a^2 r_r}{s} \right)$$

$$V_{an}^2 g_c = \frac{850 \text{ W}}{3 \text{ phases}}$$

$$I_R^2 r_s = \frac{550 \text{ W}}{3 \text{ phases}}$$

$$I_R^2 \frac{a^2 r_r}{s} = \frac{25{,}000 \text{ W} - 850 \text{ W} - 550 \text{ W}}{3 \text{ phases}}$$

$$= 7867 \text{ W}$$

$$s = \frac{1800 \text{ rpm} - 1700 \text{ rpm}}{1800 \text{ rpm}} = \frac{1}{18}$$

$$I^2 a^2 r_r = 437 \text{ W}$$

The shaft power is then

$$\frac{P_{\text{shaft}}}{q} = I_R^2 a^2 r_r \left(\frac{1}{s} - 1 \right)$$

$$= 7430 \text{ W/phase}$$

$$P_L = (3 \text{ phases}) \left(7430 \, \frac{\text{W}}{\text{phase}} \right) \left(\frac{1 \text{ hp}}{746 \text{ W}} \right)$$

$$= \boxed{29.9 \text{ hp}}$$

$$P_L = 22{,}290 \text{ W}$$

$$\eta = \left(\frac{22.29 \text{ kW}}{25 \text{ kW}} \right) (100\%) = \boxed{89.2\%}$$

Warmup 6

$$r_c = \frac{1}{g_c} = \frac{V_{ln}^2}{\dfrac{P_{\text{no load}}}{q}} = \frac{\left(\dfrac{440}{\sqrt{3}} \right)^2}{\dfrac{1200}{3 \text{ phases}}}$$

$$= \boxed{161 \ \Omega}$$

$$x_\Phi = \frac{-1}{b_c} = \frac{V_{ln}^2}{\dfrac{Q_{\text{no load}}}{q}}$$

$$= \frac{\left(\dfrac{440}{\sqrt{3}} \right)^2}{\dfrac{\sqrt{S_{\text{no load}}^2 - P_{\text{no load}}^2}}{3 \text{ phases}}}$$

$$= \frac{(440)^2}{[(2500)^2 - (1200)^2]^{1/2}} = \boxed{88.3 \ \Omega}$$

Warmup 7

$$I^2 R_e = \frac{P_{\text{blocked rotor}}}{3 \text{ phases}}$$

$$R_e = \frac{\dfrac{375 \text{ W}}{3 \text{ phases}}}{(21 \text{ A})^2} = \boxed{0.28 \ \Omega}$$

$$I^2 X_e = \frac{Q_{\text{blocked rotor}}}{3 \text{ phases}}$$

$$= \left(\frac{P_{\text{blocked rotor}}}{3 \text{ phases}} \right) \left(\frac{\sqrt{1 - \text{PF}^2}}{\text{PF}} \right)$$

$$X_e = \left[\frac{375 \text{ W}}{(3)(21 \text{ A})^2} \right] \left[\frac{\sqrt{1 - (0.37)^2}}{0.37} \right] = \boxed{0.71 \ \Omega}$$

Warmup 8

$$\frac{P_L}{q} = \frac{(20 \text{ hp}) \left(\dfrac{746 \text{ W}}{\text{hp}} \right)}{3 \text{ phases}} = 4.97 \, \frac{\text{kW}}{\text{phase}}$$

$$\frac{P_L}{q} = I_R'^2 a^2 r_r \left(\frac{1}{s} - 1 \right) = I_R'^2 a^2 r_r \left(\frac{1}{0.03} - 1 \right)$$

$$I_R'^2 a^2 r_r = \left(\frac{0.03}{0.97} \right) (4.97 \text{ kW}) = 154 \text{ W}$$

With 1200 W of fixed losses (Warmup 6), the power to r_s and $a^2 r_r$ is

$$I_R'^2 \left(r_s + \frac{a^2 r_r}{s} \right) = \frac{16{,}950 \text{ W} - 1200 \text{ W}}{3 \text{ phases}} = 5250 \text{ W}$$

$$\frac{r_s + \dfrac{a^2 r_r}{0.03}}{a^2 r_r} = \frac{5250 \text{ W}}{154 \text{ W}}$$

$$a^2 r_r = 1.217 r_s$$

$$r_e = r_s + a^2 r_r = 2.217 \, r_s$$

From Warmup 7,

$$r_e = 0.28 \ \Omega$$

$$r_s = \frac{0.28 > \Omega}{2.217} = \boxed{0.126 \ \Omega}$$

$$a^2 r_r = 1.217 \, r_s = \boxed{0.154 \ \Omega}$$

Warmup 9

The required volt-amps per phase are

$$\frac{Q}{3 \text{ phases}} = V_a I_a = \frac{V_a(E_g - V_a)}{X_s}$$

$$E_g = \left(\frac{Q}{3 \text{ phases}}\right)\left(\frac{X_s}{V_a}\right) + V_a$$

$$= \left(\frac{10^4 \text{ VA}}{3 \text{ phases}}\right)\left(\frac{20 \ \Omega}{254 \text{ V}}\right) + 254 \text{ V} = 516 \text{ V}$$

$$I_f = \left(\frac{5 \text{ A}}{254 \text{ V}}\right)(516 \text{ V}) = \boxed{10.16 \text{ A}}$$

Warmup 10

$$V_a = \frac{13,800 \text{ V}}{\sqrt{3}} = 7967 \text{ V}$$

$$|I_a| = \frac{\dfrac{50 \times 10^6 \text{ VA}}{3 \text{ phases}}}{7967 \text{ V}} = 2092 \text{ A}$$

$$\underline{/I_a} = -\arccos 0.88 = -28.36°$$

$$jX_s I_a = -(2.8 \ \Omega\underline{/90°})(2092 \text{ A}\underline{/-28.36°})$$

$$= 5858\underline{/61.64°} \text{ V}$$

$$E_{g1} = V_a - jX_s I_a = 5184 - j5155 \text{ V}$$

$$|E_{g1}| = 7311 \text{ V}$$

$$\delta_1 = -44.8°$$

$$|E_{g2}| = 1.1|E_{g1}| = 8042 \text{ V}$$

$$|E_{g1}|\sin\delta_1 = |E_{g2}|\sin\delta_2$$

$$\sin\delta_2 = \left|\frac{E_{g1}}{E_{g2}}\right|\sin\delta_1 = \frac{1}{1.1}\sin\delta_1$$

Because the motor load is not changed,

$$\sin\delta_2 = \frac{1}{1.11}\sin(-44.8°) = -0.635$$

$$\delta_2 = -39.44°$$

$$\cos\delta = 0.772$$

$$E_{g2} = (8042 \text{ V})(\cos\delta_2 + j\sin\delta_2)$$

$$= 6211 - j5109 \text{ V}$$

$$(j2.8 \ \Omega)I_2 = V_a - E_{g2} = 1756 + j5109 \text{ V}$$

$$I_2 = 1929\underline{/-18.97°} \text{ A}$$

$$PF_2 = \cos(-18.97°)$$

$$= \boxed{0.946 \text{ lagging}}$$

Concentrate 1

$$E_G = V_T + (I_T + I_F)R_a$$

$$E_N = 260 \text{ V}$$

$$\frac{E_G}{E_N} = \frac{V_T + I_T R_a}{E_N} + \left(\frac{R_a I_N}{E_N}\right)\left(\frac{I_F}{I_N}\right)$$

$$V_T = 240 \text{ V}$$

$$I_T = \frac{10^4}{240} \text{ A}$$

$$R_a = 1 \ \Omega$$

$$I_N = 2.75 \text{ A}$$

$$\frac{E_G}{E_N} = 1.0833 + 0.0106\frac{I_F}{I_N}$$

At $I_F/I_N = 1$,

$$\frac{E_G}{E_N} = 1.094$$

This is above the curve in Fig. 7.2. At $I_F/I_N = 1.25$,

$$\frac{E_G}{E_N} = 1.097$$

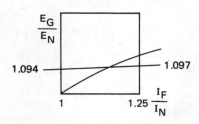

This is below the curve. Connecting these two points, the intersection with the curve is at $E_G/E_N = 1.096$, and $I_F/I_N \approx 1.15$. The necessary resistance is then

$$R_f = \frac{V_T}{I_F} = \frac{240 \text{ V}}{(1.15)(2.75 \text{ A})} = \boxed{75.9 \ \Omega}$$

Concentrate 2

Assume that the self-excitation results in a full-load voltage of 240 V. (See Concentrate 1; the stated R_f is too high, so it is a little low.) At no load ($I_L = 0$),

$$E_G = I_F(R_a + R_f) = 78I_F$$

Normalized,

$$\frac{E_G}{E_N} = (78 \ \Omega)\left(\frac{I_F}{I_N}\right)\left(\frac{I_N}{E_N}\right)$$

$$= (78 \ \Omega)\left(\frac{2.75 \text{ A}}{260 \text{ V}}\right)\frac{I_F}{I_N} = (0.825)\frac{I_F}{I_N}$$

This straight line through the origin intersects the curve of Fig. 7.7 at approximately

$$\frac{E_G}{E_N} = 1.2$$

$$\frac{I_F}{I_N} = 1.45$$

$$E_G = (1.2)(260 \text{ V}) = 312 \text{ V}$$

$$I_F = 3.99 \text{ A}$$

$$V_L = E_G - (3.99 \text{ A})R_a = 308 \text{ V}$$

$$\text{regulation} = \left(\frac{308 \text{ V} - 240 \text{ V}}{240 \text{ V}}\right)(100\%) = \boxed{28.3\%}$$

Concentrate 3

$$I_T = 25 \text{ A} = I_A + I_F$$

$$I_F = \frac{200 \text{ V}}{100 \text{ }\Omega} = 2 \text{ A}$$

$$I_A = 23 \text{ A}$$

$$E_G = 200 \text{ V} - (23 \text{ A})R_a = 188.5 \text{ V}$$

$$P_{\text{air gap}} = E_G I_A = 4335.5 \text{ W}$$

$$P_{\text{load}} = (5 \text{ hp})\left(\frac{746 \text{ W}}{\text{hp}}\right) = 3730 \text{ W}$$

(a) $P_{\text{rot}} = \boxed{605.5 \text{ W}}$

$$E_G = k\Phi n \quad (n \text{ in rpm})$$

$$k\Phi = \frac{188.5 \text{ V}}{1000 \text{ rpm}}$$

Assuming the rotational losses are fixed,

$$E_G I_A = 605.5$$

$$I_A = \frac{200 \text{ V} - E_G}{0.5 \text{ }\Omega}$$

$$200 E_G - E_G^2 = 302.75$$

$$E_G = 100 \pm \sqrt{(100)^2 - 302.75} = 198.5 \text{ V}$$

Taking the + sign,

(b) $n = \left(\frac{1000 \text{ rpm}}{188.5 \text{ V}}\right)(198.5 \text{ V})$

$$= \boxed{1053 \text{ rpm}}$$

Concentrate 4

Starting,

$$I_{\text{starting}} = \frac{500 \text{ V}}{0.8 \text{ }\Omega} = \boxed{6250 \text{ A}}$$

At 900 rpm,

$$T\Omega_R = (200 \text{ hp})\left(746 \frac{\text{W}}{\text{hp}}\right)$$

$$= 149,200 \text{ W}$$

$$\Omega_R = (900 \text{ rpm})\left(\frac{\pi \frac{\text{rad}}{\text{s}}}{30 \text{ rpm}}\right) = 30\pi \text{ rad/s}$$

$$T = \frac{149,200 \text{ W}}{30\pi \frac{\text{rad}}{\text{s}}} = 1583 \text{ N·m}$$

$$T = k\Phi I_A = kLI_A^2$$

$$kL = \frac{1583 \text{ N·m}}{(330 \text{ A})^2}$$

$$T_{\text{starting}} = \left[\frac{1583 \text{ N·m}}{(330 \text{ A})^2}\right](6250 \text{ A})^2$$

$$= \boxed{568,000 \text{ N·m}}$$

Concentrate 5

The parameters given are the per-phase values with the machine in the delta connection but calculated as if in wye.

$$T_{\text{starting}}\Omega_S = 3|V_{an}^2|\frac{a^2 r_r}{(r_s + a^2 r_r)^2 + X_E^2}$$

$$\Omega_S = (1200 \text{ rpm})\left(\frac{\pi \frac{\text{rad}}{\text{s}}}{30 \text{ rpm}}\right) = 40\pi \text{ rad/s}$$

$$|V_{an}| = \frac{440 \text{ V}}{\sqrt{3}} = 254 \text{ V}$$

$$R_E = r_s + a^2 r_r = 0.283 \text{ }\Omega$$

$$r_s = 0.126 \text{ }\Omega$$

$$a^2 r_r = 0.157 \text{ }\Omega$$

$$X_E = 0.712 \text{ }\Omega$$

(a) For windings in delta, using a delta-wye transformation, the impedance line to neutral is

$$Z_{ln} = \frac{Z_{ll}^2}{Z_{ll} + Z_{ll} + Z_{ll}} = \frac{Z_{ll}}{3}$$

$$Z_{ll} = 0.283 + j0.712 \text{ }\Omega$$

$$|I_{\text{line}}| = \frac{254 \text{ V}}{|0.283 + j0.712 \text{ }\Omega|} = \boxed{331.5 \text{ A}}$$

(b) For windings in wye,

$$Z_{ln} = (3)(0.283 + j0.712) \text{ }\Omega$$

$$|I_{\text{line}}| = \frac{331.5 \text{ A}}{3} = \boxed{110.5 \text{ A}}$$

Concentrate 6

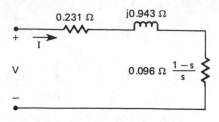

$$Z = 0.135\ \Omega + \frac{0.096\ \Omega}{s} + j0.943\ \Omega$$

On starting,

$$s = 1$$
$$Z = 0.231 + j0.943\ \Omega = 0.971\underline{/76^\circ}\ \Omega$$

To limit I_{starting} to 150 A,

$$V_1 = (150\ \text{A})(0.971\ \Omega) = 145.7\ \text{V}$$

Switching will take place when $I \to 100$ A, for which

$$|Z| = \frac{145.7\ \text{V}}{100\ \text{A}} = 1.457\ \Omega$$
$$Z^2 = R^2 + (0.943\ \Omega)^2 = (1.457\ \Omega)^2$$
$$R = \sqrt{1.234} = 1.111\ \Omega$$
$$R = 0.135\ \Omega + \frac{0.096\ \Omega}{s}$$
$$\frac{0.096\ \Omega}{s} = 0.976\ \Omega$$
$$s = \frac{0.096\ \Omega}{0.976\ \Omega} = 0.0984\ \Omega$$
$$n_{\text{switching 1}} = (1200\ \text{rpm})(1 - 0.0984\ \Omega)$$
$$= 1082\ \text{rpm}$$

The next tap voltage is found from the present impedance and 150 A,

$$V_2 = (150\ \text{A})(1.457\ \Omega) = 218.6\ \text{V}$$

The next switching occurs when

$$|Z| = \frac{218.6\ \text{V}}{100\ \text{A}} = 2.186\ \Omega$$
$$Z^2 = 4.7786\ \Omega^2 = R^2 + (0.943\ \Omega)^2$$
$$R = \sqrt{3.8894} = 1.972\ \Omega$$
$$1.972\ \Omega = 0.135\ \Omega + \frac{0.096\ \Omega}{s}$$
$$s = \frac{0.096\ \Omega}{1.837\ \Omega} = 0.052$$
$$n_{\text{switching 2}} = (1 - 0.052)(1200\ \text{rpm}) = 1138\ \text{rpm}$$

The next voltage is

$$V_3 = (150\ \text{A})(2.186\ \Omega) = 328\ \text{V}$$

The full 254 V is applied.

voltage	switching speed
1. 145.7 V	1082 rpm
2. 218.6 V	1138 rpm
3. 254 V	–

Concentrate 7

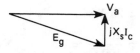

At no-load with minimum I_a, $jX_sI_a \perp V_a$, so I_a is in phase with V_a.

$$\frac{P}{q} = \frac{900\ \text{W}}{3\ \text{phases}} = V_aI_a$$
$$I_a = \frac{300\ \text{W}}{254\ \text{V}} = 1.18\ \text{A}$$
$$E_g = \sqrt{V_a^2 + I_a^2X_s^2}$$
$$= \sqrt{(254\ \text{V})^2 + (1.18\ \text{A})(20\ \Omega)^2} = 255\ \text{V}$$

Under load, $I_a = 12$ A.

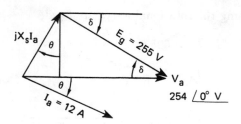

$$V_a = 254\ \text{V} = E_g\cos\delta + X_sI_a\sin\theta$$
$$254\ \text{V} = 255\cos\delta + 240\sin\theta$$
$$X_sI_a\cos\theta = |E_g\sin\delta|$$
$$(240\ \text{V})\cos\theta = (255\ \text{V})\sin\delta$$

Using $\sin^2\theta + \cos^2\theta = 1$,

$$\cos\delta = \frac{V_a^2 + E_g^2 - X_s^2I_a^2}{2|V_a||E_g|}$$

(a) $\delta = \boxed{-56.29^\circ}$

(b) $\theta = \boxed{27.89°}$

$P_{\text{in}} = (3 \text{ phases})V_a I_a \cos\theta = 8.08 \text{ kW}$
$P_{\text{out}} = 900 \text{ W}$
$I_a^2 R_a = 216 \text{ W}$

(c) $P_L = 8080 \text{ W} - 900 \text{ W} - 216 \text{ W} = \boxed{6.96 \text{ kW}}$

(d) $\eta = \left(\dfrac{6.96 \text{ kW}}{8.08 \text{ kW}}\right)(100\%) = \boxed{86\%}$

(e) For 5 kVAR of power factor correction,

$$S = P - jQ = (3 \text{ phases})V_a I_a^*$$
$$= (3 \text{ phases})V_a|I_a|(\cos\theta - j\sin\theta)$$
$$= 8080 \text{ W} - j5000 \text{ VAR}$$
$$I_a^* = \frac{8080 - j5000 \text{ VA}}{(3 \text{ phases})(254 \text{ V})}$$
$$= 10.6 - j6.56 \text{ A}$$
$$jX_s I_a = (j20 \ \Omega)(10.6 + j6.56 \text{ A})$$
$$= -131.2 + j212 \text{ V}$$
$$E_g = V_a - jX_s I_a = 439.7\underline{/-28.83°} \text{ V}$$
$$|E_g| = k_r I_R = 255 \text{ V at } I_R = 5 \text{ A}$$
$$I_R = \left(\frac{5 \text{ A}}{255 \text{ V}}\right)(440 \text{ V}) = \boxed{8.63 \text{ A}}$$

Concentrate 8

Running at rated conditions,

$$T\,\Omega_R = (50 \text{ hp})\left(\frac{746 \text{ W}}{\text{hp}}\right)$$
$$\Omega_R = (1746)\left(\frac{\pi}{30}\right) \text{ rad/s}$$
$$T = 204 \text{ N·m}$$
$$|I_{\text{line}}| = \frac{\dfrac{50 \text{ kVA}}{3 \text{ phases}}}{\dfrac{440 \text{ V}}{\sqrt{3}}} = 65.61 \text{ A}$$
$$|Z_{\text{phase}}| = \frac{254 \text{ V}}{65.61 \text{ A}} = 3.87 \ \Omega$$

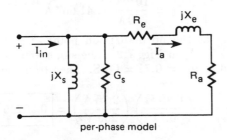

per-phase model

$$R_a = a^2 r_r \frac{1-s}{s}$$
$$I_a^2 R_a = \frac{P_{\text{out}}}{3} = \frac{(50 \text{ hp})\left(746 \dfrac{W}{\text{hp}}\right)}{3 \text{ phases}} = 12{,}430 \text{ W}$$

Note: All losses will be assigned to G_s, except $I_a^2 R_e$.

$$G_s = \frac{P_{\text{no load}}}{(3 \text{ phases})(254 \text{ V})^2} = \frac{3342 \text{ W}}{(3 \text{ phases})(254 \text{ V})^2}$$
$$= 17.3 \times 10^{-3} S$$
$$\frac{1}{G_s} = 57.8 \ \Omega$$
$$\frac{1}{X_s} = \frac{Q_{\text{no load}}}{(3 \text{ phases})(254 \text{ V})^2} = \frac{19{,}750 \text{ VA}}{(3 \text{ phases})(254 \text{ V})^2}$$
$$X_s = 9.80 \ \Omega$$

The starting conditions are (because G_s models rotational losses, which are not present at starting, G_s is ignored in these calculations),

$$I_{\text{in}} = \frac{V_a}{jX_s} + I_a = 367\underline{/-68°} \text{ A}$$
$$I_a = 367\underline{/-68°} - \frac{254}{j9.8} \text{ A}$$
$$I_a = 137.5 - j314.4 = 343.2\underline{/-66.38°} \text{ A}$$
$$R_e + jX_e = \frac{254 \text{ V}}{343.2\underline{/-66.38°} \text{ A}}$$
$$= 0.297 + j0.678 \ \Omega$$

Returning to the rated conditions,

$$\frac{P}{\text{phase}} = \frac{(50 \text{ hp})\left(746 \dfrac{W}{\text{hp}}\right)}{3 \text{ phases}} = 12{,}430 \text{ W}$$
$$I_a = \frac{V_a}{R_a + R_e + jX_e}$$
$$I_a^2 R_a = \frac{(254 \text{ V})^2 R_a}{|R_a + R_e + jX_e|^2} = 12{,}430 \text{ W}$$
$$R_a^2 - 4.597 R_a + 0.584 = 0$$
$$R_a = 2.298 \pm \sqrt{(2.298)^2 - 0.584} \ \Omega$$

The positive sign is taken because

$$\frac{(254 \text{ V})^2}{R_a} \approx 12{,}430 \text{ W}$$
$$R_a \approx 5 \ \Omega$$
or $$R_a = 4.465 \ \Omega = a^2 r_r\left(\frac{1-s}{s}\right)$$

Taking $s = 0.03$,

$$a^2 r_r = \left(\frac{0.03}{0.097}\right)(4.465\ \Omega)$$
$$= 0.138\ \Omega$$

From Eq. 7.79,

$$T_{\text{starting}} = \frac{(3\ \text{phases})(254\ \text{V})^2}{(1800\ \text{rpm})\left(\pi\dfrac{\frac{\text{rad}}{\text{sec}}}{30\ \text{rpm}}\right)}$$

$$\times \left[\frac{0.138\ \Omega}{(0.435)^2 + (0.678)^2\ \Omega^2}\right]$$

$$= \boxed{218\ \text{N·m} \ (161\ \text{ft-lbf})}$$

Concentrate 9

$$P_{\text{in}} = \frac{(45\ \text{hp})\left(746\dfrac{\text{W}}{\text{hp}}\right)}{0.93\ (\text{efficiency})} = 36.1\ \text{kW}$$

At minimum line current, the current is in phase with the voltage.

$$I = \frac{\dfrac{36.1 \times 10^3\ \text{W}}{3\ \text{phases}}}{\dfrac{440\ \text{V}}{\sqrt{3}}} = 47.37\ \text{A}$$

$$Z_{\text{base}} = \frac{254\ \text{V}}{47.37\ \text{A}} = 5.36\ \Omega$$

A synchronous reactance of 100% is common, and is therefore assumed.

$$X_s = 5.36\ \Omega$$
$$I_a X_s = (5.36\ \Omega)(47.37\ \text{A}) = 254\ \text{V}$$
$$E_g = V_a - jX_s I_a = (254\ \text{V})(1 - j)\ \text{V}$$
$$|E_g| = 359\ \text{V}$$

This required a rotor current of

$$I_R = 8.2\ \text{A}$$

To provide a leading power factor of 0.8, it is necessary to retain the same power.

$$I_a \cos\theta = 47.37\ \text{A}$$
$$I_a = \frac{47.37\ \text{A}}{0.8} = 59.2\ \text{A}$$
$$I_a = (59.2\ \text{A})(\cos\theta + j\sin\theta)$$
$$= 47.37\ \text{A} + j35.52\ \text{A}$$
$$= 59.2\underline{/36.87°}\ \text{A}$$
$$E_g = 254\ \text{V} - (j5.36\ \Omega)\,I_a$$
$$= 512\underline{/-29.74°}\ \text{V}$$
$$I_R = \left(\frac{8.2\ \text{A}}{359\ \text{V}}\right)(512\ \text{V}) = \boxed{11.7\ \text{A}}$$

Concentrate 10

For the plant initially,

$$S = 1000 + j750\ \text{kVA}$$
$$\text{induction motor,}\ S = 80 + j50\ \text{kVA}$$
$$\text{synchronous motor,}\ S = 80 - j60\ \text{kVA}$$

For the plant finally,

$$S = 1000 + j750 - (80 + j50) + 80 - j60$$
$$= 1000 + j640\ \text{kVA}$$

$$\boxed{\text{The new power factor is } \cos 32.62° = 0.842.}$$

$$|S_{\text{initial}}| = 1250\ \text{kVA}$$
$$|S_{\text{final}}| = 1187\ \text{kVA}$$
$$\frac{I_{\text{final}}}{I_{\text{initial}}} = \frac{1187\ \text{kVA}}{1250\ \text{kVA}} = 0.95$$

The current decreases by 5%.

Timed 1

$$I_A = \frac{10^4\ \text{W}}{240\ \text{V}} = 41.667\ \text{A}$$

Beginning at the normalization point, $E_G = 260$ V, MMF= 2.75 A on Fig. 7.2. The slope at this point is measured as $m_n = 0.71 = \text{OPS}$. Then from Eq. 7.20,

$$\frac{N_s}{N_f} = \left(\frac{0.48\ \Omega}{0.71}\right)\left(\frac{2.75\ \text{A}}{260\ \text{V}}\right) = \boxed{0.00725}$$

The normalized MMF is

$$\left(I_F + \frac{N_s}{N_f} 41.667\ \text{A}\right) = 2.75\ \text{A}$$

$$I_F = 2.448\ \text{A}$$

Checking at rated conditions,

$$E_G = 240\ \text{V} + (0.48\ \Omega)(I_F + I_A) = 261.2\ \text{V}$$

$$\frac{F_G}{E_N} = 1.0046$$

This is sufficiently close to the assumed operating point that no iteration is necessary.

$$\frac{N_s}{N_f} = \boxed{0.00725}$$

$$R_f = \frac{240\ \text{V}}{2.448\ \text{A}} = \boxed{98\ \Omega}$$

Timed 2

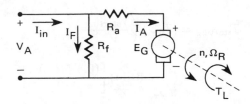

$$P_{\text{in}} = V_A I_{\text{in}} = (60\ \text{A})(120\ \text{V}) = 7200\ \text{W}$$

$$P_{\text{out}} = (7.5\ \text{hp})\left(746\ \frac{\text{W}}{\text{hp}}\right) = 5595\ \text{W}$$

As load torque is constant,

$$P_{\text{out}} = K_T n$$

$$K_T = \frac{5595\ \text{W}}{1000\ \text{rpm}}$$

$$= 5.595n \text{ with } n \text{ in rpm}$$

The losses are the difference between P_{in} and P_{out}.

$$P_{\text{loss}} = 1605\ \text{W}$$

With no information given, it is necessary to assign these losses to rotational losses, $I_A^2 R_a$ and $I_F^2 R_f$. Make them equal.

$$I_A^2 R_a = I_F^2 R_f = P_{\text{rot}} = 535\ \text{W}$$

$$I_F^2 R_f = \frac{V_A^2}{R_f} = 535\ \text{W}$$

$$R_f = \frac{(120\ \text{V})^2}{535\ \text{W}} = 26.9\ \Omega$$

$$I_F = \frac{120\ \text{V}}{26.9\ \Omega} = 4.46\ \text{A}$$

This makes $I_A = 60\ \text{A} - 4.46\ \text{A}$ or $I_A = 55.54\ \text{A}$.

$$R_a = \frac{535\ \text{W}}{(55.54\ \text{A})^2} = 0.173\ \Omega$$

Because of rounding, the powers are recalculated and the remainder assigned to rotational losses.

$$P_{\text{rot}} = 1605\ \text{W} - \frac{(120\ \text{V})^2}{26.9\ \Omega} - (0.173\ \Omega)(55.54\ \text{A})^2$$

$$= 536\ \text{W}$$

The air-gap power must then be

$$P_{\text{air gap}} = P_{\text{out}} + P_{\text{rot}} = 5.595n + 536\ \text{W}$$

The air-gap power is also $E_G I_A$, and E_G is proportional to I_F and n.

$$E_G = k' I_F n = k'' \frac{n}{R_f}$$

At $n = 1000$ rpm and $R_f = 26.9\ \Omega$,

$$E_G = 120\ \text{V} - (55.54\ \text{A})(0.173\ \Omega) = 110.4\ \text{V}$$

$$k'' = \frac{(110.4\ \text{V})(26.9\ \Omega)}{1000\ \text{rpm}} = 2.97\ \text{V-}\Omega/\text{rpm}$$

$$E_G = 2.97 \frac{n}{R_f}$$

$$I_A = \frac{120\ \text{V} - E_G}{R_a} = \frac{120\ \text{V} - 2.97 \dfrac{n}{R_f}}{0.173\ \Omega}$$

$$= 694\ \text{A} - 17.2 \frac{n}{R_f}$$

$$P_{\text{air gap}} = E_G I_A = 2061 \frac{n}{R_f} - 51.08 \left(\frac{n}{R_f}\right)^2$$

Equating with the mechanical side,

$$(51.08)\left(\frac{n}{R_f}\right)^2 + \left(5.595 - \frac{2061}{R_f}\right)n + 536\ \text{W} = 0$$

$$0 = R_f^2 - \left(\frac{2061n}{5.595n + 536\ \text{W}}\right)R_f + \frac{51.08n^2}{5.595n + 536\ \text{W}}$$

(a) For $n = 1150$ rpm,

$$R_f^2 - (340.0\ \Omega)R_f + 9692\ \Omega^2 = 0$$

$$R_f = \boxed{31.4\ \Omega}$$

(b) For $n = 750$ rpm,

$$R_f^2 - (326.6\ \Omega)R_f + 6072\ \Omega^2 = 0$$

$$R_f = \boxed{19.8\ \Omega}$$

Timed 3

Initially, $E_G = 0$, $I_A = (2.5)(125\text{ A})$.

$$R_1 = \frac{250\text{ V}}{312.5\text{ A}} = 0.8\ \Omega$$

When $I_A \to 125\text{ A}$,

$$E_G = 250\text{ V} - (125\text{ A})(0.8\ \Omega) = 150\text{ V}$$

$$R_2 = \frac{250\text{ V} - 150\text{ V}}{312.5\text{ A}} = 0.32\ \Omega$$

When $I_A \to 125\text{ A}$,

$$E_G = 250\text{ V} - (125\text{ A})(0.32\ \Omega) = 210\text{ V}$$

$$R_3 = \frac{250\text{ V} - 210\text{ V}}{312.5\text{ A}} = 0.128\ \Omega$$

$R_a = 0.15\ \Omega$, so R_3 is not needed.

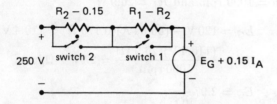

$$R_2 - 0.15\ \Omega = 0.32\ \Omega - 0.15\ \Omega = \boxed{0.17\ \Omega}$$

$$R_1 - R_2 = 0.8\ \Omega - 0.17\ \Omega - 0.15\ \Omega = \boxed{0.48\ \Omega}$$

Initially, both switches are open.

Switch 1 closes at

$$E_G + (0.15\ \Omega)I_A = 150\text{ V} + 18.75\text{ V} = \boxed{169\text{ V}}$$

Switch 2 closes at

$$E_G + (1.5\ \Omega)I_A = 210\text{ V} + 18.75\text{ V} = \boxed{229\text{ V}}$$

Timed 4

At no-load, $s \to 0$.

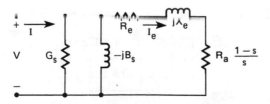

At no-load, $I_e \to 0$.

$$I = V(G_s - jB_s)$$

$$V^2 G_s = \frac{P}{3} = 1500\text{ W}$$

$$G_s = 0.0213\text{ S}$$

$$V^2 |Y_s| = \left(\frac{460}{\sqrt{3}\text{ V}}\right)(135\text{ A})$$

$$|Y_s| = \frac{(135\text{ A})\sqrt{3}}{460\text{ V}} = 0.508\text{ S}$$

$$B_s^2 = Y_s^2 - G_s^2$$

$$B_s = 0.508\text{ S}$$

(a) From Eq. 7.78, the starting torque is proportional to the voltage squared.

$$T_{\text{starting}} = (T_{\text{b.r.}})\left(\frac{V_{\text{starting}}}{V_{\text{b.r.}}}\right)^2$$

$$= (17.2\text{ ft-lbf})\left[\frac{(0.8)(460\text{ V})}{78\text{ V}}\right]^2$$

$$= \boxed{383\text{ ft-lbf}}$$

The no-load test is at running speed, and G_s accounts for the rotational losses, so it is not present at starting.

(b) The blocked rotor test is at low voltage, so the stator reactance $(-1/B_s)$ is not excited. Upon starting, the current will be

$$I_{\text{starting}} = -jB_s V_{\text{starting}} + V_{\text{starting}}\frac{1}{R_e + jX_e}$$

$$X_e \gg R_e$$

$$I_{\text{starting}} \approx -j\left(B_s + \frac{1}{X_e}\right)V_{\text{starting}}$$

$$= -j\left[(0.508\text{ S})(0.8)\left(\frac{460\text{ V}}{\sqrt{3}}\right)\right]$$

$$+ (-j)\left(\frac{460\text{ V}}{78\text{ V}}\right)(I_{\text{b.r.}})(0.8)$$

$$= -j(107.9 + 1132)\text{ A}$$

$$= \boxed{-j\,1240\text{ A}}$$

Timed 5

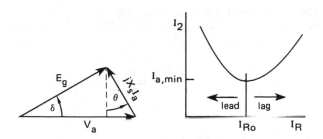

$$E_g \sin \delta = X_s I_a \cos \theta = \text{constant}$$
$$= X_s I_{a,\text{min}}$$
$$I_a = \frac{I_{a,\text{min}}}{\cos \theta}$$

(a) For an 80° lagging power factor,

$$I_a = \frac{15}{0.8} = 18.75 \text{ A}$$

The vee curve is approximately parabolic, so it can be represented as

$$I_a - A = k(I_R - B)^2$$

I_a lies between points $(I_R, I_a) = (20, 32)$ and $(15, 18)$, but is much closer to the latter. With three parameters it requires three points, so the third point is $(12, 15)$. This results in three equations with three unknowns which are solved, giving

$$k = 0.225 \text{ A}^{-1}$$
$$B = 11.277 \text{ A}$$
$$A = 14.882 \text{ A}$$

Putting in $I_a = 18.75$ A,

$$18.75 \text{ A} - 14.88 \text{ A} = (0.225 \text{ A}^{-1})(I_R - 11.277 \text{ A})$$
$$\boxed{I_R = \boxed{15.4 \text{ A}}}$$

(b) For $I_a = 40$ A with leading power factor (left side), use the three points $(I_R, I_a) = (2, 60)(3, 45)$ and $(5.5, 30)$.

From the three resulting equations, in the unknowns A, B, and k,

$$k = \frac{18}{7} = 2.57 \text{ A}^{-1}$$
$$B = \frac{65}{12} = 5.417 \text{ A}$$
$$A = 29.98 \text{ A}$$

At $I_a = 40$ A,

$$40 \text{ A} - 29.98 \text{ A} = \left(\frac{18}{7} \text{ A}^{-1}\right)(I_R - 5.417 \text{ A})^2$$
$$\pm 1.974 \text{ A} = I_R - 5.417 \text{ A}$$
$$I_R = 5.417 \text{ A} \mp 1.974 \text{ A}$$
$$= \boxed{3.44 \text{ A}}$$

(c) $\cos \theta = \dfrac{15}{40} = \boxed{0.375 \text{ leading}}$

Timed 6

The bases for the motor and transformer are the same.

$$I_{\text{rated}} = \frac{\dfrac{50 \text{ kVA}}{3 \text{ phases}}}{254 \text{ V}} = 65.62 \text{ A}$$

$$Z_{\text{base}} = \frac{254 \text{ V}}{65.62 \text{ A}} = 3.87 \ \Omega$$

From the blocked rotor test,

$$P + jQ = I^2(R_e + jX_e)$$
$$1097 \text{ W} + j2791 \text{ VAR} = (65.62 \text{ A})^2(R_e + jX_e)$$
$$R_e + jX_e = 0.2548 + j0.6482 \ \Omega$$

On a per-unit basis,

$$R_e + jX_e = 0.0658 + j0.1615 \text{ P.U.}$$

The per-unit circuit for starting is

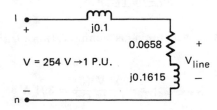

By voltage division,

$$|V_{\text{line}}| = \left| \frac{0.0658 + j0.1615}{0.0658 + j0.2615} \right| = 0.647 \text{ P.U.}$$

$$\text{dip} = \boxed{1 - 0.647 \text{ P.U.} \rightarrow 35\%}$$

Timed 7

From the blocked rotor test,

$$R_e + jX_e = 0.255 + j0.643 \ \Omega$$

Obtained at rated current,

$$I_{\text{rated}} = \frac{\dfrac{50 \text{ kVA}}{3}}{254} = 65.62 \text{ A}$$

$$I_{\text{rated}}(R_e + jX_e) \rightarrow 45.4\underline{/68.37°} \text{ A}$$

The stator reactance $-1/B_s$ has not been excited. The light running test yields

$$G_s + jB_s = \frac{1}{1.614 + j9.531} \ \Omega$$

$$= 0.0173 - j0.102 \text{ S}$$

G_s models rotational losses, and does not enter starting calculations. For starting purposes,

$$Y_{\text{starting}} = jB_s + \frac{1}{R_e + jX_e}$$

$$= -j0.102 \text{ S} + \frac{1}{0.255 + j0.643 \ \Omega}$$

$$= 0.5329 \text{ S} - j1.446 \text{ S} = 1.54\underline{/-69.77°} \text{ S}$$

$$Z_{\text{starting}} = 0.649\underline{/69.77°} \ \Omega$$

However, this is the wye equivalent of a delta connection, so the actual phase impedance is three times that value.

$$Z_{\text{phase}} = 3Z_{\text{starting}} = 1.947\underline{/69.77°} \ \Omega$$

When 440 V is applied across this phase, the starting current will be

(a) $$I_{\text{starting}} = \frac{440 \text{ V}}{1.947\underline{/69.77°} \ \Omega}$$

$$= \boxed{226\underline{/-69.77°} \text{ A}}$$

Note that in the previous configuration, with 254 V line-to-neutral,

$$|I_{\text{starting}}| = \frac{(254 \text{ V})(3)}{1.947 \ \Omega} = 391 \text{ A}$$

(b)
> In the new configuration, the kVA rating remains the same. The voltage rating increases from 440 to $440\sqrt{3} = 762$ V. The line current rating is reduced to
>
> $$I_{\text{rated}} = \frac{65.61 \text{ A}}{\sqrt{3}} = 37.9 \text{ A}$$

Timed 8

The impedance for wye starting will be three times that for delta starting, so the current will be only one-third the delta current.

$$I_{\text{starting}} = \frac{367 \text{ A}}{3} = \boxed{122.3 \text{ A}}$$

The starting torque can be seen to be diminished by the same factor. From Eq. 7.78,

$$T_{\text{starting,delta}} = \left(\frac{3|V_{an}|^2}{\Omega_S}\right)\left[\frac{a^2 r_r}{(r_s + a^2 r_r)^2 + X_e^2}\right]$$

For the wye configuration, impedances are multiplied by three.

$$T_{\text{starting,wye}} = \left(\frac{3|V_{an}|^2}{\Omega_S}\right)\left[\frac{3a^2 r_r}{(9)(r_s + a^2 r_r)^2 + 9X_e^2}\right]$$

$$= \frac{T_{\text{starting,delta}}}{3}$$

$$= \frac{190}{3} \text{ ft-lbf} = \boxed{63.3 \text{ ft-lbf}}$$

Timed 9

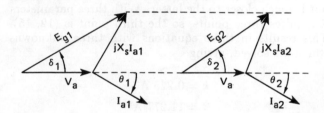

Initially,

$$V_a = |X_s I_{a1}| = 1 \text{ P.U.}$$

$$I_{a1}\cos\theta_1 = 0.9$$

$$|I_{a1}| = 1 \text{ P.U.}$$

$$E_{g1}\sin\delta_1 = 0.9 \text{ P.U.} = X_s I_s \cos\theta_1$$

$$E_{g1}\cos\delta_1 = V_a + X_s I_s \sin\theta_1$$

$$= 1 + \sqrt{1 - (0.9)^2}$$

$$= 1.436 \text{ P.U.}$$

$$E_{g1}^2\sin^2\delta_1 + E_{g1}^2\cos^2\delta_1 = (0.9 \text{ P.U.})^2$$
$$+ (1.436 \text{ P.U.})^2$$

$$E_{g1} = 1.695 \text{ P.U.}$$

$$E_{g2} = 0.9 \, E_{g1} = 1.525 \text{ P.U.}$$

$$E_{g2}\sin\delta_2 = 1.525\sin\delta_2 = 0.9 \text{ P.U.}$$

The power is assumed to be constant.

$$\delta_2 = \arcsin\left(\frac{0.9}{1.525}\right) = 36.17°$$

$$\cos\delta_2 = 0.8073$$

$$V_a + I_2 X \sin\theta_2 = E_{g2}\cos\delta_2 = 1.231 \text{ P.U.}$$

$$V_a = 1 \text{ P.U.}$$

$$X = 1 \text{ P.U.}$$

$$I_2\sin\theta_2 = 0.231 \text{ P.U.}$$

$$I_2\cos\theta_2 = 0.9 \text{ P.U.}$$

$$I_2^2\sin^2\theta_2 + I_2^2\cos^2\theta_2 = (0.9 \text{ P.U.})^2 + (0.231 \text{ P.U.})^2$$

$$I_2 = 0.929 \text{ P.U.}$$

$$\cos\theta_2 = \frac{0.9}{0.929} = \boxed{0.97}$$

$$\Delta I_2 = 1 - 0.929$$

$$= \boxed{0.71 \text{ P.U. } (7.1\%)}$$

Timed 10

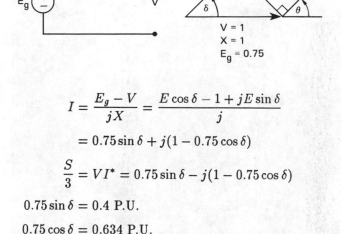

$$I = \frac{E_g - V}{jX} = \frac{E\cos\delta - 1 + jE\sin\delta}{j}$$

$$= 0.75\sin\delta + j(1 - 0.75\cos\delta)$$

$$\frac{S}{3} = VI^* = 0.75\sin\delta - j(1 - 0.75\cos\delta)$$

$$0.75\sin\delta = 0.4 \text{ P.U.}$$

$$0.75\cos\delta = 0.634 \text{ P.U.}$$

$$I = 0.4 + j(1 - 0.634) = 0.5422\underline{/42.46°} \text{ P.U.}$$

(a) $|I| = \boxed{0.5422 \text{ P.U.}}$

$$\cos\theta = \cos 42.46° = \boxed{0.738}$$

(b) Increasing the power by a factor of two,

$$\frac{S}{3} = E\sin\delta + j(1 - E\cos\delta)$$

$$= I\cos\theta - jI\sin\theta$$

To make the power 80% (0.8 P.U.) and maintain rating limits,

$$|IX| = 1 \text{ P.U.}$$

$$|IX|\cos\theta = 0.8 \text{ P.U.}$$

$$\cos\theta = 0.8$$

$$\sin\theta = 0.6$$

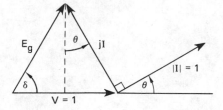

$$E_g\sin\delta = 0.8 \text{ P.U.}$$

$$E_g\cos\delta = 1 - \sin\theta = 0.4 \text{ P.U.}$$

$$E_g^2 = (0.8 \text{ P.U.})^2 + (0.4 \text{ P.U.})^2 = (0.8944 \text{ P.U.})^2$$

Rotor current must increase from its initial value by a factor of

$$\frac{E_{g2}}{E_{g1}} = \frac{0.894 \text{ P.U.}}{0.75 \text{ P.U.}} = \boxed{1.193 \ (19.3\% \text{ increase})}$$

(c) $$\boxed{\begin{array}{l} I = 1 \text{ P.U. (by specification)} \\ PF = 0.8 \end{array}}$$

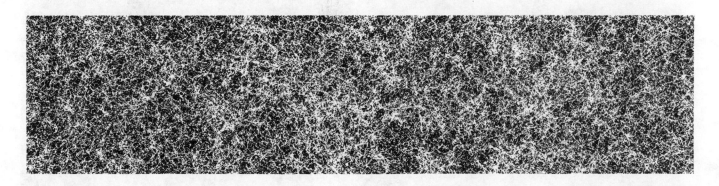

FUNDAMENTAL SEMICONDUCTOR CIRCUITS

Warmup 1

$$i_{PN} = I_S(e^{\frac{v_{PN}}{\eta V_T}} - 1) \approx I_S e^{\frac{v_{PN}}{\eta V_T}}$$

At 20°C, $V_T = 25.26$ mV.

At $v_{PN} = 0.6$ V, $i_{PN} = 10^{-3}$ mA.

At $v_{PN} = 0.7$ V, $i_{PN} = 9.83 \times 10^{-3}$ mA.

Taking the ratio,

$$9.83 = \frac{e^{\frac{0.7\,V}{\eta V_T}}}{e^{\frac{0.6\,V}{\eta V_T}}} = e^{\frac{0.7\,V}{\eta V_T}} e^{-\frac{0.6\,V}{\eta V_T}}$$

$$= e^{\frac{0.7\,V - 0.6\,V}{\eta V_T}} = e^{\frac{0.1\,V}{\eta V_T}}$$

$$\frac{0.1\,V}{\eta V_T} = \ln 9.83$$

$$\eta = \frac{0.1\,V}{(0.02526\,V)\ln 9.83}$$

$$= \boxed{1.732}$$

Warmup 2

$$\frac{\Delta v}{\Delta T} = -2.2 \text{ mV/°C}$$

$$\Delta T = -50°C$$

$$\Delta v = \left(-2.2\,\frac{mV}{°C}\right)(-50°C)$$

$$= 110 \text{ mV}$$

$$= \boxed{0.110 \text{ V}}$$

Warmup 3

$$i_{PN} = I_S e^{\frac{v_{PN}}{\eta V_T}}$$

$$v_{PN} = \eta V_T[\ln(i_{PN}) - \ln I_S]$$

$$i_{PN} \text{ (mA)} = 1000 i_{PN} \text{ (A)}$$

$$i_{PN} = \frac{i_{PN} \text{ (mA)}}{1000}$$

$$\ln\left[\frac{i_{PN} \text{ (mA)}}{1000}\right] = \ln[i_{PN} \text{ (mA)}] - \ln 1000$$

$$v_{PN} = \eta V_T[\ln(i_{PN} \text{ (mA)}) - \ln(I_S \text{ (mA)})]$$

From the circuit,

$$v_{PN} = (10 \text{ V}) - (1000 \text{ }\Omega)i_{PN}$$

$$= (10 \text{ V}) - i_{PN} \text{ (mA)}$$

Taking $\eta = 2, V_T = 0.025$ V,

$$10 \text{ V} - (1000 \text{ }\Omega)i_{PN}$$
$$= (0.05 \text{ V})[\ln(i_{PN} \text{ (mA)}) - \ln(I_S \text{ (mA)})]$$

$$i_{PN} \text{ (mA)} = 10 \text{ mA} + (0.05 \text{ mA})\ln[I_S \text{ (mA)}]$$
$$- (0.05 \text{ mA})\ln[i_{PN} \text{ (mA)}]$$

$$I_S = i_{PN} e^{-\frac{v_{PN}}{0.05}}$$

At $v_{PN} = 0.6$, $i_{PN} = 1$ mA.

$$I_S = e^{-12} \text{ (mA)}$$

$$\ln[I_S \text{ (mA)}] = -12$$

$$i_{PN} = 10 \text{ mA} - (0.05 \text{ mA})(12)$$
$$- (0.05 \text{ mA})\ln[i_{PN} \text{ (mA)}]$$

Beginning with i_{PN} (mA) = 9.3 mA,

$$i_{PN1} = 9.4 \text{ mA} - (0.05 \text{ mA})\ln 9.3 = 9.288 \text{ mA}$$

Iterating,

$$i_{PN2} = 9.4 \text{ mA} - (0.05)\ln 9.288 = 9.289 \text{ mA}$$

This repeats when iterated again. The error is

$$\text{error} = \frac{9.3 \text{ mA} - 9.289 \text{ mA}}{9.289 \text{ mA}}$$

$$= \boxed{0.0012 \text{ or } 0.12\%}$$

Warmup 4

$$i_{PN} = I_S e^{\frac{v_{PN}}{(1.5)(0.025 \text{ V})}}$$

At $v_{PN} = 0.6$ V, $i_{PN} = 1$ mA.

$$I_S = 1e^{\frac{-0.6 \text{ V}}{(1.5)(0.025 \text{ V})}} = e^{-16} \text{ (mA)}$$

$$i_{PN} = e^{-16}e^{\left[\frac{0.6 \text{ V}}{(1.5)(0.025 \text{ V})}\right]\left(\frac{v_{PN}}{0.6 \text{ V}}\right)}$$

$$= e^{(16)\left(\frac{v_{PN}}{0.6 \text{ V}} - 1\right)} \text{ (mA)}$$

$$P = v_{PN}e^{(16)\left(\frac{v_{PN}}{0.6 \text{ V}} - 1\right)} \text{ (mW)}$$

Trying $v_{PN} = 0.7$ V,

$$P = 10.07 \approx 10 \text{ mW}$$

$$i_{PN\text{-rated}} \approx e^{(16)\left(\frac{0.7 \text{ V}}{0.6 \text{ V}} - 1\right)} = \boxed{14.4 \text{ mA}}$$

Warmup 5

$$i_D = I_{DSS}\left(1 - \frac{v_{GS}}{V_T}\right)^2$$

$$= (5 \text{ mA})\left(1 - \frac{-3 \text{ V}}{-5 \text{ V}}\right)^2 = \boxed{0.8 \text{ mA}}$$

Warmup 6

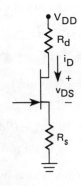

From Kirchhoff's voltage law,

$$V_{DD} = i_D R_d + v_{DS} + i_D R_s$$
$$30 \text{ V} = 5R_d + 15 \text{ V} + 5R_s$$

R_d and R_s are in kΩ and i_D is in mA.

$$R_d + R_s = \frac{15 \text{ V}}{5 \text{ mA}} = 3 \text{ k}\Omega$$

From the given characteristic, $v_{GS} \approx -1.8$ V. With self-biasing, the gate is at ground, and

$$v_{GS} = v_G - v_S = 0 - i_D R_s$$
$$-1.8 \text{ V} = -5R_d$$

$$R_d = 0.36 \text{ k}\Omega \text{ or } 360 \text{ }\Omega$$

$$R_s = \boxed{2.64 \text{ k}\Omega \text{ or } 2640 \text{ }\Omega}$$

Warmup 7

$$v_{DS} = 16 \text{ V} - 1500i_D$$

With i_D in mA and R in kΩ,

$$v_{DS} = 16 \text{ V} - 1.5i_D \quad \text{(load-line)}$$

The load-line plotted on the characteristic chart is

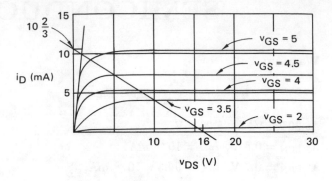

The linear (pinchoff) region is for $v_{DS} > 5$ V, so the useful amplifier range is from 5 V to about 15 V. The bias point should be at $v_{DS} = 10$ V, $i_D \approx 4.2$ mA, and $v_{GS} = 3.5$ V.

As $v_S = (1 \text{ k}\Omega)i_D = 4.2$ V,

$$v_{GS} = 3.5 \text{ V} = v_G - v_S = v_G - 4.2 \text{ V}$$

$$v_G = 7.7 \text{ V}$$

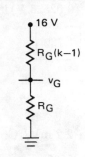

$$v_G = \frac{16R_g}{R_g + R_g(k-1)} = \frac{16}{k}$$

$$k = \frac{16}{7.7} = \boxed{2.078}$$

Warmup 8

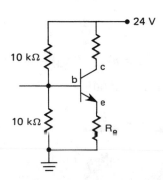

The Thevenin equivalent from b, looking left, is 5 kΩ in series with 12 V. From b, looking right, there is a 0.7-V drop in series with a resistance, R_e, fed by two current sources.

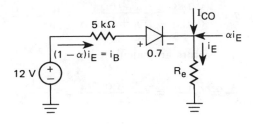

(a) $i_C = I_{CO} + \alpha i_E = 15$ mA

$I_{CO} \approx 10^{-3}$ mA, which is negligible, so

$$i_E = \frac{15 \text{ mA}}{\alpha_o} = 15.79 \text{ mA}$$

$$i_B = (1 - \alpha)i_E = \boxed{0.79 \text{ mA}}$$

Using Kirchhoff's voltage law, with resistance in kΩ,

$$12 \text{ V} = (5 \text{ k}\Omega)i_B + 0.7 \text{ V} + R_e i_E$$
$$= (5 \text{ k}\Omega)(0.79 \text{ mA}) + 0.7 \text{ V} + R_e(15.79 \text{ mA})$$
$$R_e = 0.466 \text{ k}\Omega = 466 \text{ }\Omega$$

(b) $\quad S_v = \dfrac{2.5\alpha_o}{(1 - \alpha_o)R_b + R_e} = 0.0033 \text{ mA/°C}$

$$\Delta i_C = S_v \Delta T = \boxed{0.41 \text{ mA}}$$

Warmup 9

At $v_{CE} = 10$ V and $i_B = 1$ mA,

$$\left.\frac{\Delta v_{CE}}{\Delta i_C}\right|_{i_B = 1 \text{ mA}} = \frac{35 \text{ V} - 5 \text{ V}}{99 \text{ mA} - 82 \text{ mA}} = 1.8 \text{ k}\Omega = r_c$$

$$\left.\frac{\Delta i_C}{\Delta i_B}\right|_{v_{CE} = 10 \text{ V}} = \frac{65 \text{ mA}}{1 \text{ mA}} = 65 = \beta$$

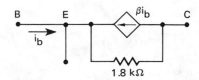

Warmup 10

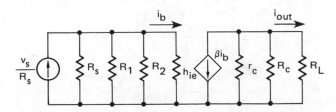

$$i_b = \left(\frac{v_s}{R_s}\right)\left(\frac{R_s\|R_1\|R_2}{R_s\|R_1\|R_2 + h_{ie}}\right) = \frac{v_s}{1750} \text{ A}$$

$$v_{out} = -\beta i_b (r_c\|R_c\|R_L)$$

$$\frac{v_{out}}{v_s} = -\frac{(50)(5 \text{ k}\Omega\|1 \text{ k}\Omega\|833 \text{ }\Omega)}{1050 \text{ }\Omega} = \boxed{-11.9}$$

Concentrate 1

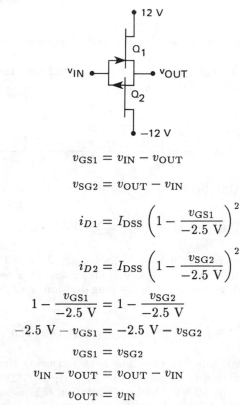

$$v_{GS1} = v_{IN} - v_{OUT}$$

$$v_{SG2} = v_{OUT} - v_{IN}$$

$$i_{D1} = I_{DSS}\left(1 - \frac{v_{GS1}}{-2.5 \text{ V}}\right)^2$$

$$i_{D2} = I_{DSS}\left(1 - \frac{v_{SG2}}{-2.5 \text{ V}}\right)^2$$

$$1 - \frac{v_{GS1}}{-2.5 \text{ V}} = 1 - \frac{v_{SG2}}{-2.5 \text{ V}}$$

$$-2.5 \text{ V} - v_{GS1} = -2.5 \text{ V} - v_{SG2}$$

$$v_{GS1} = v_{SG2}$$

$$v_{IN} - v_{OUT} = v_{OUT} - v_{IN}$$

$$v_{OUT} = v_{IN}$$

In order to remain in pinchoff, $v_{DS} > -V_P$, so

$$v_{OUT} < 12 \text{ V} - 2.5 \text{ V} = 9.5 \text{ V}$$

For Q_2, $v_{SD} > -V_P$, so

$$v_{OUT} > -12 \text{ V} + 2.5 \text{ V} = -9.5 \text{ V}$$

$$\boxed{-9.5 \text{ V} < v_{IN} < 9.5 \text{ V}}$$

Concentrate 2

The same drain current flows through both transistors, which are operating in the pinchoff mode. Note that v_{GS2} is 0.

$$i_D = I_{DSS1}\left(1 + \frac{v_{GS1}}{V_P}\right)^2\left(1 + \frac{v_{DS1}}{V_A}\right)$$

$$= I_{DSS2}\left(1 + \frac{v_{DS2}}{V_A}\right)$$

The quiescent point is with $v_{\text{IN}} = 0$ V. Under that condition, the voltage $v_{\text{GS1}} = -v_{\text{OUT}}$. Also note that $v_{\text{DS1}} = 12$ V $- v_{\text{OUT}}$ and that $v_{\text{DS2}} = 12$ V $+ v_{\text{OUT}}$. Putting in the given parameter values and these voltages in the above equation,

$$(12 \text{ mA})(1 + v_{\text{OUT}})^2(162 \text{ V} - v_{\text{OUT}})$$
$$= (8 \text{ mA})(162 \text{ V} + v_{\text{OUT}})$$

$$(1.5)(v_{\text{OUT}})^3 - (246)(v_{\text{OUT}})^2 + 488.5 v_{\text{OUT}} - 81 \text{ V} = 0$$

This third-degree equation is solved numerically. The iteration formula is obtained from this last equation. The present value of v_{OUT} is $v_{\text{OUT}}(n)$ and the next value calculated is $v_{\text{OUT}}(n+1)$.

$$v_{\text{OUT}}(n+1)$$
$$= \frac{81 \text{ V} + (246)[v_{\text{OUT}}(n)]^2 - (1.5)[v_{\text{OUT}}(n)]^3}{488.5}$$

Taking $v_{\text{OUT}}(0) = 0$ V,

$$v_{\text{OUT}}(1) = \frac{81 \text{ V}}{488.5} = 0.1658 \text{ V}$$

Then $v_{\text{OUT}}(2) = 0.1796$ V and $v_{\text{OUT}}(3) = 0.1820$ V, which converges to 0.1826 V. This root is extracted from the third-degree equation by long division (see Chap. 1) to leave

$$1.5 v_{\text{OUT}}^2 - 246.726 v_{\text{OUT}} + 443.635 = 0$$

This second-degree equation is solved using the binomial equation to obtain the roots $v_{\text{OUT}} = 1.818$ V and $v_{\text{OUT}} = 161.99$ V. The latter solution is non-physical, leaving two possible conditions for the quiescent v_{OUT}.

If $v_{\text{OUT}} = 0.183$ V,

$$i_D = (8 \text{ mA})\left(1 + \frac{12.183 \text{ V}}{150 \text{ V}}\right) = 8.65 \text{ mA}$$

If $v_{\text{OUT}} = 1.818$ V,

$$i_D = (8 \text{ mA})\left(1 + \frac{13.818 \text{ V}}{150 \text{ V}}\right) = 8.74 \text{ mA}$$

When the circuit is first energized, it will reach the lower current first and remain at that value, so the quiescent condition is

$$V_{\text{OUTQ}} = 0.183 \text{ V}$$
$$I_{\text{DQ}} = 8.65 \text{ mA}$$
$$V_{\text{DS1Q}} = 11.82 \text{ V}$$
$$V_{\text{DS2Q}} = 12.18 \text{ V}$$
$$V_{\text{GS1Q}} = -0.183 \text{ V} \ (-V_{\text{OUTQ}})$$

The transconductance of T1 is obtained.

$$g_m = \frac{\partial i_{\text{DS1}}}{\partial v_{\text{GS1}}} = \frac{2 I_{\text{DQ}}}{V_P + V_{\text{GS1Q}}} = 0.0212 \text{ S}$$

The drain resistors are calculated.

$$\frac{1}{r_{d1}} = \frac{\partial i_{\text{DS1}}}{\partial v_{\text{DS1}}} = \frac{I_{\text{DQ}}}{V_A + V_{\text{DS1Q}}} = \frac{1}{18.71 \text{ k}\Omega}$$

$$\frac{1}{r_{d2}} = \frac{\partial i_{\text{DS2}}}{\partial v_{\text{DS2}}} = \frac{I_{\text{DQ}}}{V_A + V_{\text{DS2Q}}} = \frac{1}{18.75 \text{ k}\Omega}$$

The small-signal equivalent circuit is shown in the figure.

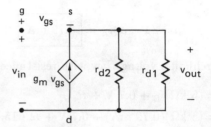

The two drain resistors appear in parallel to the output current source ($g_m v_{\text{gs}}$), and $v_{\text{gs}} = v_{\text{in}} - v_{\text{out}}$.

$$v_{\text{out}} = g_m \left[\frac{(r_{d1})(r_{d2})}{r_{d1} + r_{d2}}\right](v_{\text{in}} - v_{\text{out}})$$

$$= (198.5)(v_{\text{in}} - v_{\text{out}})$$

The output small-signal voltage gain is

$$A_v = \frac{v_{\text{out}}}{v_{\text{in}}} = \frac{198.5}{1 + 198.5} = \boxed{0.995}$$

To determine the output resistance, set the input voltage to 0 and apply a test voltage v_t at the output. The resulting test current, i_t, supplied by the test voltage is

$$i_t = \frac{v_t}{r_{d1}} + \frac{v_t}{r_{d2}} - g_m(v_{\text{IN}} - v_t)$$

v_{in} has been set to 0, so

$$\frac{i_t}{v_t} = \frac{1}{r_{\text{out}}} = \frac{1}{r_{d1}} + \frac{1}{r_{d2}} + g_m$$

$$\frac{1}{r_{\text{out}}} = \frac{1}{18,710 \ \Omega} + \frac{1}{18,750 \ \Omega} + 0.0212 \text{ S}$$

$$r_{\text{out}} = \boxed{46.9 \ \Omega}$$

Concentrate 3

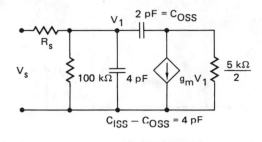

$$V_{Th} = \frac{100 \text{ k}\Omega}{100 \text{ k}\Omega + R_s} V_S$$

$$R_{Th} = \frac{(100 \text{ k}\Omega)R_s}{100 \text{ k}\Omega + R_s}$$

For $R_s = 5$ kΩ,

$$V_{Th} = 0.952 V_s$$

$$R_{Th} = 4.76 \text{ k}\Omega$$

For $R_s = 50$ Ω,

$$V_{Th} = 0.9995 V_s \approx V_s$$

$$R_{Th} = 49.98 \ \Omega \approx 50 \ \Omega$$

$$V_{out} = -g_m R_L V_1 = (-2 \times 10^{-3} \text{ S})\left(\frac{5}{2} \times 10^3 \ \Omega\right) V_1$$

$$= -5 V_1$$

The Miller capacitance is

$$C_m = (2 \text{ pF})(1 + g_m R_L) = 12 \text{ pF}$$

$$C_T = 12 \text{ pF} + 4 \text{ pF} = 16 \text{ pF}$$

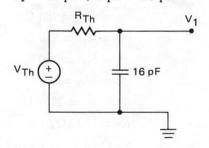

$$V_1 = V_{Th} \frac{\frac{1}{sC}}{R_{Th} + \frac{1}{sC}} = \frac{V_{Th}}{sCR_{Th} + 1}$$

$$V_{Th} = 0.952 V_s \text{ for (a)}$$

$$= V_s \text{ for (b)}$$

The voltage gain is

(a) $A_v = (0.952)(-5) = \boxed{-4.76}$

(b) $A_v = \boxed{-5}$

The high corner frequency is

$$\omega_{cf} = \frac{1}{R_{Th}(16 \text{ pF})}$$

(a) $R_{Th} = 4760 \ \Omega$

$$\omega_{cf} = 13.13 \text{ Mrad/s} = \boxed{2.09 \text{ MHz}}$$

(b) $R_{Th} = 50 \ \Omega$

$$\omega_{cf} = 1250 \text{ Mrad/s} = \boxed{199 \text{ MHz}}$$

Concentrate 4

In order to operate in pinchoff, T1, must have $v_{GS1} \geq 1$ V, and because $v_{GS1} = v_{DS1} = 12 \text{ V} - v_{out}$, the maximum value of v_{out} will be 11 V.

The same drain current flows through both transistors.

$$i_D = K[v_{GS1} - V_{GS(on)}]^2 \left(1 + \frac{v_{DS1}}{V_A}\right)$$

$$= K[v_{GS2} - V_{GS(on)}]^2 \left(1 + \frac{v_{DS2}}{V_A}\right)$$

Substituting values and the above voltage relations for the circuit given,

$$i_D \text{ (mA)} = (11 \text{ V} - v_{OUT})^2 \left(1 + \frac{12 \text{ V} - v_{OUT}}{125 \text{ V}}\right)$$

$$= (v_{IN} - 1)^2 \left(1 + \frac{v_{OUT}}{125 \text{ V}}\right)$$

Eliminating i_D,

$$(11 \text{ V} - v_{OUT})^2 (137 \text{ V} - v_{OUT})$$

$$= (v_{IN} - 1)^2 (125 \text{ V} + v_{OUT})$$

To find the point where T2 leaves pinchoff, set $v_{IN} - 1 = v_{OUT}$, which results in the following equation:

$$(2)(v_{OUT})^3 - (34)(v_{OUT})^2 + 3135 v_{OUT} - 16{,}577 \text{ V} = 0$$

The iteration formula is

$$v_{OUT}(n + 1)$$

$$= \frac{16{,}577 + (34)[v_{OUT}(n)]^2 - (2)[v_{OUT}(n)]^3}{3135}$$

This equation is solved numerically. The present value of v_{OUT} is $v_{OUT}(n)$ and the next value calculated is $v_{OUT}(n + 1)$.

Taking $v_{\text{OUT}}(0) = 0$ V,

$$v_{\text{OUT}}(1) = \frac{16{,}577 \text{ V}}{3135} = 5.29 \text{ V}$$

Then, $v_{\text{OUT}}(2) = 5.50$ V, and $v_{\text{OUT}}(3) = 5.51$ V, which has converged.

This root is extracted from the third-degree equation by long division (see Chap. 1) to leave a quadratic expression with two complex roots, so this is the only physical solution.

An operating point is then chosen at the average of the two extremes: $v_{\text{OUT}} = 5.51$ V and $v_{\text{OUT}} = 11$ V, which average to $v_{\text{OUT}} = 8.255$ V. Solving with the T1 equation, using $K = 1$ mA/V^2 and $v_{\text{OUT}} = 8.244$ V,

$$i_D = (11 \text{ V} - v_{\text{OUT}})^2 \left(1 + \frac{12 \text{ V} - v_{\text{OUT}}}{125 \text{ V}}\right) = 7.761 \text{ mA}$$

Using the T2 equation,

$$7.761 \text{ mA} = (v_{\text{IN}} - 1)^2 \left(1 + \frac{8.255 \text{ V}}{125 \text{ V}}\right)$$

$$v_{\text{IN}} = 3.698 \text{ V}$$

$$v_{\text{OUTQ}} = \boxed{8.255 \text{ V}}$$

$$i_{\text{DQ}} = \boxed{7.761 \text{ mA}}$$

$$v_{\text{DS1Q}} = \boxed{3.745 \text{ V}}$$

$$v_{\text{DS2Q}} = \boxed{8.255 \text{ V}}$$

$$V_{\text{GS2Q}} = \boxed{3.693 \text{ V}}$$

The transconductance of T2 is obtained.

$$g_{m2} = \frac{\partial i_{\text{DS2}}}{\partial v_{\text{GS2}}} = \frac{2i_{\text{DQ}}}{v_{\text{GS2Q}} - V_{\text{GS(on)}}} = 0.00575 \text{ S}$$

The drain resistor for T2 is calculated.

$$\frac{1}{r_{d2}} = \frac{\partial i_{\text{DS2}}}{\partial v_{\text{DS2}}} = \frac{i_{\text{DQ}}}{V_A + v_{\text{DS2Q}}} = \frac{1}{17.2 \text{ k}\Omega}$$

For T1, the voltage current relation is

$$i_{\text{DS1}} = I_{\text{DSS}}[v_{\text{DS1}} - V_{\text{GS(on)}}]^2 \left(1 + \frac{v_{\text{DS1}}}{V_A}\right)$$

From this, the drain resistance for T1 is

$$\frac{1}{r_{d1}} = \frac{\partial i_{\text{DS1}}}{\partial v_{\text{DS1}}} = \frac{2i_{\text{DQ}}}{v_{\text{DS1Q}} - V_{\text{GS(on)}}} + \frac{i_{\text{DQ}}}{V_A + v_{\text{DS1Q}}}$$

$$= \frac{1}{175 \text{ }\Omega}$$

The small-signal equivalent circuit is shown in the figure.

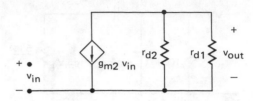

The two drain resistors appear in parallel to the output current source of T1, $g_{m2}v_{\text{gs2}}$, and $v_{\text{gsS2}} = v_{\text{in}}$.

$$v_{\text{out}} = -g_{m2} \frac{r_{d1}r_{d2}}{r_{d1} + r_{d2}} v_{\text{in}}$$

The output small-signal voltage gain is

$$A_V = \frac{v_{\text{out}}}{v_{\text{in}}} = \boxed{-0.996}$$

Concentrate 5

The small-signal mid-frequency equivalent circuit is

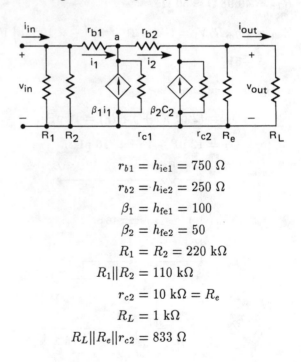

$$r_{b1} = h_{\text{ie1}} = 750 \text{ }\Omega$$
$$r_{b2} = h_{\text{ie2}} = 250 \text{ }\Omega$$
$$\beta_1 = h_{\text{fe1}} = 100$$
$$\beta_2 = h_{\text{fe2}} = 50$$
$$R_1 = R_2 = 220 \text{ k}\Omega$$
$$R_1 \| R_2 = 110 \text{ k}\Omega$$
$$r_{c2} = 10 \text{ k}\Omega = R_e$$
$$R_L = 1 \text{ k}\Omega$$
$$R_L \| R_e \| r_{c2} = 833 \text{ }\Omega$$

The simplified circuit is

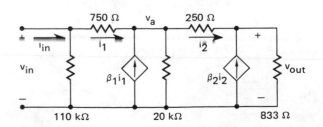

$$i_2 = \frac{v_a - v_{\text{out}}}{250\ \Omega}$$

$$v_{\text{out}} = (1 + \beta_2)(833\ \Omega)i_2$$

$$= (42{,}480\ \Omega)i_2$$

$$v_a = 1.0059 v_{\text{out}}$$

An independent calculation gives

$$i_2 = (23.54 \times 10^{-6}\ \text{S})v_{\text{out}}$$

At node a,

$$(1 + \beta_1)i_1 = i_2 + \frac{v_a}{20\ \text{k}\Omega}$$

$$= (73.84 \times 10^{-6}\ \text{S})v_{\text{out}}$$

$$i_1 = (0.731 \times 10^{-6}\ \text{S})v_{\text{out}}$$

$$= \frac{v_{\text{in}} - v_a}{750\ \Omega} = \frac{v_{\text{in}} - 1.0059 v_{\text{out}}}{750\ \Omega}$$

$$v_{\text{in}} = 1.0064 v_{\text{out}}$$

$$v_{\text{out}} = \frac{v_{\text{in}}}{1.0064}$$

$$i_1 = (0.726 \times 10^{-6}\ \text{S})v_{\text{in}}$$

$$i_{\text{in}} = \frac{v_{\text{in}}}{110\ \text{k}\Omega} + i_1$$

$$= (9.817 \times 10^{-6}\ \text{S})v_{\text{in}}$$

$$i_{\text{out}} = \frac{v_{\text{out}}}{833\ \Omega} = \frac{v_{\text{in}}}{(833\ \Omega)(1.0064)}$$

$$\frac{i_{\text{out}}}{i_{\text{in}}} = \boxed{122 = A_i}$$

Note: A reasonable approximation includes $v_{\text{out}} = v_{\text{in}}$, and

$$i_{\text{out}} = (1 + \beta_1)(1 + \beta_2)i_1$$

$$= \frac{v_{\text{in}}}{833\ \Omega}$$

$$= (51)(101\ \Omega)i_1$$

$$i_1 = \frac{v_{\text{in}}}{4.29 \times 10^6\ \Omega}$$

$$i_{\text{in}} = \frac{v_{\text{in}}}{110\ \text{k}\Omega} + i_1$$

$$= \frac{v_{\text{in}}}{107{,}300\ \Omega}$$

$$\frac{i_{\text{out}}}{i_{\text{in}}} = \frac{107{,}300\ \Omega}{833\ \Omega} = 129$$

(for a 5.7% error)

Concentrate 6

With C_1 shorted, the impedance seen at the base is $6\ \text{k}\Omega\|3\ \text{k}\Omega\|1\ \text{k}\Omega = 667\ \Omega$. The emitter output impedance is then

$$\frac{667\ \Omega + h_{\text{ie}}}{1 + \beta} = 29.2\ \Omega$$

Therefore, C_e sees $29.2\ \Omega\|200\ \Omega$, which is $25.5\ \Omega$. The low-corner frequency is

(a) $$f_1 = \frac{1}{2\pi C_e (25.5\ \Omega)} = \boxed{62.4\ \text{Hz}}$$

The worst-case effect on C_1 is with C_e shorted, in which case C_1 sees $1\ \text{k}\Omega$ in series with the parallel combination $6\ \text{k}\Omega\|3\ \text{k}\Omega\|h_{\text{ie}}$, which is $400\ \Omega$.

(b) $$C_1 \geq \frac{1}{(2\pi)(10\ \text{Hz})(1\ \text{k}\Omega + 400\ \Omega)} = \boxed{11.4\ \mu\text{F}}$$

The high-frequency circuit is

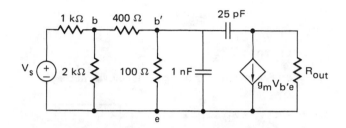

$$R_{\text{out}} = r_c\|1\ \text{k}\Omega\|833\ \Omega = 417\ \Omega$$

$$g_m = \frac{\beta}{r_{b'e}} = (0.39\ \text{S})\quad g_m R_{\text{out}} = 163\ \text{S}$$

The Miller capacitance is

$$C_m = (1 + g_m R_{\text{out}})(25\ \text{pF}) = 4.1\ \text{nF}$$

The Thevenin equivalent seen to the left of b'e has

$$V_{\text{Th}} = V_s \left(\frac{2\ \text{k}\Omega\|500\ \Omega}{1\ \text{k}\Omega + 2\ \text{k}\Omega\|500\ \Omega}\right) \left(\frac{100\ \Omega}{100\ \Omega + 400\ \Omega}\right)$$

$$= 0.0571 V_s$$

$$R_{\text{Th}} = 100\ \Omega\|[400\ \Omega + (1000\ \Omega\|2000\ \Omega)] = 91.4\ \Omega$$

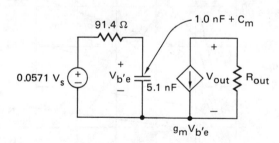

$$V_{\text{out}} = -g_m R_{\text{out}} V_{b'e}$$

$$V_{b'e} = \frac{0.0571 V_s}{s(91.4\ \Omega)(5.1 \times 10^{-9}\ \text{F}) + 1}$$

$$\frac{V_{\text{out}}}{V_s} = \frac{(0.0571)(163\ \text{V})}{\dfrac{s}{2.145 \times 10^6\ \dfrac{\text{rad}}{\text{s}}} + 1}$$

$$\omega_2 = 2.145 \times 10^6\ \text{rad/s}$$

$$f_2 = 341\ \text{kHz}$$

(c)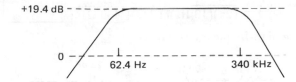

$$\frac{V_{\text{out}}}{V_s} = \frac{9.3}{\left(\dfrac{s}{2.1 \times 10^6 \,\frac{\text{rad}}{\text{s}}} + 1\right)\left(\dfrac{s}{392\,\frac{\text{rad}}{\text{s}}} + 1\right)}$$

$A_{\text{mid}} = 20 \log 9.3 = 19.4 \text{ dB}$

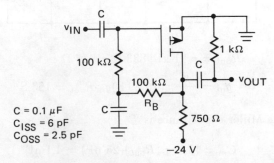

Concentrate 7

The correct circuit for analysis is shown here.

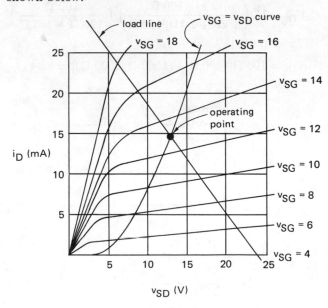

$C = 0.1\ \mu\text{F}$
$C_{\text{ISS}} = 6 \text{ pF}$
$C_{\text{OSS}} = 2.5 \text{ pF}$

For voltage feedback bias, the curve $v_{\text{GS}} = v_{\text{DS}}$ is plotted on the characteristic together with the load line, shown below.

The operating point on the given characteristic is at $v_{\text{SD}} = v_{\text{SG}} = 13.0$ V and $i_D = 14.5$ mA. r_{ds} is obtained from the average of the slopes of the characteristic curves for $v_{\text{SG}} = 12$ V and $v_{\text{SG}} = 14$ V. On $v_{\text{SG}} = 12$ V, there is 5.8 mA over 25 V for a resistance of 4.3 kΩ. On $v_{\text{SG}} = 14$ V, there is 8.1 mA over 25 V or

$R = 3.1$ kΩ. So $r_d = \left(\frac{1}{2}\right)(4.3 \text{ k}\Omega + 3.1 \text{ k}\Omega) = 3.7$ kΩ. At $v_{\text{SD}} = 13.5$ V, the distance between these curves is 4.5 mA, so

$$g_m = \frac{4.5 \text{ mA}}{2 \text{ V}} = 2.25 \times 10^{-3} \text{ S}$$

At low frequency, the time constant is set by the two input circuit capacitances with some feedback effect. Ignoring the feedback, using voltage division,

$$V_{\text{sg}} \approx V_{\text{in}} \frac{R + \dfrac{1}{sC}}{R + \dfrac{1}{sC} + \dfrac{1}{sC}} = V_{\text{in}} \frac{sCR + 1}{sCR + 2}$$

$$= \frac{\dfrac{s}{100} + 1}{\dfrac{s}{100} + 2} V_{\text{in}}$$

The output equivalent circuit is shown.

$$r_d \| 750\ \Omega \| 50 \text{ k}\Omega = 620\ \Omega$$

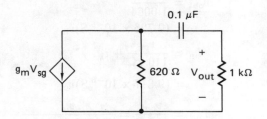

The output capacitance sees approximately 1620 Ω.

$$V_{\text{out}} = -g_m V_{\text{sg}} \left(\frac{620}{1620 + \dfrac{10^7}{s}}\right)(1 \text{ k}\Omega)$$

$$= \frac{(-1.395 \times 10^{-4})s}{\dfrac{s}{6170\,\frac{\text{rad}}{\text{s}}} + 1}$$

The output circuit sets the lower corner frequency.

At high frequency, the circuit capacitors act as short circuits. The Miller effective capacitor will appear across the 100-kΩ resistance.

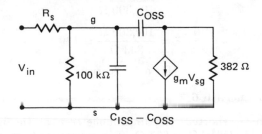

$$C_{\text{OSS}}(1 + g_m R_o) = 4.6 \text{ pF} = C_m$$

$$C_{\text{ISS}} - C_{\text{OSS}} + C_m = 8.15 \text{ pF} = C_T$$

Using voltage division,

$$\frac{V_{sg}}{V_{in}} = \left(\frac{100 \text{ k}\Omega}{100 \text{ k}\Omega + R_s} \right) \left[\frac{1}{\dfrac{sC_T R_s (100 \text{ k}\Omega)}{R_{out} + 100 \text{ k}\Omega} + 1} \right]$$

Assuming $R_s \ll 100 \text{ k}\Omega$,

$$\frac{V_{sg}}{V_{in}} = \frac{1}{sC_T R_s + 1} = \frac{1}{\dfrac{s}{2.45 \times 10^9 \frac{\text{rad}}{\text{s}}} + 1}$$

Combining the low- and high-frequency transfer functions,

$$A = \frac{v_{out}}{v_{in}}$$

$$= \left[-\frac{(0.5)\left(\frac{s}{100} + 1 \right)}{\frac{s}{200} + 1} \right] \left[\frac{(1.395 \times 10^{-4})s}{\frac{s}{6170} + 1} \right]$$

$$\times \left(\frac{1}{\dfrac{s}{2.45 \times 10^9} + 1} \right)$$

The Bode diagram for amplitude is shown.

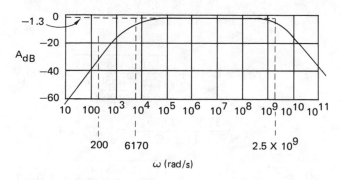

ω (rad/s)

Concentrate 8

As $i_{DQ} = 10$ mA, the voltage drop across the 600-Ω resistance is 6 V. With $v_{DS} = 5$ V, then the voltage across R_s must be 4 V.

$$R_s = \frac{4 \text{ V}}{0.01 \text{ A}} = 400 \ \Omega$$

From the characteristic at the Q point ($v_{DS} = 5$ V, $i_D = 10$ mA), the interpolated value of v_{GS} is -3.4 V.

$$v_{GS} = v_G - v_S = v_G - 4 \text{ V} = -3.4 \text{ V}$$

$$v_G = 0.6 \text{ V}$$

$$v_G = \left(\frac{R_2}{R_1 + R_2} \right) (15 \text{ V})$$

$$\frac{R_2}{R_1 + R_2} = \frac{0.6 \text{ V}}{15 \text{ V}}$$

It is required that

$$\frac{R_1 R_2}{R_1 + R_2} = 100 \text{ k}\Omega$$

$$R_1 = \frac{15 \times 10^5}{0.6} = 2.5 \text{ M}\Omega$$

$$R_2 = 104 \text{ k}\Omega$$

$$\frac{R_1}{R_2} + 1 = \frac{15 \text{ V}}{0.6 \text{ V}}$$

From the characteristic at $v_{DS} = 5$ V, the distance from the $v_{GS} = -3$ V curve to the $v_{GS} = -4$ V curve is 2.2 mA, so $g_m = 2.2 \times 10^{-3}$ S.

With R_s shorted by a large capacitance,

$$v_{OUT} = -g_m (600 \ \Omega) v_{GS}$$

$$A_v = -g_m (600 \ \Omega) = \boxed{-1.32}$$

Concentrate 9

In pinchoff operation,

$$i_{D1} = (5) \left(1 + \frac{v_{GS1}}{2} \right)^2 \text{ mA}$$

$$i_{D2} = (5) \left(1 + \frac{v_{GS2}}{2} \right)^2 \text{ mA}$$

These have the ranges of

$$-2 \text{ V} \le v_{GS} \le 0 \text{ V}$$

With $v_{GS2} = -2$ V and $v_{GS1} = 0$ V,

$$i_{D1} = 5 \text{ mA}$$

$$i_{D2} = 0 \text{ mA}$$

$$v_{D1} = 10 \text{ V}$$

$$v_{D2} = 16 \text{ V}$$

$$v_{OUT} = v_{D2} - v_{D1} = 6 \text{ V}$$

Reversing the voltages,

$$v_{GS1} = -2 \text{ V}$$
$$v_{GS2} = 0 \text{ V}$$
$$i_{D1} = 0 \text{ mA}$$
$$i_{D2} = 5 \text{ mA}$$
$$v_{OUT} = -6 \text{ V}$$

The full output swing occurs for an input swing of 2 V on each input terminal.

The worst case is the transistor that is carrying 5 mA when $v_{OUT} = 6$ V. For that transistor, $v_D = 10$ V and $v_{GS} = 0$ V, so $v_S = v_G$.

To remain in pinchoff with $v_{GS} = 0$ V, $v_{DS} \geq V_P = 2$ V. Therefore, v_S can be no greater than 8 V.

Let

$$v_1 = v_{CM} + \frac{v_{dm}}{2}$$
$$v_2 = v_{CM} - \frac{v_{dm}}{2}$$

With $v_S = 8$ V, $v_{GS1} = 0$ V and $v_{GS2} = -2$ V, $v_1 = 8$ V and $v_2 = 6$ V.

$$v_1 = 8 \text{ V} = v_{CM} + \frac{v_{dm}}{2}$$
$$v_2 = 6 \text{ V} = v_{CM} - \frac{v_{dm}}{2}$$
$$v_{CM} = 7 \text{ V}$$
$$v_{dm} = 2 \text{ V}$$

The maximum common-mode voltage will be 7 V. The negative maximum will depend on the current source. Assume the current source is the same type of transistor with the gate shorted to the source. For this current source transistor to remain in pinchoff operation, its drain-source voltage must equal or exceed V_P, which is 2 V. Then the source voltage of the differential pair cannot become more negative than -14 V, so the most negative common-mode voltage will be -13 V, to allow a ± 1 V swing of v_{dm}.

(a) $\boxed{-13 \text{ V} < v_{CM} < 7 \text{ V}}$

(b) At $i_{D1} = i_{D2} = 2.5$ mA,

$$v_{GS1} = v_{GS2} : 1 + \frac{v_{GS}}{V_P} = \sqrt{0.5} \text{ V}$$

$$g_m = \frac{2}{V_P} I_{DSS} \left(1 + \frac{v_{GS}}{V_P} \right) = \frac{5}{\sqrt{2}} \text{ mS}$$

$$v_{d1} = -g_m R_c \frac{v_{dm}}{2}$$

$$v_{d2} = -g_m R_c \left(-\frac{v_{dm}}{2} \right)$$

$$v_{OUT} = v_{d2} - v_{d1} = g_m R_c v_{dm}$$

$$A_v = \frac{v_{OUT}}{v_{dm}} = g_m R_c$$

$$= \left(\frac{5 \text{ mS}}{\sqrt{2}} \right) (1.2 \text{ k}\Omega) = \boxed{4.24}$$

Concentrate 10

$$v_{DS1} = v_{GS} : I_{REF} = \frac{32 \text{ V} - v_{GS}}{11.3 \text{ k}\Omega}$$

T1 is always in pinchoff.

$$I_{REF} \text{ (mA)} = \left(\frac{1}{2} \right) (v_{GS} - 1.5 \text{ V})^2 \left(1 + \frac{v_{GS}}{120 \text{ V}} \right)$$

$$v_{GS} = 1.5 \text{ V} + \sqrt{\frac{2 I_{REF} \text{ (mA)}}{1 + \frac{v_{GS}}{120 \text{ V}}}}$$

The solution for I_{REF} and v_{GS} is found by iteration.

(1) $v_{GS} = 0$

$$I_{REF} = \frac{32 \text{ V}}{11.3 \text{ k}\Omega} = 2.832 \text{ mA}$$

(2) $$v_{GS} = 1.5 \text{ V} + \sqrt{\frac{(2)(2.832 \text{ mA})}{1 + \frac{0 \text{ V}}{120 \Omega}}} = 3.880 \text{ V}$$

$$I_{REF} = \frac{32 \text{ V} - 3.880 \text{ V}}{11.3 \text{ k}\Omega} = 2.488 \text{ mA}$$

(3) $$v_{GS} = 1.5 \text{ V} + \sqrt{\frac{(2)(2.488 \text{ mA})}{1 + \frac{3.880 \text{ V}}{120 \Omega}}} = 3.695 \text{ V}$$

$$I_{REF} = \frac{32 \text{ V} - 3.695 \text{ V}}{11.3 \text{ k}\Omega} = 2.505 \text{ mA}$$

(4) $$v_{GS} = 1.5 \text{ V} + \sqrt{\frac{(2)(2.505 \text{ mA})}{1 + \frac{3.695 \text{ V}}{120 \Omega}}} = 3.705 \text{ V}$$

This converges to

(a) $I_{REF} = \boxed{2.504 \text{ mA}}$

$v_{GS} = \boxed{3.704 \text{ V}}$

(b) To remain in pinchoff,

$$v_{DS2} > v_{GS2} - V_T = 2.204 \text{ V}$$
$$v_{OUT} > 2.204 \text{ V} - 16 \text{ V} = -13.80 \text{ V}$$
$$v_{OUT} < 16 \text{ V} - 2.204 \text{ V} = 13.80 \text{ V}$$

$$\boxed{-13.8 \text{ V} < v_{OUT} < 13.8 \text{ V}}$$

(c)
$$i_S = \left(5 \times 10^{-4} \frac{\text{A}}{\text{V}^2}\right)(v_{GS} - 1.5 \text{ V})^2$$
$$\times \left(1 + \frac{v_{DS1}}{120 \text{ V}}\right)$$
$$v_{DS1} = v_{OUT} + 16 \text{ V}$$
$$v_{GS} - 1.5 \text{ V} = 2.204 \text{ V}$$
$$i_S = (2.429 \text{ mA})\left(1 + \frac{v_{OUT}}{120 \text{ V}} + \frac{16 \text{ V}}{120 \text{ V}}\right)$$
$$= 2.753 \text{ mA} + \frac{v_{OUT}}{43.59 \text{ k}\Omega}$$
$$\frac{13.80 \text{ V}}{43.59 \text{ k}\Omega} = 0.317 \text{ mA}$$

$$2.753 \text{ mA} - 0.317 \text{ mA} < i_S < 2.753 \text{ mA} + 0.317 \text{ mA}$$

$$\boxed{2.436 \text{ mA} < i_S < 3.070 \text{ mA}}$$

Timed 1

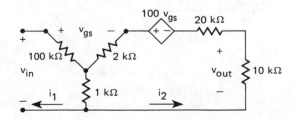

$$i_B + \alpha i_E = i_E$$
$$i_C = 19 i_B$$
$$i_E = 20 i_B$$
$$i_B = \frac{10.44 \text{ V} - v_{BE}}{163 \text{ k}\Omega + (20)(8.1 \text{ k}\Omega)} = \frac{10.44 \text{ V} - v_{BE}}{325 \text{ k}\Omega}$$

(a) For $v_{BE} = 0.6$ V,

$$i_B = 30.28 \ \mu\text{A}$$
$$i_C = 0.5753 \text{ mA}$$
$$i_E = 0.6056 \text{ mA}$$

Kirchhoff's voltage law around output circuit is

$$v_{CE} = 16 \text{ V} - (8.1 \text{ k}\Omega)(i_C + i_E)$$
$$= \boxed{6.435 \text{ V}}$$

(b)
$$\frac{\partial i_B}{\partial v_{BE}} = -\frac{1}{325 \text{ k}\Omega}$$
$$\frac{\partial i_C}{\partial v_{BE}} = (19)\left(\frac{\partial i_B}{\partial v_{CE}}\right) = \frac{-19}{325 \text{ k}\Omega}$$
$$\frac{\partial v_{BE}}{\partial T} = -2.5 \times 10^{-3} \text{ V/°C}$$
$$\frac{\partial i_C}{\partial T} = \frac{\left(-2.5 \times 10^{-3} \frac{\text{V}}{\text{°C}}\right)(-19)}{325 \text{ k}\Omega}$$
$$= 0.146 \ \mu\text{A/°C}$$
$$\frac{\frac{\partial i_C}{\partial T}}{i_C} = \frac{0.146 \times 10^{-6} \frac{\text{A}}{\text{°C}}}{0.575 \times 10^{-3} \text{ A}}$$
$$\approx \frac{0.25 \times 10^{-3}}{\text{°C}}$$
$$\approx \boxed{0.025\%/\text{°C}}$$

(c)
$$r_{b'e} \approx \frac{0.026 \text{ V}}{i_B} = 860 \ \Omega$$
$$r_{bb'} + r_{b'e} = 1210 \ \Omega$$

The small-signal circuit is

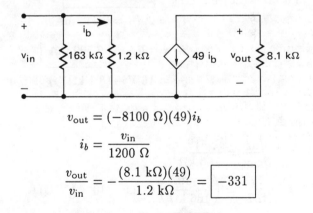

$$v_{out} = (-8100 \ \Omega)(49)i_b$$
$$i_b = \frac{v_{in}}{1200 \ \Omega}$$
$$\frac{v_{out}}{v_{in}} = -\frac{(8.1 \text{ k}\Omega)(49)}{1.2 \text{ k}\Omega} = \boxed{-331}$$

Timed 2

The small-signal equivalent circuit is

$$v_{in} = (101 \text{ k}\Omega)i_1 + (1 \text{ k}\Omega)i_2$$

$$v_{gs} = (100 \text{ k}\Omega)i_1 - (2 \text{ k}\Omega)i_2$$

$$100v_{gs} = (10 \text{ k}\Omega + 20 \text{ k}\Omega + 2 \text{ k}\Omega + 1 \text{ k}\Omega)i_2 + (1 \text{ k}\Omega)i_1$$

$$v_{out} = (-10 \text{ k}\Omega)i_2$$

(a) $A_v = \boxed{-2.98}$

(b) $Z_{in} = \boxed{144 \text{ k}\Omega}$

Timed 3

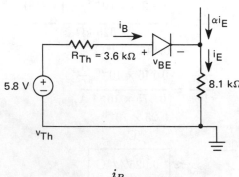

$$i_E = \frac{i_B}{1 - \alpha} = 20i_B$$

(a) With $v_{BE} = 0.7$ V,

$$\frac{5.8 \text{ V} - v_{BE}}{3.6 \text{ k}\Omega + (20)(8.1 \text{ k}\Omega)} = \boxed{31.5 \text{ }\mu\text{A} = i_B}$$

$$i_E = 20i_B = 0.630 \text{ mA}$$

$$i_C = 19i_B = \boxed{0.599 \text{ mA}}$$

$$v_{CE} = 16 \text{ V} - (8.1 \text{ k}\Omega)(i_E + i_C)$$

$$= \boxed{6.05 \text{ V}}$$

(b) $\dfrac{\partial i_C}{\partial v_{BE}} = \dfrac{-19}{166 \text{ k}\Omega}$

$$\frac{\partial i_C}{\partial T} = \left(\frac{-19}{166 \text{ k}\Omega}\right)(-2.5 \times 10^{-3} \text{ V/}^\circ\text{C})$$

$$= \boxed{0.286 \text{ }\mu\text{A/}^\circ\text{C}}$$

$$\frac{\frac{\partial i_C}{\partial T}}{i_C} = \frac{0.286 \times 10^{-6} \frac{A}{^\circ C}}{0.599 \times 10^{-3} \text{ A}}$$

$$= 0.48 \times 10^{-3}/^\circ\text{C} \ (0.048\%/^\circ\text{C})$$

$$\boxed{\text{This is adequate.}}$$

(c) The small-signal analysis is

$$r_{b'e} = \frac{0.026 \text{ V}}{i_B} = 825 \text{ }\Omega$$

$$r_{bb'} = 350 \text{ }\Omega$$

$$r_{b'e} + r_{bb'} = 1175 \text{ }\Omega$$

$$r_c = \frac{V_A}{i_C} = \frac{100 \text{ V}}{0.599 \text{ mA}} = 167 \text{ k}\Omega$$

The source transformation is

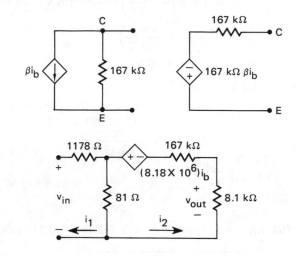

$$v_{in} = (1175 \text{ }\Omega + 81 \text{ }\Omega)i_1 + (81 \text{ }\Omega)i_2$$

$$(8.18 \times 10^6)i_1 = (81 \text{ }\Omega)i_1 + (175 \text{ k}\Omega)i_2$$

$$v_{out} = (-8.1 \text{ k}\Omega)i_2$$

$$A_v = \frac{v_{out}}{v_{in}} = \boxed{-75}$$

(d) $\dfrac{R_c}{R_e} = \dfrac{8.1 \text{ k}\Omega}{81 \text{ }\Omega} = 100$

$$\boxed{\text{The error is } 25\%.}$$

Timed 4

The small-signal circuit is

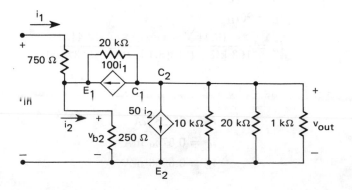

Note: Bias resistance is not needed for these calculations.

$$i_1 = \frac{v_{\text{in}} - v_{\text{b2}}}{750 \ \Omega}$$

$$i_2 = \frac{v_{\text{b2}}}{250 \ \Omega}$$

Kirchhoff's current law at E_1 is

$$i_1 - i_2 + 100i_1 + \frac{v_{\text{out}} - v_{\text{b2}}}{20 \ \text{k}\Omega} = 0$$

$$101v_{\text{in}} = 104.4v_{\text{b2}} - 0.0375v_{\text{out}}$$

Kirchhoff's current law at C_2 is

$$v_{\text{out}}\left(\frac{1}{1 \ \text{k}\Omega} + \frac{1}{10 \ \text{k}\Omega} + \frac{2}{20 \ \text{k}\Omega}\right) - v_{\text{b2}}\left(\frac{1}{20 \ \text{k}\Omega}\right)$$

$$+ \ 100i_1 + 50i_2 = 0$$

$$A_v = \frac{v_{\text{out}}}{v_{\text{in}}} = \boxed{-161.1}$$

Timed 5

With $v_1 = 0$ V,

$$i_{E1} = i_{E2} = \frac{I_2}{2}$$

$$i_E = I_{E0}e^{\frac{v_{\text{BEQ}}}{V_T}} = \frac{I_2}{2}$$

With signal v_1,

$$v_{\text{BE1}} = v_{\text{BEQ}} + v_1$$

$$i_{E1} = I_{E0}e^{\frac{v_{\text{BEQ}} + v_1}{V_T}}$$

$$= I_{E0}e^{\frac{v_{\text{BEQ}}}{V_T}}e^{\frac{v_1}{V_T}} = \frac{I_2}{2}e^{\frac{v_1}{V_T}}$$

When $v_1 \ll V_T$,

$$e^{\frac{v_1}{V_T}} \approx 1 + \frac{v_1}{V_T}$$

$$i_{E1} = \left(\frac{I_2}{2}\right)\left(1 + \frac{v_1}{V_T}\right)$$

$$i_{E2} = I_2 - i_{E1} = \left(\frac{I_2}{2}\right)\left(1 - \frac{v_1}{V_T}\right)$$

Note that with $\alpha \to 1$,

$$v_{C1} = V_{\text{CC}} - i_{E1}R$$

$$v_{C2} = V_{\text{CC}} - i_{E2}R$$

$$v_{\text{OUT}} = v_{C2} - v_{C1} = R(i_{E1} - i_{E2})$$

$$= \frac{RI_2}{2}\left[1 + \frac{v_1}{V_T} - \left(1 - \frac{v_1}{V_T}\right)\right]$$

$$= \frac{RI_2}{V_T}v_1$$

$$A_v = \frac{v_{\text{OUT}}}{v_1} = \frac{RI_2}{V_T} = \frac{RI_2}{0.025 \ \text{V}}$$

For $A_v = 10^4 I_2$, $R = \boxed{250 \ \Omega.}$

Timed 6

Kirchhoff's current law at the collector is

$$0.01 \ \text{A} = i_C + \frac{v_{\text{out}}}{1 \ \text{k}\Omega}$$

$$i_C = \beta i_B\left(1 + \frac{v_{\text{CE}}}{50 \ \text{V}}\right)$$

$$i_B = I_B + i_b$$

$$= (10^{-3} \ \text{A})(0.175 + 0.04 \ \cos\omega t)$$

$$v_{\text{CE}} = V_{\text{CE}} + v_{\text{out}}$$

$$10 \ \text{mA} = (49)(0.175 \ \text{mA} + 0.04\cos\omega t \ \text{mA})$$

$$\times \left(1 + \frac{v_{\text{CE}} + v_{\text{out}}}{50 \ \text{V}}\right) + v_{\text{out}} \ (\text{mA})$$

$$10 \ \text{mA} = (8.575 \ \text{mA})\left(1 + \frac{v_{\text{CE}}}{50 \ \text{V}}\right)$$

$$+ \left(\frac{8.575 \ \text{mA}}{50 \ \text{V}} + 1\frac{\text{mA}}{\text{V}}\right)v_{\text{out}}$$

$$+ (1.96 \ \text{mA})\left(1 + \frac{v_{\text{CE}}}{50 \ \text{V}} + \frac{v_{\text{out}}}{50 \ \text{V}}\right)\cos\omega t$$

As DC terms must match,

$$1 + \frac{V_{\text{CE}}}{50 \ \text{V}} = \frac{10 \ \text{V}}{8.575 \ \text{V}} = 1.166$$

$$V_{\text{CE}} = 8.309 \ \text{V}$$

From the remainder of the equation,

$$\left(1.172\frac{\text{mA}}{\text{V}}\right)v_{\text{out}}$$

$$+ \ (1.96 \ \text{mA})\left(1.166 + \frac{v_{\text{out}}}{50 \ \text{V}}\right)\cos\omega t = 0$$

As $|v_{\text{out}}| \approx 1$ V, $\frac{v_{\text{out}}}{50 \ \text{V}}$ is ignored.

(a) $v_{\text{out}} = -\dfrac{(1.96 \text{ mA})(1.166)}{1.172 \dfrac{\text{mA}}{\text{V}}} \cos \omega t$

$= \boxed{-1.95 \ \cos \omega t \ \text{V}}$

(b) $P_{16} = (16 \text{ V})(10 \text{ mA}) = \boxed{160 \text{ mW}}$

(c) $P_{10 \text{ mA}} = (10 \text{ mA})(8.309 \text{ V} - 16 \text{ V})$

$= \boxed{-76.9 \text{ mW}}$

Timed 7

$$i_D = (4 \text{ mA})\left(1 + \frac{v_{\text{GS}}}{2.5 \text{ V}}\right)^2 \left(1 + \frac{v_{\text{DS}}}{100 \text{ V}}\right)$$

$$= 2 \text{ mA}$$

$$v_{\text{DS}} = 16 \text{ V} - (4.7 \text{ k}\Omega + 0.47 \text{ k}\Omega)(2 \text{ mA})$$

$$= 5.66 \text{ V}$$

$$1 + \frac{v_{\text{GS}}}{2.5 \text{ V}} = \left(\frac{0.5}{1 + 0.0566}\right)^{\frac{1}{2}} = 0.688$$

$$v_{\text{GS}} = -0.780 \text{ V}$$

$$= \frac{16R}{R + 2 \text{ M}\Omega} - (470 \ \Omega)I_D$$

(a) $R = \boxed{20.2 \text{ k}\Omega}$

(b) $g_m = \dfrac{\partial 2i_D}{\partial v_{\text{GS}}}$

$$= \frac{2i_D \left(1 + \dfrac{v_{\text{GS}}}{V_P}\right)\left(1 + \dfrac{v_{\text{DS}}}{V_A}\right)}{V_P}$$

$$= \frac{(2)(4 \text{ mA})\left(1 - \dfrac{0.78 \text{ V}}{2.5 \text{ V}}\right)\left(1 + \dfrac{5.66 \text{ V}}{100 \text{ V}}\right)}{2.5 \text{ V}}$$

$$= \boxed{2.3 \text{ mS}}$$

Timed 8

The Thevenin equivalent voltage seen from the collector of transistor T2 is 0.99 V, and the Thevenin equivalent resistance is 220 Ω. With no differential mode input, the 2-mA current source splits between the two transistors, so that the quiescent voltage at the output is

$$v_{\text{OUTQ}} = 0.99 \text{ V} - (0.001 \text{ A})(220 \ \Omega) = 0.77 \text{ V}$$

Therefore, the common-mode voltage, v_{CM}, cannot exceed about 1.5 V, or transistor T2 will come out of linear operation because the collector will be forward biased. The common-mode voltage is −4 V, which will result in the quiescent collector-emitter voltages of

$$v_{\text{EC2Q}} = 0.8 \text{ V} + 4.7 \text{ V} = 5.5 \text{ V}$$
$$v_{\text{EC1Q}} = 12 \text{ V} + 4.7 \text{ V} = 16.7 \text{ V}$$

The collector resistances are

$$r_{c1} = \frac{V_A + v_{\text{EC1Q}}}{i_{\text{C1Q}}} = \frac{50 \text{ V} + 16.7 \text{ V}}{0.001 \text{ A}} = 67.5 \text{ k}\Omega$$

$$r_{c2} = \frac{V_A + v_{\text{EC2Q}}}{i_{\text{C1Q}}} = \frac{50 \text{ V} + 5.5 \text{ V}}{0.001 \text{ A}} = 55.5 \text{ k}\Omega$$

$$r_b = \frac{(1 + \beta)V_T}{i_{\text{CQ}}} = \frac{(50)(0.025 \text{ V})}{0.001 \text{ A}} = 1250 \ \Omega$$

The small-signal equivalent circuit is

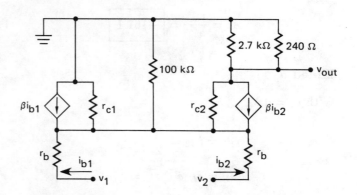

$$v_1 = v_{\text{CM}} + \frac{v_{\text{dm}}}{2} \qquad [1]$$

$$v_2 = v_{\text{CM}} - \frac{v_{\text{dm}}}{2} \qquad [2]$$

Kirchhoff's current law at the emitter node (indicated by v_e) is

$$(1 + \beta)\left(\frac{v_1 - v_e}{r_b}\right) + (1 + \beta)\left(\frac{v_2 - v_e}{r_b} + \frac{v_{\text{out}}}{r_{c2}}\right)$$

$$= v_e\left(\frac{1}{r_{c1}} + \frac{1}{r_{c2}} + \frac{1}{100 \text{ k}\Omega}\right)$$

$$(v_1 + v_2) + 0.000450 v_{\text{out}} = 2.001071 v_e$$

With Eqs. 1 and 2,

$$v_e = 0.000225 v_{\text{OUT}} + 0.999465 v_{\text{CM}} \qquad [3]$$

Kirchhoff's current law at the output node is

$$-\beta\frac{v_2 - v_e}{r_b} + \frac{v_e}{r_{c2}} = v_{\text{OUT}}\left(\frac{1}{r_{c2}} + \frac{1}{240\ \Omega} + \frac{1}{2.7\ \text{k}\Omega}\right)$$

$$v_2 - 1.000460v_e + 0.116200v_{\text{OUT}} = 0$$

From this and Eq. 2,

$$v_e = 0.116147v_{\text{OUT}} - 0.499770v_{\text{dm}} + 0.999540v_{\text{CM}} \quad [4]$$

Eliminating v_e from Eqs. 3 and 4,

$$v_{\text{OUT}} = 4.31v_{\text{dm}} + 0.000646v_{\text{CM}}$$

(a) $A_{dm} = \boxed{4.31}$

The common-mode rejection ratio is

$$\text{CMRR} = \frac{0.000646}{4.31} = 0.000150$$

(b) $\text{CMRR}_{\text{dB}} = 20\log\text{CMRR}$

$$= \boxed{-76.5\ \text{dB}}$$

The input impedance to the differential mode is $2r_b$.

(c) $Z_{\text{in}} = \boxed{2500\ \Omega}$

Timed 9

Any common-mode voltage above $+0.7$ V will forward bias the collector of T2. The solution here uses a common-mode voltage of -4 V.

In the quiescent condition, with $v_{\text{CM}} = -4$ V and $v_{\text{dm}} = 0$ V, the current mirror consisting of T3 and T4 causes the collector currents of T4 and T2 to be almost equal at 1 mA, so that there is almost no current flowing in the output resistor. This means that the output voltage is nearly 0. This establishes the quiescent collector to emitter voltages of T2 and T4, which in turn set their small-signal collector resistances $v_{\text{CE2}Q} = 0$ V $- (-4$ V$) = 4$ V, so with the early voltage $V_A = 50$ V,

$$r_{c2} = \frac{50\ \text{V} + 4\ \text{V}}{1\ \text{mA}} = 54\ \text{k}\Omega$$

With $v_{\text{CE4}Q} = 12$ V,

$$r_{c4} = \frac{50\ \text{V} + 12\ \text{V}}{1\ \text{mA}} = 62\ \text{k}\Omega$$

Transistor T3 is connected in a diode mode, so the collector-emitter voltage, v_{CE3}, will be about 0.7 V.

$$r_{c3} = \frac{50\ \text{V} + 0.7\ \text{V}}{1\ \text{mA}} = 50.7\ \text{k}\Omega$$

The collector-emitter voltage of T1 is then 11.3 V + 4 V = 15.3 V.

$$r_{c1} = \frac{50\ \text{V} + 15.3\ \text{V}}{1\ \text{mA}} = 65.3\ \text{k}\Omega$$

$$r_b = \frac{(1 + \beta)V_T}{i_{CQ}} = \frac{(50)(0.025\ \text{V})}{0.001\ \text{A}} = 1250\ \Omega$$

The small-signal equivalent circuit is

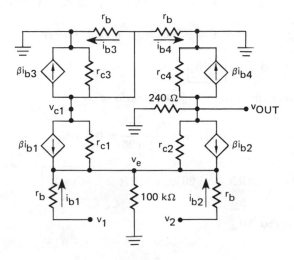

$$v_1 = v_{\text{CM}} + \frac{v_{\text{dm}}}{2} \quad [1]$$

$$v_2 = v_{\text{CM}} - \frac{v_{\text{dm}}}{2} \quad [2]$$

Kirchhoff's current law at the collector of T2 (indicated by v_{c1}) is

$$\beta(i_{b1} + i_{b3}) + i_{b3} + i_{b4} + \frac{v_{c1}}{r_{c3}} + \frac{v_{c1} - v_e}{r_{c1}} = 0$$

$$i_{b3} = i_{b4} = \frac{v_{c1}}{r_b}$$

$$i_{b1} = \frac{v_1 - v_e}{r_b}$$

With $\beta = 49$, and substituting values,

$$v_{c1} = 0.95996v_e - 0.96033v_1 \quad [3]$$

Kirchhoff's current law at the emitter node (indicated by v_e) is

$$(1 + \beta)\left(\frac{v_1 - v_e}{r_b}\right) + (1 + \beta)\left(\frac{v_2 - v_e}{r_b}\right)$$

$$+ \frac{v_{\text{out}} - v_e}{r_{c2}} + \frac{v_{c1} - v_e}{r_{c1}} = \frac{v_e}{100\ \text{k}\Omega}$$

Substituting for v_{c1} from Eq. 3 and values, solve for v_e.

$$v_e = 0.49991v_1 + 0.49973v_2 + 0.00023v_{\text{OUT}} \quad [4]$$

Kirchhoff's current law at the output node is

$$\frac{v_e - v_{\text{OUT}}}{r_{c2}} = \beta \frac{v_2 - v_e}{r_b} + \frac{v_{\text{OUT}}}{r_{c4}} + \frac{v_{\text{OUT}}}{240\ \Omega} + \beta \frac{v_{c1}}{r_b}$$

Substituting from Eqs. 3 and 4 together with values,

$$v_{\text{OUT}} = 9.15107 v_1 - 9.14080 v_2$$

Putting in the expressions for v_1 and v_2 from Eqs. 1 and 2,

$$v_{\text{OUT}} = 9.14626 v_{\text{dm}} + 0.00774 v_{\text{CM}}$$

(a) $A_{\text{dm}} = \boxed{9.15}$

The comon-mode rejection ratio is

$$\text{CMRR} = \frac{0.00774}{9.14626} = 0.00085$$

(b) $\text{CMRR}_{\text{dB}} = 20 \log \text{CMRR} = \boxed{-61\ \text{dB}}$

Timed 10

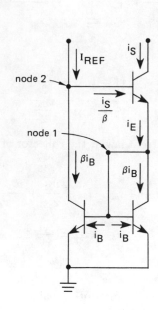

(a) Node 1:

$$i_S \left(1 + \frac{1}{\beta} \right) = i_E$$

$$i_E = (2 + \beta) i_B$$

$$\beta i_B = \frac{\beta + 1}{\beta + 2} i_S$$

Node 2:

$$I_{\text{REF}} = \beta i_B + \frac{i_S}{\beta}$$

$$= \left(\frac{\beta + 1}{\beta + 2} + \frac{1}{\beta} \right) i_S$$

$$= \frac{\beta^2 + 2\beta + 2}{\beta^2 + 2\beta} i_S$$

$$= \boxed{\left(1 + \frac{2}{\beta^2 + 2\beta} \right) i_S}$$

(b) The collector resistances can be neglected for the two lower transistors.

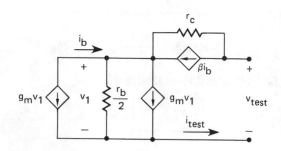

$$i_{\text{test}} = (2) \left(g_m + \frac{1}{r_b} \right) v_1$$

$$i_b = -g_m v_1$$

$$v_{\text{test}} = v_1 + (i_{\text{test}} - \beta i_b) r_c$$

$$\frac{v_{\text{test}}}{i_{\text{test}}} = r_c \left[1 + \frac{\beta g_m r_b}{(2)(g_m r_b + 1)} \right] + \frac{r_b}{(2)(g_m r_b + 1)}$$

$$g_m r_b = \beta$$

$$r_b = r_{\text{bb}'} + \frac{V_T}{i_B}$$

$$r_b = r_{\text{bb}'} + \beta \frac{V_T}{i_S}$$

$$r_c = \frac{V_A}{i_S}$$

$$R_{\text{out}} = \frac{V_A}{i_S} \left[1 + \frac{\beta^2}{(2)(\beta + 1)} \right] + \frac{r_{\text{bb}'} + \beta \dfrac{V_T}{I_S}}{(2)(\beta + 1)}$$

$$\approx \boxed{\frac{V_A}{i_S} \left(1 + \frac{\beta}{2} \right)}$$

AMPLIFIER APPLICATIONS

Warmup 1

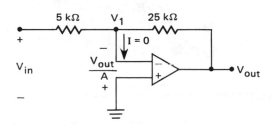

$$\frac{V_1 + \dfrac{V_{out}}{A}}{5\text{ k}\Omega} + \frac{V_{out} + \dfrac{V_{out}}{A}}{25\text{ k}\Omega} = 0$$

$$\frac{V_{out}}{A} = V_{out}\frac{\dfrac{s}{\omega_b} + 1}{A_0}$$

$$= V_{out}\left(\frac{s}{\omega_t} + \frac{1}{A_0}\right)$$

The term $1/A_0$ is negligible.

$$\left(\frac{25\text{ k}\Omega}{5\text{ k}\Omega}\right)\left(V_1 + \frac{s}{\omega_t}V_{out}\right) + V_{out}\left(1 + \frac{s}{\omega_t}\right) = 0$$

$$\frac{V_{out}}{V_1} = \frac{-5}{\dfrac{s}{\left(\dfrac{\omega_t}{6}\right)} + 1}$$

The DC gain is $\boxed{-5.}$

The bandwidth is

$$\frac{\omega_t}{6} = \frac{2\pi \times 10^7}{6}\text{ rad/s}$$

$$\text{BW} = 10.5\text{ Mrad/s} = \boxed{1.67\text{ MHz}}$$

Warmup 2

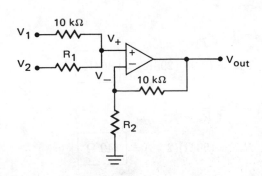

$$V_+ = \frac{R_1 V_1 + (10\text{ k}\Omega)V_2}{R_1 + 10\text{ k}\Omega}$$

$$R_1 = \boxed{10\text{ k}\Omega}$$

$$V_+ = \frac{V_1 + V_2}{2}$$

$$V_- = \frac{10\text{ k}\Omega}{R_2 + 10\text{ k}\Omega}V_{out}$$

$$V_{out} = V_-\left(1 + \frac{R_2}{10\text{ k}\Omega}\right)$$

The ideal opamp has

$$V_+ = V_-$$

$$V_{out} = \left(\frac{V_1 + V_2}{2}\right)\left(1 + \frac{R_2}{10\text{ k}\Omega}\right) = V_1 + V_2$$

Then it is necessary that

$$R_2 = \boxed{10\text{ k}\Omega}$$

Warmup 3

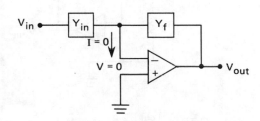

$$V_{in}Y_{in} + V_{out}Y_f = 0$$

$$\frac{V_{out}}{V_{in}} = -\frac{Y_{in}}{Y_f}$$

Let

$$Y_{in} = \frac{1}{R_1}$$

$$Y_f = sC + \frac{1}{R_2}$$

$$\frac{V_{out}}{V_{in}} = \frac{-\dfrac{R_2}{R_1}}{sCR_2 + 1}$$

The specification is

$$\frac{V_{out}}{V_{in}} = \frac{-10}{\dfrac{s}{(2)\left(30\pi\,\dfrac{\text{rad}}{\text{s}}\right)} + 1}$$

$$C = 10^{-7}\text{ F}$$

$$R_2 \times 10^{-7} \, \text{F} = \frac{1}{60\pi \, \dfrac{\text{rad}}{\text{s}}}$$

$$R_2 = \boxed{53 \, \text{k}\Omega}$$

$$R_1 = \frac{R_2}{10} = \boxed{5.3 \, \text{k}\Omega}$$

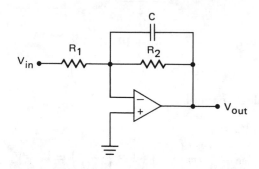

Warmup 4

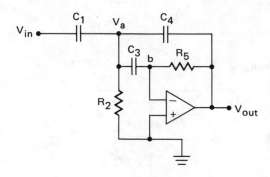

$$sC_3 V_a + \frac{V_{\text{out}}}{R_5} = 0 \quad \text{at node b}$$

$$V_a = \frac{-V_{\text{out}}}{sC_3 R_5}$$

Kirchhoff's current law at node a is

$$sC_1 V_{\text{in}} + sC_4 V_{\text{out}} = V_a \left[s(C_1 + C_3 + C_4) + \frac{1}{R_2} \right]$$

From this,

$$\frac{V_{\text{out}}}{V_{\text{in}}} = \frac{-s^2 C_1 C_3 R_2 R_5}{s^2 C_3 C_4 R_2 R_5 + s R_2 (C_1 + C_3 + C_4) + 1}$$

For a pole frequency of 100 rad/s and critical damping,

$$\frac{V_{\text{out}}}{V_{\text{in}}} = \frac{k \left(\dfrac{s}{\omega_p} \right)^2}{\left(\dfrac{s}{\omega_p} + 1 \right)^2}$$

At high frequency,

$$\frac{V_{\text{out}}}{V_{\text{in}}} \rightarrow k = 1$$

$$C_3 C_4 R_2 R_5 = \frac{1}{\omega_p^2}$$

$$R_2 (C_1 + C_3 + C_4) = \frac{2}{\omega_p}$$

Choose capacitor values:

$$\boxed{C_1 = C_3 = C_4 = 10^{-6} \, \text{F}}$$

$$R_2 = \frac{2 \times 10^6}{3 \, \omega_p} = \boxed{6.67 \, \text{k}\Omega}$$

$$R_5 = \frac{3 \times 10^6}{2 \, \omega_p} = \boxed{15.0 \, \text{k}\Omega}$$

Warmup 5

$$P_{\text{out(noise)}} = N_{\text{out}} = (k' T \, BW)(FG) = 10^{-12}$$

Given that $R_s = R_{\text{in}} = 50 \, \Omega$,

$$F_{\text{dB}} = 10 \log_{10} F = 6$$

$$F = 3.98$$

$$G = \frac{10^{-12}}{\left[\underbrace{(1.38 \times 10^{-23})(293)}_{kT} \right] \left(3.98 \times \underbrace{10^5}_{BW} \right)}$$

(a) $G = \boxed{621}$

(b) $F_n - 1 = \dfrac{T_{\text{en}}}{T_0}$

$$T_{\text{en}} = (2.98)(290\text{K}) = \boxed{864\text{K}}$$

(c) $F_n - 1 = \dfrac{R_{\text{en}}}{R_{\text{sn}}}$

$$R_{\text{en}} = (50 \, \Omega)(2.98) = \boxed{149 \, \Omega}$$

Warmup 6

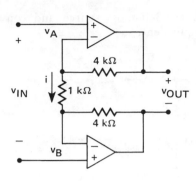

$$v_A = 0 \text{ V}$$
$$v_B = 0 \text{ V}$$
$$v_{IN} = i(1 \text{ k}\Omega)$$
$$i = \frac{v_{IN}}{1 \text{ k}\Omega}$$
$$v_{OUT} = (4 \text{ k}\Omega + 1 \text{ k}\Omega + 4 \text{ k}\Omega)i$$
$$= \frac{9 \text{ k}\Omega}{1 \text{ k}\Omega} v_{IN} = \boxed{9v_{IN}}$$

Warmup 7

Except while slewing from one saturation level to the other, the opamp is not operating in its linear region.

The current flowing in the resistors is

$$i_{IN} = \frac{v_{IN} - v_{OUT}}{1 \text{ k}\Omega + R}$$

The voltage of the positive terminal is

$$v_{IN} - i_{IN}(1 \text{ k}\Omega) = v_{IN} - \frac{(1 \text{ k}\Omega)v_{IN} - (1 \text{ k}\Omega)v_{OUT}}{1 \text{ k}\Omega + R}$$
$$v_+ = \frac{Rv_{IN} + (1 \text{ k}\Omega)v_{OUT}}{R + 1 \text{ k}\Omega}$$

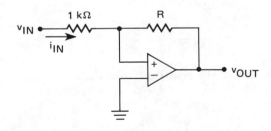

For v_+ positive, v_{OUT} is $+12$ V. v_{OUT} will reverse when v_+ becomes negative.

$$v_{IN} = (-1 - \delta) \text{ V}$$
$$-R(1 \text{ V} + \delta) + (1 \text{ k}\Omega)(12 \text{ V}) < 0$$
$$-R + 12 \text{ k}\Omega - \delta R < 0$$

Let δ approach zero, then

$$R = \boxed{12 \text{ k}\Omega}$$

Warmup 8

$$v_{OUT} = 5 \sin \omega_m t$$
$$\frac{dv_{OUT}}{dt} = 5\omega_m \cos \omega_m T$$
$$\frac{dv_{OUT}}{dt}\bigg|_{max} = 5\omega_m = 0.75 \times 10^6 \text{ V/s}$$
$$\omega_m = \frac{0.75 \times 10^6 \frac{\text{V}}{\text{s}}}{5 \text{ V}} = 375 \text{ krad/s}$$
$$f_m = \frac{375 \frac{\text{krad}}{\text{s}}}{2\pi \frac{\text{rad}}{\text{cycle}}} = \boxed{59.7 \text{ kHz}}$$

Warmup 9

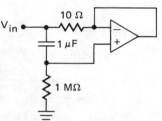

$$V_+ = \frac{1 \text{ M}\Omega}{1 \text{ M}\Omega + \frac{10^6}{s}} V_{in}$$
$$= \frac{s}{s+1} V_{in}$$
$$V_{in} - V_+ = \frac{V_{in}}{s+1}$$
$$V_- = V_+$$
$$I_{10\Omega} = \left(\frac{V_{in}}{10 \text{ }\Omega}\right)\left(\frac{1}{s+1}\right)$$
$$I_c = 10^{-6}s(V_{in} - V_+) = (10^{-6}sV_{in})\left(\frac{1}{s+1}\right)$$
$$I_{total} = I_{10\Omega} + I_c = \frac{10^{-6}s + 10^{-1}}{s+1} V_{in}$$
$$V_{in} = \frac{10s + 10}{10^{-5}s + 1} V_{in}$$

This appears as $10s + 10$ for $10^{-5}|\omega| < 0.1$ rad/s or $\omega < 10^4$ rad/s.

$$L = \boxed{10\ \text{H}}$$

$$R = \boxed{10\ \Omega}$$

$$f < \frac{10^4\ \dfrac{\text{rad}}{\text{s}}}{2\pi\ \dfrac{\text{rad}}{\text{cycle}}} = \boxed{1.6\ \text{kHz}}$$

Warmup 10

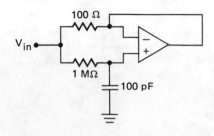

$$100\ \text{pF} = 10^{-10}\ \text{F}$$

$$V_+ = V_\text{in}\ \frac{\dfrac{10^{10}}{s}}{10^6 + \dfrac{10^{10}}{s}} = \frac{V_\text{in}}{10^{-4}s + 1}$$

$$V_\text{in} - V_+ = \frac{10^{-4}s}{10^{-4}s + 1}\ V_\text{in}$$

$$V_- = V_+ : I_{100\Omega} = \left(\frac{1}{100\ \Omega}\right)(V_\text{in} - V_+)$$

$$I_{100\Omega} = \frac{10^{-6}s}{10^{-4}s + 1}\ V_\text{in}$$

$$I_{1\text{M}\Omega} = \frac{10^{-10}s}{10^{-4}s + 1}\ V_\text{in}$$

$$I_\text{total} \to I_{100\Omega} = \frac{10^{-6}s V_\text{in}}{10^{-4}s + 1} \approx (10^{-6}s)V_\text{in}$$

$$C_\text{eq} = \boxed{1\ \mu\text{F}}$$

This is valid for $|10^{-4}s| < 0.1$ rad/s.

$$\omega < \boxed{1000\ \text{rad/s}}$$

$$f < \boxed{159\ \text{Hz}}$$

Concentrate 1

Begin with the left-most source and convert to the Thevenin equivalent.

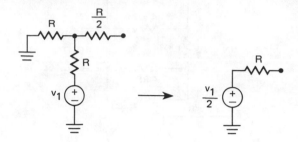

Next, combine with the second left-most source.

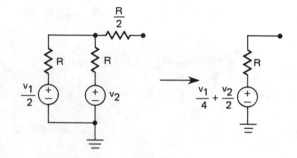

Combining with the next source,

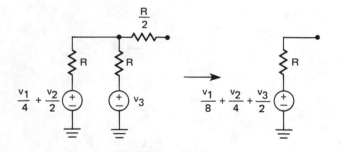

Combining with the last source, the Thevenin equivalent voltage source is

$$v_\text{Th} = \frac{v_1}{16} + \frac{v_2}{8} + \frac{v_3}{4} + \frac{v_4}{2}$$

Connected to the positive terminal,

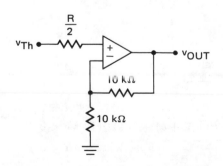

$$v_- = \frac{v_{\text{OUT}}}{2} = v_+$$

$$\frac{v_{\text{OUT}}}{2} = v_{\text{Th}}$$

$$v_{\text{OUT}} = 2v_{\text{Th}}$$

$$v_{\text{OUT}} = \boxed{\frac{v_1}{8} + \frac{v_2}{4} + \frac{v_3}{2} + v_4}$$

Concentrate 2

$$E_{\text{out}} = -\frac{Z_{\text{fb}}}{Z_{\text{in}}} V_s$$

$$Z_{\text{fb}} = \frac{0.225d}{j\omega A}$$

$$Z_{\text{in}} = \frac{1}{j\omega C}$$

$$E_{\text{out}} = \boxed{-\frac{0.225dC}{A} V_s}$$

Concentrate 3

$$G_1 = 12 \text{ dB} \rightarrow 15.8$$
$$F_1 = 6 \text{ dB} \rightarrow 4.0$$
$$G_2 = -6 \text{ dB} \rightarrow 0.25$$
$$F_2 = 12 \text{ dB} \rightarrow 15.9$$
$$G_3 = 40 \text{ dB} \rightarrow 10^4$$
$$F_3 = 6 \text{ dB} \rightarrow 4.0$$

(a) $F = F_1 + \dfrac{F_2 - 1}{G_1} + \dfrac{F_3 - 1}{G_1 G_2}$

$$= \boxed{5.69 \text{ or } 7.6 \text{ dB}}$$

Note: Bandwidth for noise set by I.F. stage.

(b) $N_{\text{in}} = 4kTR_{\text{in}}BW$

Assuming $R_{\text{in}} = 72 \text{ }\Omega$,

$S_{\text{in}} = FN_{\text{in}}$

$= (5.69)\left[(4)\left(1.38 \times 10^{-23} \dfrac{\text{J}}{\text{K}}\right)(293\text{K})(72 \text{ }\Omega)(10^7 \text{ Hz})\right]$

$= \boxed{6.6 \times 10^{-11} \text{ W}}$

Concentrate 4

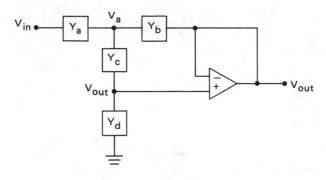

At the V_a node,

$$V_{\text{in}}Y_a + V_{\text{out}}(Y_b + Y_c) = V_a(Y_a + Y_b + Y_c)$$

At the V_+ node,

$$V_{\text{out}}(Y_c + Y_d) = V_a Y_c$$

$$V_{\text{in}}Y_a + V_{\text{out}}(Y_b + Y_c) = V_{\text{out}}\frac{(Y_c + Y_d)}{Y_c}(Y_a + Y_b + Y_c)$$

$$V_{\text{in}}Y_a Y_c + V_{\text{out}}(Y_b Y_c + Y_c^2)$$

$$= V_{\text{out}}[Y_a Y_c + Y_b Y_c + Y_c^2 + Y_d(Y_a + Y_b + Y_c)]$$

$$V_{\text{in}}Y_a Y_c = V_{\text{out}}[Y_a Y_c + Y_d(Y_a + Y_c) + Y_d Y_b]$$

$$\frac{V_{\text{out}}}{V_{\text{in}}} = \frac{Y_a Y_c}{Y_a Y_c + Y_d(Y_a + Y_c) + Y_b Y_d}$$

$$Y_a = sC_1$$
$$Y_b = G_2$$
$$Y_c = sC_2$$
$$Y_d = G_1$$

$$\frac{V_{\text{out}}}{V_{\text{in}}} = \frac{s^2 C_1 C_2}{s^2 C_1 C_2 + \frac{1}{R_1}(sC_1 + sC_2) + \frac{1}{R_2 R_1}}$$

$$= \frac{s^2 C_1 C_2 R_1 R_2}{s^2 C_1 C_2 R_1 R_2 + s(C_1 + C_2)R_2 + 1}$$

$$C_1 C_2 R_1 R_2 = (10^{-3} \text{ s})^2 = \frac{1}{\omega_p^2}$$

$$R_1 R_2 = \frac{10^{-6} \text{ s}^2}{(10^{-7} \text{ F})(10^{-7} \text{ F})} = 10^8 \text{ }\Omega^2$$

At $\omega = \omega_p$,

$$\left|\frac{V_{\text{out}}}{V_{\text{in}}}\right| = 1$$

$$s^2 C_1 C_2 R_1 R_2 \rightarrow -1$$

$$\left|\frac{V_{\text{out}}}{V_{\text{in}}}\right| = \frac{1}{\omega_p(C_1 + C_2)R_2} = 1$$

$$R_2 = \frac{1}{\left(10^3 \frac{\text{rad}}{\text{s}}\right)(2 \times 10^{-7}\,\text{F})} = \boxed{5\,\text{k}\Omega}$$

$$R_1 = \boxed{20\,\text{k}\Omega}$$

Concentrate 5

This topology is the same as Concentrate 4, with an added admittance from node a to ground. The node a equation then is

$$V_{\text{in}}Y_a + V_{\text{out}}(Y_b + Y_c) = V_a(Y_a + Y_b + Y_c + Y_d)$$

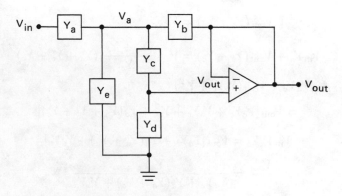

As in Concentrate 4,

$$V_a = V_{\text{out}}\left(\frac{Y_c + Y_d}{Y_c}\right)$$

$$\frac{V_{\text{out}}}{V_{\text{in}}} = \frac{Y_aY_c}{Y_aY_c + Y_eY_c + Y_d(Y_a + Y_b + Y_c + Y_e)}$$

For this problem,

$$Y_a = G_1$$
$$Y_b = G_1$$
$$Y_c = sC$$
$$Y_d = G_2$$
$$Y_e = sC$$

$$\frac{V_{\text{out}}}{V_{\text{in}}} = \frac{sCG_1}{sCG_1 + s^2C^2 + G_2(2sC + 2G_1)}$$

$$= \frac{sC\dfrac{1}{R_1}}{s^2C^2 + sC\left(\dfrac{1}{R_1} + \dfrac{2}{R_2}\right) + \dfrac{2}{R_1R_2}}$$

$$= \frac{sCR_2}{s^2C^2R_1R_2 + sC(R_2 + 2R_1) + 2}$$

(continued)

$$\frac{V_{\text{out}}}{V_{\text{in}}} = \frac{sC\dfrac{R_2}{2}}{s^2C^2R_1\dfrac{R_2}{2} + sC\left(\dfrac{R_2}{2} + R_1\right) + 1}$$

$$= \frac{As}{\dfrac{s^2}{\omega_1\omega_2} + \dfrac{s}{Q\sqrt{\omega_1\omega_2}} + 1}$$

$$\omega_1 = 10^2\,\text{rad/s}$$
$$\omega_2 = 10^4\,\text{rad/s}$$
$$\sqrt{\omega_1\omega_2} = 10^3\,\text{rad/s}$$

A_{mid} at $\omega^2 = \omega_1\omega_2$,

$$A_{\text{mid}} = \frac{R_2}{R_2 + 2R_1}$$

To have pole frequencies of 10^2 rad/s and 10^4 rad/s, the denominator must be

$$(10^{-4}s + 1)(10^{-2}s + 1)$$

To maximize the gain, R_2 should be large compared with R_1. Let

$$\frac{R_2}{2}C = 10^{-2}\,\text{s}$$
$$R_1C = 10^{-4}\,\text{s}$$
$$C = \boxed{10^{-7}\,\text{F}}$$
$$R_2 = 2 \times 10^5\,\Omega = \boxed{200\,\text{k}\Omega}$$
$$R_1 = 10^3\,\Omega = \boxed{1\,\text{k}\Omega}$$

Note that

$$A_{\text{mid}} = \frac{200\,\text{k}\Omega}{202\,\text{k}\Omega} = 0.99$$

Concentrate 6

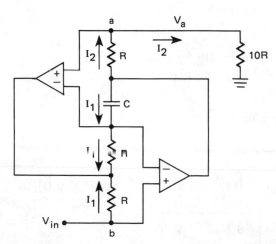

With the amplifiers operating in their linear regions, the input voltages are driven to zero by the feedback.

For the lower opamp, the currents flowing in the 1-kΩ resistors must be equal and opposite.

Because opamp input currents are negligible, the same current must also flow down in C, causing a voltage drop of I_1/sC.

To make the upper opamp input voltage zero, the voltage across the resistor must be equal and opposite to I_1/sC.

$$RI_2 = \frac{I_1}{sC}$$

$$I_2 = \frac{I_1}{sCR}$$

$$I_1 = sCRI_2$$

Because the opamp input voltages are zero, $V_a = V_{\text{in}}$ and $I_2 = V_a/10R$.

$$I_1 = sCR\frac{V_a}{10R} = \frac{sC}{10}V_a$$

$$Z_{\text{in}} = \frac{10}{sC}$$

$$C_{\text{eq}} = \frac{C}{10} = \boxed{10 \text{ nF}}$$

Concentrate 7

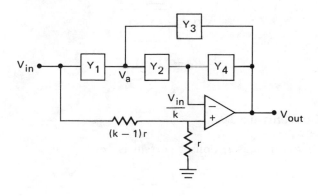

$$Y_1 = sC$$
$$Y_2 = G_2$$
$$Y_3 = G_3$$
$$Y_4 = sC$$

Kirchhoff's current law at the negative terminal, where $V_- = V_{\text{in}}/k$ is

$$V_a Y_2 + V_{\text{out}} Y_4 = \frac{V_{\text{in}}}{k}(Y_2 + Y_4)$$

At node a,

$$V_{\text{in}} Y_1 + V_{\text{out}} Y_3 + \frac{V_{\text{in}}}{k} Y_2 = V_a(Y_1 + Y_2 + Y_3)$$

Eliminating V_a,

$$\frac{V_{\text{in}}}{k}[Y_2(Y_1 + Y_3) + Y_4(Y_1 + Y_2 + Y_3) - kY_1Y_2]$$
$$= V_{\text{out}}[Y_2Y_3 + Y_4(Y_1 + Y_2 + Y_3)]$$

Substituting for Y's,

$$\frac{V_{\text{out}}}{V_{\text{in}}} = \left(\frac{1}{k}\right)\left(\frac{s^2C^2 + sC[G_1 + G_2(2-k)] + G_1G_2}{s^2C^2 + sC(G_1 + G_2) + G_1G_2}\right)$$

Dividing by C^2 with $G_1 = \frac{1}{R_1}$ and $G_2 = \frac{1}{R_2}$,

$$\frac{V_{\text{out}}}{V_{\text{in}}} = \left(\frac{1}{k}\right)\left[\frac{s^2 + s\frac{1}{C}\left(\frac{1}{R_1} + \frac{2-k}{R_2}\right) + \frac{1}{C^2R_1R_2}}{s^2 + s\frac{1}{C}\left(\frac{1}{R_1} + \frac{1}{R_2}\right) + \frac{1}{C^2R_1R_2}}\right]$$

$$\frac{1}{C^2R_1R_2} = 10^6 \text{ (rad/s)}^2$$

$$\frac{1}{C} = (10^3 \text{ rad/s})\sqrt{R_1R_2}$$

$$\frac{1}{C}\left(\frac{1}{R_1} + \frac{1}{R_2}\right) = 2 \times 10^3 \text{ rad/s}$$

$$\frac{1}{R_1} + \frac{1}{R_2} = \frac{2}{\sqrt{R_1}\sqrt{R_2}}$$

$$\sqrt{R_1}^2 - 2\sqrt{R_1}\sqrt{R_2} + \sqrt{R_2}^2 = 0 \ \Omega$$

This requires $R_1 = R_2 = R$.

$$\frac{1}{RC} = 10^3$$

$$C = 10^{-7} \text{ F}$$

$$R_1 = \boxed{10^4 \ \Omega}$$

$$R_2 = \boxed{10^4 \ \Omega}$$

$$\frac{1}{R} + \frac{2-k}{R} = -\frac{2}{R}$$

$$k = 3 + 2 = \boxed{5}$$

Concentrate 8

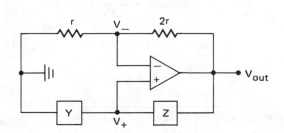

$$V_- = \frac{r}{r+2r}V_{out} = \frac{V_{out}}{3}$$

$$V_+ \left(Y + \frac{1}{Z} \right) = \frac{V_{out}}{Z}$$

$$V_+ = \frac{V_{out}}{1+YZ}$$

$$V_+ = V_- : 1 + YZ = 3$$

$$YZ = 2$$

$$Y = (10^{-6}\ \text{F})s + 10^{-3}\ \text{S} = \frac{s + 10^3\ \frac{\text{rad}}{\text{s}}}{10^6\ \text{F}^{-1}}$$

$$Z = \frac{10^6\ \text{F}^{-1}}{s} + 10^3\ \Omega = (10^3\ \Omega)\left(\frac{s + 10^3\ \frac{\text{rad}}{\text{s}}}{s} \right)$$

$$YZ = \frac{\left(s + 10^3\ \frac{\text{rad}}{\text{s}} \right)^2}{\left(10^3\ \frac{\text{rad}}{\text{s}} \right)s} = 2$$

$$s^2 + \left(2 \times 10^3\ \frac{\text{rad}}{\text{s}} \right)s + 10^6 \left(\frac{\text{rad}}{\text{s}} \right)^2 = \left(2 \times 10^3\ \frac{\text{rad}}{\text{s}} \right)s$$

$$s^2 + 10^6 \left(\frac{\text{rad}}{\text{s}} \right)^2 = 0$$

For $s = j\omega_0$,

$$\boxed{\omega_0 = 10^3\ \text{rad/s}}$$

Concentrate 9

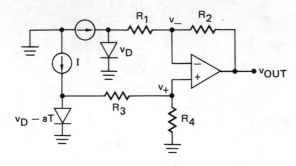

$$v_- = \frac{R_2 v_D + R_1 v_{OUT}}{R_1 + R_2}$$

$$v_+ = (v_D - aT)\left(\frac{R_4}{R_3 + R_4} \right)$$

$$v_+ = v_-$$

$$\frac{v_D R_4}{R_3 + R_4} - \frac{a\Delta T R_4}{R_3 + R_4} = \frac{R_2 v_D + R_1 v_{OUT}}{R_1 + R_2}$$

Then it is necessary that

$$\frac{v_D R_4}{R_3 + R_4} = \frac{v_D R_2}{R_1 + R_2}$$

However, it is required that

$$\frac{R_1 R_2}{R_1 + R_2} = \frac{R_3 R_4}{R_3 + R_4}$$

Therefore, $R_1 = R_3$. It follows that $R_2 = R_4$, which leaves

$$-a\Delta T R_4 = R_1 v_{OUT}$$

$$v_{OUT} = -a\frac{R_4}{R_1}\Delta T$$

$$a = 2 \times 10^{-3}\ \text{V/}^\circ\text{C}$$

At $\Delta T = 100^\circ\text{C}$,

$$v_{OUT} \to -10\ \text{V}$$

$$-10\ \text{V} = \left(-2 \times 10^{-3}\frac{\text{V}}{^\circ\text{C}} \right)\left(\frac{R_4}{R_1} \right)(100^\circ\text{C})$$

$$\frac{R_4}{R_1} = 50$$

Taking $R_1 = \boxed{1\ \text{k}\Omega}$,

$$R_4 = \boxed{50\ \text{k}\Omega}$$

$$R_2 = \boxed{50\ \text{k}\Omega}$$

$$R_3 = \boxed{1\ \text{k}\Omega}$$

Concentrate 10

Bias current is I_B, offset current is I_F.

$$I_{BIAS} = \frac{i_+ + i_-}{2}$$

$$I_{OFF} = |i_+ - i_-|$$

$$i_+ = I_{BIAS} \pm \frac{I_{OFF}}{2}$$

The worse case is at the positive terminal, with

$$i_+ = 105\ \text{nA}$$

A current into a 10-nF capacitor for a period of $(1/40\ \text{kHz})$ second results in a voltage of

$$\Delta v = \frac{I}{C}\Delta t = \left(\frac{105\ \text{nA}}{10\ \text{nF}} \right)\left(\frac{1}{40\ \text{kHz}} \right) = \boxed{262\ \mu\text{V}}$$

Timed 1

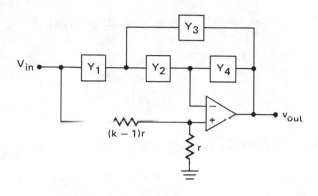

$$Y_1 = G_1 = \frac{1}{R_1}$$

$$Y_4 = G_2 = \frac{1}{R_2}$$

$$Y_2 = Y_3 = sC$$

$$(k-1)r = 1000\ \Omega$$

This is the same topology as Concentrate 7, so

$$\frac{V_{\text{out}}}{V_{\text{in}}} = \left(\frac{1}{k}\right)\left[\frac{Y_2(Y_1 + Y_3) + Y_4(Y_1 + Y_2 + Y_3) - kY_1Y_2}{Y_2Y_3 + Y_4(Y_1 + Y_2 + Y_3)}\right]$$

Substituting,

$$\frac{V_{\text{out}}}{V_{\text{in}}} = \left(\frac{1}{k}\right)\left(\frac{s^2C^2 + sC[2G_2 + (1-k)G_1] + G_1G_2}{s^2C^2 + s2G_2C + G_1G_2}\right)$$

Dividing through by C^2,

$$\frac{V_{\text{out}}}{V_{\text{in}}} = \left(\frac{1}{k}\right)\left[\frac{s^2 + s\dfrac{1}{C}\left(\dfrac{2}{R_2} + \dfrac{1-k}{R_1}\right) + \dfrac{1}{C^2R_1R_2}}{s^2 + s\dfrac{1}{C}\left(\dfrac{2}{R_2}\right) + \dfrac{1}{C^2R_1R_2}}\right]$$

$$\frac{1}{C^2R_1R_2} = \left[(2\pi)\left(400\ \frac{\text{rad}}{\text{s}}\right)\right]^2 : (\omega_p^2)$$

$$\frac{2}{R_2} + \frac{1-k}{R_1} = 0 : (\text{notch})$$

$$\frac{2}{CR_2} = (2\pi)\left(80\ \frac{\text{rad}}{\text{s}}\right) : (\text{bandwidth})$$

$$C = 10^{-8}\ \text{F}$$

$$R_2 = \frac{10^8\ \text{F}^{-1}}{80\pi\ \dfrac{\text{rad}}{\text{s}}} = \boxed{398\ \text{k}\Omega \rightarrow 400\ \text{k}\Omega}$$

$$R_1 = \left[\frac{10^{16}\ \text{F}^{-2}}{\left((2\pi)\left(400\ \dfrac{\text{rad}}{\text{s}}\right)\right)^2}\right]\left(\frac{80\pi\ \dfrac{\text{rad}}{\text{s}}}{10^8\ \text{F}^{-1}}\right)$$

$$= \boxed{3.98\ \text{k}\Omega \rightarrow 4\ \text{k}\Omega}$$

$$k - 1 = (2)\left(\frac{R_1}{R_2}\right) = 0.02$$

$$k = 1.02$$

$$1000\ \Omega = (k-1)r = 0.02r$$

$$R_3 = r = \boxed{50\ \text{k}\Omega}$$

Timed 2

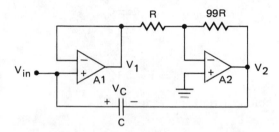

Ignoring frequency effects,

$$V_1 = V_{\text{in}}$$

$$V_2 = \frac{-99R}{R}V_1 = -99V_{\text{in}}$$

$$V_c = V_{\text{in}} - (-99V_{\text{in}}) = 100V_{\text{in}}$$

$$I_c = 100sCV_{\text{in}}$$

$$Z_{\text{in}} = \boxed{\frac{1}{100sC}}$$

This multiplies C by 100.

Frequency response is limited by $A2$. $A1$ will have bandwidth equal to the gain-bandwidth product because it is in the voltage-follower configuration.

For $A2$,

$$V_- = -\frac{s}{\omega_t}V_2 - \frac{1}{A_0}V_2$$

The term V_2/A_0 is negligible.

$$\frac{V_1 + \dfrac{s}{\omega_t} V_2}{R} + \frac{V_2 + \dfrac{s}{\omega_t} V_2}{99R} = 0 \text{ A-sec}$$

$$\frac{V_2}{V_1} = \frac{-99}{\dfrac{100s}{\omega_t} + 1}$$

$$\text{BW} = \frac{\omega_t}{100}$$

$$= 10^5 \frac{\text{rad}}{\text{s}} = 15.9 \text{ kHz}$$

The range is

$$\boxed{0 < f < 15.9 \text{ kHz}}$$

Timed 3

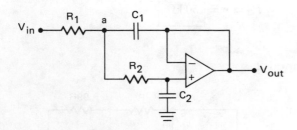

$$V_- = V_+ = V_{\text{out}}$$

Kirchhoff's current law at node a is

$$G_1 V_{\text{in}} + V_{\text{out}}(sC_1 + G_2) = V_a(sC_1 + G_1 + G_2)$$

At the positive terminal,

$$V_a G_2 = V_{\text{out}}(sC_2 + G_2)$$

Eliminating V_a,

$$G_1 G_2 V_{\text{in}} + V_{\text{out}}(sC_1 G_2 + G_2^2)$$
$$= V_{\text{out}}[s^2 C_1 C_2 + sC_2(G_1 G_2) + G_2(sC_1 + G_2) + G_1 G_2]$$

$$\frac{V_{\text{out}}}{V_{\text{in}}} = \frac{G_1 G_2}{s^2 C_1 C_2 + sC_2(G_1 + G_2) + G_1 G_2}$$

$$= \frac{1}{s^2 C_1 C_2 R_1 R_2 + sC_2(R_1 + R_2) + 1}$$

The high-frequency asymptote is

$$\frac{1}{s^2 C_1 C_2 R_1 R_2}$$

This is -1 at the pole frequency.

$$\left.\begin{array}{r} -10^8 C_1 C_2 R_1 R_2 = -1 \\ C_2 = 10^{-7} \text{ F} \end{array}\right\} C_1 R_1 R_2 = \frac{1}{10} \text{ F}^{-1} \text{ (rad/s)}^{-2}$$

At $\omega = 10^4$ rad/s,

$$\left| \frac{V_{\text{out}}}{V_{\text{in}}} \right| = \frac{1}{\sqrt{2}}$$

$$\left(10^4 \frac{\text{rad}}{\text{s}} \right) C_2(R_1 + R_2) = \sqrt{2}$$

$$C_2 = 10^{-7} \text{ F}$$

$$R_1 + R_2 = 1000\sqrt{2} \ \Omega$$

Choose $C_1 = 10^{-7}$ F, then $R_1 R_2 = 10^6 \ \Omega^2$.

$$R_1 + \frac{10^6 \ \Omega^2}{R_1} = 1000\sqrt{2} \ \Omega$$

This gives an imaginary answer. Choose

$$C_1 = 10^{-6} \text{ F}$$

$$R_1 R_2 = 10^5 \ \Omega$$

$$R_1^2 - (1000\sqrt{2} \ \Omega) R_1 + 10^5 \ \Omega^2 = 0 \ \Omega^2$$

$$R_{1,2} = 500\sqrt{2} \pm \sqrt{(500)^2(2) - 10^5} \ \Omega$$

$$= 1340 \ \Omega, \ 74.65 \ \Omega$$

$$C_1 = \boxed{1 \ \mu\text{F}}$$

$$R_1 = \boxed{1340 \ \Omega}$$

$$R_2 = \boxed{74.65 \ \Omega}$$

Timed 4

This is similar to the circuit of Timed 3, but with $V_- = V_+ = V_{\text{out}}/k$. Kirchhoff's current law at node a is

$$G_1 V_{\text{in}} + V_{\text{out}} \left(sC_1 + \frac{G_2}{k} \right) = V_a(sC_1 + G_1 + G_2)$$

At the positive terminal,

$$V_a G_2 = \frac{V_{\text{out}}}{k}(sC_2 + G_2)$$

$$\frac{V_{\text{out}}}{V_{\text{in}}} = \frac{k}{s^2 C^2 R^2 + sCR(3 - k) + 1}$$

The high-frequency asymptote is

$$10^8 C^2 R^2 = 1$$
$$CR = 10^{-4} \text{ s}$$

The DC gain is $20 \log k = 6$.

$$k = \boxed{2}$$

The pole frequency gain is also k.

$10^4 CR = 1$ (This is already met.)

$$R = \boxed{10^3 \ \Omega}$$

$$C = \boxed{10^{-7} \ \text{F}}$$

Timed 5

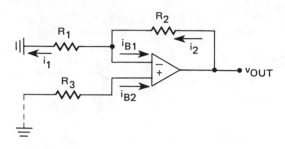

$$i_1 = i_2$$

$$i_1 = I_O \left(e^{\frac{q v_{\text{IN}}}{k T_{\text{REF}}}} - 1 \right)$$

$$i_2 = I_O \left(e^{-\frac{q v_{\text{OUT}}}{kT}} - 1 \right)$$

For positive v_{IN}, v_{OUT} is negative, then

$$\frac{v_{\text{IN}}}{T_{\text{REF}}} = -\frac{v_{\text{OUT}}}{T}$$

(a) $v_{\text{OUT}} = \boxed{-\dfrac{v_{\text{IN}}}{T_{\text{REF}}} T}$

(b) The sensitivity can be multiplied by putting n sensing diodes in series. They will equally divide v_{OUT}, so each will have the same voltage.

$$i_2 = I_o \left(e^{-\frac{8 v_{\text{OUT}}}{nkT}} - 1 \right) = i_1$$

$$v_{\text{OUT}} = \boxed{\dfrac{n v_{\text{IN}}}{T_{\text{REF}}} T}$$

Timed 6

The non-inverting gain $= 1 + R_2/R_1$, since $A = 2$, $R_2 = R_1$. Assume no input signal. Offset current is I_F, bias current is I_B.

$$v_+ = -i_{B2} R_3 = v_-$$

$$i_1 = \frac{v_+}{R_1} = -\frac{i_{B2} R_3}{R_1}$$

$$i_2 = i_{B1} + i_1 = i_{B1} - \frac{R_3}{R_1} i_{B2}$$

$$v_{\text{OUT}} = v_+ + i_2 R_2$$

$$= -i_{B2} R_3 + i_{B1} R_2 - \frac{R_2}{R_1} R_3 i_{B2}$$

$$R_2 = R_1$$

$$v_{\text{OUT}} = i_{B1} R_2 - i_{B2} 2 R_3$$

$$i_{B1} = I_B + \frac{I_{\text{OFF}}}{2}$$

$$i_{B2} = I_B - \frac{I_{\text{OFF}}}{2}$$

$$v_{\text{OUT}} = (R_2 - 2R_3) I_B + (R_2 + 2R_3) \frac{I_{\text{OFF}}}{2}$$

Set $R_3 = R_2/2$, then $v_{\text{OUT}} = R_2 I_{\text{OFF}}$.

For 12-bit digital representation of $+5$ V, the most significant bit has a value of $5/2$ V or $5/2^1$ V. The least significant digit (12th) has a place value of $5/2^{12}$ V. Half the value of the least significant bit is then

$$\frac{5 \text{ V}}{2^{13}} = 610 \ \mu\text{V}$$

$$I_{\text{OFF}} R_2 < 610 \ \mu\text{V}$$

$$I_{\text{OFF}} = 10 \text{ nA} = 10^{-8} \text{ A}$$

$$R_2 \leq 610 \times 10^{-6} \times 10^8 \ \Omega$$

$$\boxed{\begin{aligned} R_2 &\leq 61 \text{ k}\Omega \\ R_1 &\leq 61 \text{ k}\Omega \\ R_3 &\leq 30.5 \text{ k}\Omega \end{aligned}}$$

Timed 7

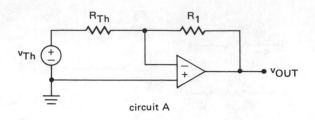

circuit A

$$v_{OUT} = -\frac{R_1}{R_{Th}}v_{Th}$$

$$dv_{OUT} = -\frac{R_1}{R_{Th}}dv_{Th} + \frac{R_1}{R_{Th}^2}v_{Th}\,dR_{Th}$$

To see these effects, it is best to look at fractional changes.

$$\frac{dv_{OUT}}{v_{OUT}}, \frac{dv_{Th}}{v_{Th}}, \frac{dR_{Th}}{R_{Th}}$$

This leads to

$$\frac{dv_{OUT}}{v_{OUT}} = \left(\frac{v_{Th}}{v_{OUT}}\right)\left(\frac{\partial v_{OUT}}{\partial v_{Th}}\right)\left(\frac{dv_{Th}}{v_{Th}}\right)$$

$$+ \left(\frac{R_{Th}}{v_{OUT}}\right)\left(\frac{\partial v_{OUT}}{\partial R_{Th}}\right)\left(\frac{dR_{Th}}{R_{Th}}\right)$$

$$\frac{\partial v_{OUT}}{\partial v_{Th}} = -\frac{R_1}{R_{Th}}$$

$$\frac{\partial v_{OUT}}{\partial R_{Th}} = \frac{R_1}{R_{Th}^2}v_{Th}$$

$$\left(\frac{v_{Th}}{v_{OUT}}\right)\left(\frac{-R_1}{R_{Th}}\right) = 1$$

$$\left(\frac{R_{Th}}{v_{OUT}}\right)\left(\frac{R_1}{R_{Th}^2}\right)v_{Th} = -1$$

$$\boxed{\frac{dv_{OUT}}{v_{OUT}} = \frac{dv_{Th}}{v_{Th}} - \frac{dR_{Th}}{R_{Th}}}$$

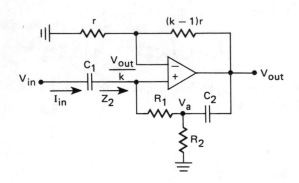

circuit B

$$v_{OUT} = kv_+$$

$$v_+ = \frac{R_2}{R_2 + R_{Th}}v_{Th}$$

$$v_{OUT} = \frac{kR_2}{R_2 + R_{Th}}v_{Th}$$

$$\frac{dv_{OUT}}{v_{OUT}} = \left(\frac{v_{Th}}{v_{OUT}}\right)\left(\frac{\partial v_{OUT}}{\partial v_{Th}}\right)\left(\frac{dv_{Th}}{v_{Th}}\right)$$

$$+ \left(\frac{R_{Th}}{v_{OUT}}\right)\left(\frac{\partial v_{OUT}}{\partial R_{Th}}\right)\left(\frac{dR_{Th}}{R_{Th}}\right)$$

$$\frac{\partial v_{OUT}}{\partial v_{Th}} = \frac{v_{OUT}}{v_{Th}}$$

$$\left(\frac{v_{Th}}{v_{OUT}}\right)\left(\frac{\partial v_{OUT}}{\partial v_{Th}}\right) = 1$$

$$\frac{\partial v_{OUT}}{\partial R_{Th}} = \frac{-kR_2}{(R_2 + R_{Th})^2}v_{Th}$$

$$\left(\frac{R_{Th}}{v_{OUT}}\right)\left(\frac{\partial v_{OUT}}{\partial R_{Th}}\right) = \frac{-R_{Th}}{R_2 + R_{Th}}$$

$$\boxed{\frac{dv_{OUT}}{v_{OUT}} = \frac{dv_{Th}}{v_{Th}} - \left(\frac{R_{Th}}{R_2 + R_{Th}}\right)\left(\frac{d\dot{R}_{Th}}{R_{Th}}\right)}$$

> Circuit B is less sensitive to changes in R_{Th}. It can be made entirely insensitive by making R_2 infinite.

Timed 8

Node a:

$$\left(\frac{V_{out}}{k}\right)\left(\frac{1}{R_1}\right) + V_{out}sC_2 = V_a\left(sC_2 + \frac{1}{R_1} + \frac{1}{R_2}\right)$$

$$I_{in} = \frac{\frac{V_{out}}{k} - V_a}{R_1}$$

$$= \left(\frac{V_{out}}{k}\right)\left[\frac{sC_2R_2(1-k) + 1}{sC_2R_1R_2 + R_1 + R_2}\right]$$

$$Z_2 = \frac{\dfrac{V_{\text{out}}}{k}}{I_{\text{in}}}$$

$$= \frac{sC_2R_1R_2 + R_1 + R_2}{sC_2R_2(1-k) + 1}$$

(a) $k = 1$

$$Z_{\text{in}} = \frac{1}{sC_1} + Z_2$$

$$\boxed{= \frac{s^2C_1C_2R_1R_2 + sC_1(R_1+R_2) + 1}{sC_1}}$$

(b) $k = 1$

$$A = \frac{Z_2k}{Z_{\text{in}}} = \boxed{\frac{ksC_1(sC_2R_1R_2 + R_1 + R_2)}{s^2C_1C_2R_1R_2 + sC_1(R_1+R_2) + 1}}$$

(c) For DC, $A = 0$ and $Z_{\text{in}} = \infty$. For $k = 1$ and $\omega_p^2 C_1C_2R_1R_2 = 1$,

$$Z_2 = j\frac{C_2R_1R_2}{\sqrt{C_1C_2R_1R_2}} + R_1 + R_2$$

$$= R_1 + R_2 + j\sqrt{\frac{C_2R_1R_2}{C_1}}$$

$$Z_{\text{in}} = R_1 + R_2$$

$$i_{\text{IN}} = \boxed{\frac{V_{\text{AC}}}{R_1 + R_2}\sin\omega_p t}$$

$$A = \frac{Z_2}{Z_{\text{in}}} = 1 + j\sqrt{\frac{C_2}{C_1}}\frac{\sqrt{R_1R_2}}{R_1 + R_2}$$

$$= 1 + j\frac{1}{\omega_p C_1(R_1 + R_2)}$$

$$V_{\text{out}} = V_{\text{AC}}\left(1 + j\sqrt{\frac{C_2}{C_1}}\frac{\sqrt{R_1R_2}}{R_1 + R_2}\right)$$

$$v_{\text{out}} = \boxed{V_{\text{AC}}\sqrt{1 + \frac{1}{[\omega_p C_1(R_1+R_2)]^2}}\sin(\omega_p t + \phi)}$$

$$\phi = \boxed{\arctan\frac{1}{\omega_p C_1(R_1+R_2)}}$$

(d) $\boxed{\text{For } k = 2, \text{ there is a righthand pole of the input impedance which will result in voltage oscillations building to saturation.}}$

Timed 9

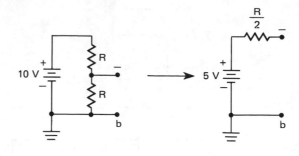

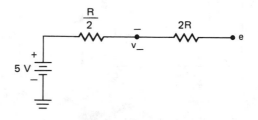

$$v_- = (5\text{ V})\left(\frac{2R}{\dfrac{R}{2} + 2R}\right) + e\,\frac{\dfrac{R}{2}}{\dfrac{R}{2} + 2R}$$

$$= 4\text{ V} + 0.2e$$

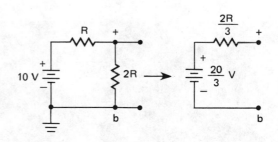

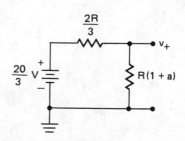

$$v_+ = \left(\frac{20}{3}\text{ V}\right)\left[\frac{R(1+a)}{\dfrac{2}{3}R + R(1+a)}\right] = \frac{(20)(1+a)}{5 + 3a}\text{ V}$$

$$= v_- : 4\text{ V} + 0.2e = \frac{(20)(1+a)}{5 + 3a}\text{ V}$$

$$e = \frac{40a \text{ V}}{5 + 3a}$$

$$\frac{e}{a} = \boxed{\frac{40 \text{ V}}{5 + 3a}}$$

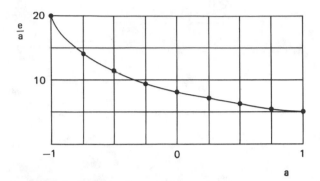

$$v_+ = v_-$$

$$= \frac{12R_2 - 12R_1}{R_1 + R_2} = 6 \text{ V}$$

$$12R_2 - 12R_1 = 6R_2 + 6R_1$$

$$6R_2 = 18R_1$$

$$R_2 = 3R_1$$

$$R_1 = \boxed{10 \text{ k}\Omega}$$

$$R_2 = \boxed{30 \text{ k}\Omega}$$

The maximum transistor voltage occurs when the load voltage is -6 V.

Timed 10

The collector voltage must remain at least 1 V above the emitter, so set $v_C = 6$ V.

$$v_{CE,\text{max}} = 6 \text{ V} - (-6 \text{ V}) = 12 \text{ V}$$

$$R_3 = \frac{6 \text{ V}}{0.01 \text{ A}} = \boxed{600 \ \Omega}$$

$$p_{\text{max}} = (12 \text{ V})(10 \text{ mA}) = \boxed{120 \text{ mW}}$$

WAVESHAPING, LOGIC, AND DATA CONVERSION

Warmup 1

Assume a -12-V supply voltage is available. Using a 6.8-V, 500-mW zener diode, $Z_z = 5\ \Omega$.

$$I_Z = 1.0\ \text{mA} = I_{ZK}$$

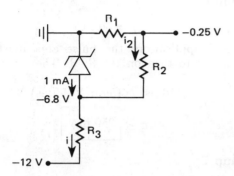

$$\frac{(6.8\ \text{V})R_1}{R_1 + R_2} = 0.25\ \text{V}$$
$$27.2R_1 = R_1 + R_2$$
$$26.2R_1 = R_2$$

Take $R_1 = 18\ \text{k}\Omega$ and $R_2 = 472\ \text{k}\Omega$, then

$$i_2 = \frac{6.8\ \text{V}}{472\ \text{k}\Omega + 18\ \text{k}\Omega} = 13.9\ \mu\text{A}$$
$$i = 1.014\ \text{mA}$$
$$R_3 = \frac{12\ \text{V} - 6.8\ \text{V}}{1.014 \times 10^{-3}\text{A}} = 5128\ \Omega$$

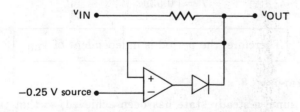

Design:

6.8-V, 500-mW zener diode
$R_1 = 18\ \text{k}\Omega$
$R_2 = 472\ \text{k}\Omega$
$R_3 = 5128\ \Omega$
opamp with silicon diode

Warmup 2

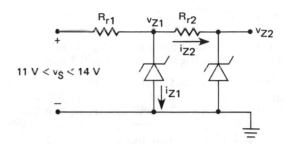

For $v_S = 14$ V, $i_{Z1} = 8$ mA, $v_{Z1} = 8.1$ V, $v_{Z2} = 4.7$ V, and $i_{Z2} = 10$ mA.

(a) $8.1\ \text{V} + R_{r1}(8\ \text{mA} + 10\ \text{mA}) = 14\ \text{V}$

$$R_{r1} = \boxed{328\ \Omega}$$

$$4.7\ \text{V} + R_{r2}(10\ \text{mA}) = 8.1\ \text{V}$$

$$R_{r2} = \boxed{340\ \Omega}$$

$$\frac{v_{Z1} - 8.1\ \text{V}}{i_{Z1} - 8\ \text{mA}} = R_{z1} = 8\ \Omega$$
$$v_{Z1} = 8.036\ \text{V} + (8\ \Omega)i_{Z1}$$
$$\frac{v_{Z2} - 4.7\ \text{V}}{i_{Z2} - 10\ \text{mA}} = R_{z2} = 35\ \Omega$$
$$v_{Z2} = 4.35\ \text{V} + (35\ \Omega)i_{Z2}$$

(b) $V_{Z01} = 8.1\ \text{V} - (0.008\ \text{A})(8\ \Omega) = 8.036\ \text{V}$
$V_{Z02} = 4.7\ \text{V} - (0.01\ \text{A})(35\ \Omega) = 4.35\ \text{V}$

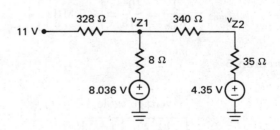

$$\frac{11\ \text{V} - v_{Z1}}{328\ \Omega} = \frac{v_{Z1} - 8.036\ \text{V}}{8\ \Omega} + \frac{v_{Z1} - 4.35\ \text{V}}{375\ \Omega}$$

$$v_{Z1} = 8.0299 \text{ V}$$

$$v_{Z2} = \frac{(35 \ \Omega)v_{Z1} + (340 \ \Omega)(4.35 \text{ V})}{340 \ \Omega + 35 \ \Omega}$$

$$v_{Z2} = 4.695 \text{ V}$$

$$\text{regulation} = \left(\frac{4.7 \text{ V} - 4.695 \text{ V}}{4.7 \text{ V}} \right) (100) = \boxed{0.1\%}$$

Warmup 3

The load line with no loads has $i_C \approx 4.9$ mA, which requires i_B to be slightly more than 0.3 mA.

To sink five additional loads in the off condition, as $I_{COE} = 0.4$ mA, i_C must increase by $(5)(0.4 \text{ mA}) = 2$ mA to ~ 6.9 mA. This will require $i_B \approx 0.4$ mA.

(a) $i_B \big|_{\text{low output}} = \boxed{0.4 \text{ mA}}$

When this transistor is off, the five loads draw 0.4 mA each, while the bases have 0.7 V.

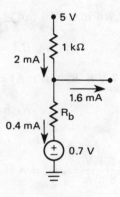

$$5 \text{ V} = (2 \text{ mA})(1 \text{ k}\Omega) + (0.4 \text{ mA})R_b + 0.7 \text{ V}$$

(b) $R_b = \dfrac{5 \text{ V} - 0.7 \text{ V} - 2 \text{ V}}{0.4 \text{ mA}} = \boxed{5.75 \text{ k}\Omega}$

Warmup 4

$$\tau_{\min} = \tau_d + \tau_r + \tau_s + \tau_f = 115 \text{ ns}$$

$$f_{\max} = \frac{1}{\tau_{\min}} = \frac{10^9}{115} = \boxed{8.7 \text{ MHz}}$$

Warmup 5

voltage table

v_A	v_B	v_C
H	H	L
H	L	H
L	H	H
L	L	H

For H = 0, L = 1.

A	B	C
0	0	1
0	1	0
1	0	0
1	1	0

$$C = \boxed{\overline{A + B}}$$

Warmup 6

$$I_{GT} = 50 \text{ mA}$$

For pulsed application, the pulse area must exceed $(50 \ \mu\text{s})(I_{GT})$ to turn on the SCR. Then, for a 10-μs pulse,

$$i_G(10 \ \mu\text{s}) \geq (50 \text{ mA})(50 \ \mu\text{s})$$

$$i_G \geq \boxed{250 \text{ mA}}$$

Warmup 7

Referring to Ex. 10.14, switching takes place when

$$v_E \rightarrow \frac{V_{BB}(10 \text{ k}\Omega)}{24 \text{ k}\Omega} = \frac{V_{BB}}{2.4}$$

The time function is

$$v_E = V_{BB} \left(1 - e^{\frac{-t}{\tau}} \right)$$

$$v_E(\text{switch}) = V_{BB} \left(1 - e^{\frac{-T}{\tau}} \right) = \frac{V_{BB}}{2.4}$$

$$1 - e^{\frac{-T}{\tau}} = \frac{1}{2.4}$$

$$\frac{T}{\tau} = \ln \left(\frac{2.4}{1.4} \right) = 0.539$$

$$T = \boxed{0.539\tau}$$

$$\boxed{\text{Therefore, the period is independent of } V_{BB}.}$$

Warmup 8

Assume a steady state has been achieved, so that the voltage at $t = 0$ s (when the switch opens) will again be the voltage when the switch opens at $t = 1$ s. At $t = 0$ s, the switch opens.

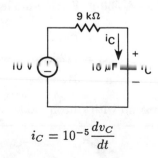

$$i_C = 10^{-5} \frac{dv_C}{dt}$$

Using Kirchhoff's voltage law,

$$10 \text{ V} = (9 \text{ k}\Omega)(10^{-5})\frac{dv_C}{dt} + v_C$$

$$= (0.09 \text{ }\Omega)\frac{dv_C}{dt} + v_C$$

This has the solution

$$v_C = 10 \text{ V} + (v_{CO} - 10 \text{ V})e^{\frac{-t}{0.09\,\text{s}}}$$

At $t = 0.5$ s, when the switch closes,

$$v_C\Big|_{t=0.5\,\text{s}} = (10 \text{ V})(1 - e^{\frac{-50}{9}}) + v_{CO}e^{\frac{-50}{9}} = v_{C1}$$

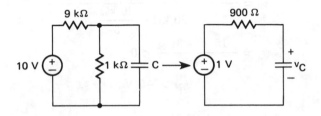

With the switch closed at $t = 0.5$ s,

$$1 \text{ V} = (900 \text{ }\Omega)(10^{-5} \text{ F})\frac{dv_C}{dt} + v_C$$

$$= (0.009 \text{ s})\frac{dv_C}{dt} + v_C$$

$$v_C = 1 \text{ V} + [v_{C1} - 1 \text{ V}]e^{-\frac{t-0.5\,\text{s}}{0.009\,\text{s}}}$$

At $t = 1$ s,

$$v_C = \left(1 - e^{-\frac{0.5}{0.009}}\right) \text{ V}$$

$$+ v_{C1}e^{-\frac{0.5}{0.009}} = v_{CO}$$

$$v_{CO} = \left(1 - e^{-\frac{500}{9}}\right) \text{ V}$$

$$+ \left[(10 \text{ V})\left(1 - e^{-\frac{50}{9}}\right)\right.$$

$$\left. + v_{CO}e^{-\frac{50}{9}}\right]e^{-\frac{500}{9}}$$

$$v_{CO}\left(1 - e^{-\frac{550}{9}}\right) = \left(1 - e^{-\frac{500}{9}}\right) \text{ V}$$

$$+ (10 \text{ V})\left(1 - e^{-\frac{50}{9}}\right)e^{-\frac{500}{9}}$$

$$v_{CO} = 1 \text{ V}$$

$$v_{C1} = 10 \text{ V} - (9 \text{ V})e^{-\frac{50}{9}} = 9.965 \text{ V}$$

$$v_C = \begin{cases} 10 - 9e^{-\frac{t}{0.09\,\text{s}}} & \text{for } 0 < t < 0.5 \text{ s} \\ 1 + 8.965e^{-\frac{t-0.5\,\text{s}}{0.009\,\text{s}}} & \text{for } 0.5 \text{ s} < t < 1 \end{cases}$$

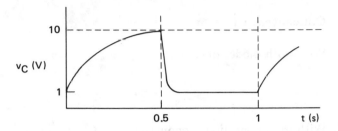

Warmup 9

In the quiescent state, B_2 is at 0.6 V and C_2 is charged to

$$v_{C2} = -(12 \text{ V} - 0.6 \text{ V}) = -11.4 \text{ V}$$

When T1 is turned on, its collector falls to about 0.3 V, putting B_2 at

$$v_{B2} = 0.3 \text{ V} - 11.4 \text{ V} = -11.1 \text{ V}$$

v_{C2} then charges toward $12 \text{ V} - 0.3 \text{ V} = 11.7$ V. However, when it reaches $+0.3$ V, v_{B2} will reach 0.6 V and turn T2 on and terminate the pulse.

$$v_{C2} = 11.7 \text{ V} + (-11.4 \text{ V} - 11.7 \text{ V})e^{\frac{-t}{R_2C_2}}$$

At $v_{C2} = 0.3$ V,

$$e^{\frac{-t}{R_2C_2}} = \frac{-11.4 \text{ V}}{-23.1 \text{ V}}$$

$$t = R_2C_2 \ln\left(\frac{23.1 \text{ V}}{11.4 \text{ V}}\right) = 0.706R_2C_2$$

$$= T_{\text{pulse}} = (0.706)(10 \text{ k}\Omega)(10^{-7} \text{ F})$$

$$T_{\text{pulse}} = \boxed{0.706 \text{ ms}}$$

Warmup 10

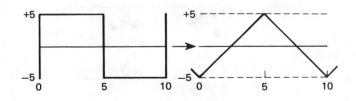

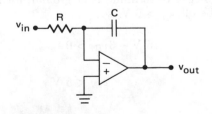

$$v_{\text{OUT}} = \frac{-1}{RC} \int_0^{0.005} 5dt + 5\text{ V} = -5\text{ V}$$

$$\frac{(0.005\text{ s})(5\text{ V})}{RC} = 10\text{ V}$$

$$\boxed{RC = 2.5 \times 10^{-3}\text{ s}}$$

Concentrate 1

With both diodes open,

$$\frac{v_{\text{OUT}}}{v_{\text{IN}}} = -1$$

With the upper diode conducting,

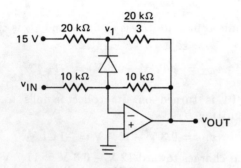

$$\frac{20\text{ k}\Omega}{3} \,\|\, 10\text{ k}\Omega = 4\text{ k}\Omega$$

$$\frac{15\text{ V}}{20\text{ k}\Omega} + \frac{v_{\text{IN}}}{10\text{ k}\Omega} + \frac{v_{\text{OUT}}}{4\text{ k}\Omega} = 0$$

$$v_{\text{OUT}} = -0.4v_{\text{IN}} - 3\text{ V}$$

For the lower diode conducting,

$$v_{\text{OUT}} = -0.4v_{\text{IN}} + 3\text{ V}$$

For both diodes open,

$$\frac{(15\text{ V})\left(\dfrac{20\text{ k}\Omega}{3}\right) + (v_{\text{OUT}})(20\text{ k}\Omega)}{\dfrac{20\text{ k}\Omega}{3} + 20\text{ k}\Omega} = v_1$$

or

$$v_1 = \frac{15\text{ V} + 3v_{\text{OUT}}}{4} = \frac{15\text{ V} - 3v_{\text{IN}}}{4}$$

Since the negative terminal is at ground, for the upper diode to be off, $v_1 > 0$ V, so

$$15\text{ V} - 3v_{\text{IN}} > 0$$

or

$$v_{\text{IN}} < 5\text{ V}$$

For the lower diode,

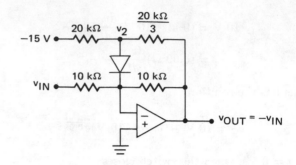

For both diodes open,

$$v_2 = \frac{(-15\text{ V})\left(\dfrac{20\text{ k}\Omega}{3}\right) - v_{\text{IN}}(20\text{ k}\Omega)}{20\text{ k}\Omega + \dfrac{20\text{ k}\Omega}{3}}$$

$$= \frac{-15\text{ V} - 3v_{\text{IN}}}{4} < 0$$

$$v_{\text{IN}} > -5\text{ V}$$

$$-5\text{ V} < v_{\text{OUT}} < 5\text{ V} : v_{\text{OUT}} = -v_{\text{IN}}$$
$$v_{\text{IN}} < -5\text{ V} : v_{\text{OUT}} = -0.4v_{\text{IN}} - 3\text{ V}$$
$$v_{\text{IN}} > 5\text{ V} : v_{\text{OUT}} = -0.4v_{\text{IN}} + 3\text{ V}$$

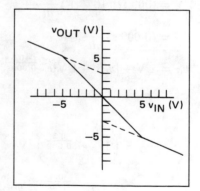

Concentrate 2

Given that $v_Z = 16$ V when $i_Z = 155$ mA, and $R_Z = 4\ \Omega$,

$$v_Z = V_{ZO} + R_Z i_Z$$
$$v_Z = 15.38\text{ V} + (4\ \Omega)i_Z$$

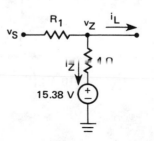

$$24 \text{ V} < v_S < 30 \text{ V}$$
$$0 < i_L < 0.25 \text{ A}$$

$$i_{Z,\text{max}} = 530 \text{ mA}$$
$$v_S - (i_L + i_Z)R_1 = v_Z$$
$$i_Z = \frac{v_Z - 15.38 \text{ V}}{4 \text{ }\Omega}$$

From this,

$$i_Z = \frac{v_S - 15.38 \text{ V} - R_1 i_L}{4 \text{ }\Omega + R_1}$$

$$v_Z = \frac{(4)(v_S - R_1 i_L) + 15.38 R_1}{4 \text{ }\Omega + R_1}$$

$$i_{Z,\text{max}} = \frac{v_{S,\text{max}} - 15.38 \text{ V}}{4 \text{ }\Omega + R_1} = \frac{14.62 \text{ V}}{4 \text{ }\Omega + R_1}$$
$$\leq 530 \text{ mA}$$
$$R_1 \geq 23.585 \text{ }\Omega$$

$$i_{Z,\text{min}} = \frac{v_{S,\text{min}} - 15.38 \text{ V} - 0.25 R_1}{4 \text{ }\Omega + R_1} \geq I_{\text{ZK}}$$

For $I_{\text{ZK}} = 15 \text{ mA}$ ($\approx I_{\text{rated}}/10$),

$$R_1 \leq 32.3 \text{ }\Omega$$

Voltage regulation is improved (made smaller) by using the largest possible R_1. Therefore,

$$R_1 = \boxed{32 \text{ }\Omega}$$

$$v_{Z,\text{max}} = \frac{(4 \text{ }\Omega)(30 \text{ V}) + (15.38 \text{ V})(32 \text{ }\Omega)}{32 \text{ }\Omega + 4 \text{ }\Omega}$$
$$= 17.00 \text{ V}$$

$$v_{Z,\text{min}} = \frac{(4 \text{ }\Omega)[24 \text{ V} - (0.25)(32 \text{ }\Omega)] + (15.38 \text{ V})(32 \text{ }\Omega)}{32 \text{ }\Omega + 4 \text{ }\Omega}$$
$$= 15.45 \text{ V}$$

$$\text{regulation} = \left(\frac{17 \text{ V} - 15.45 \text{ V}}{15.45 \text{ V}} \right)(100\%) = \boxed{10\%}$$

To improve on this regulation significantly, it is necessary to (a) use a pass transistor, (b) use an opamp, or (c) use both.

Concentrate 3

The worse-case load current occurs with the minimum resistance and minimum diode drop.

$$i_{\text{Load,max}} = \frac{5 \text{ V} - 0.6 \text{ V} - 0.2 \text{ V}}{(0.8)(2 \text{ k}\Omega)} = 2.63 \text{ mA}$$

The minimum base current occurs with maximum resistance and maximum P-N drops for the diodes and base-emitter.

$$i_{B,\text{min}} = \frac{5 \text{ V} - (3)(0.8 \text{ V})}{(1.2)(2 \text{ k}\Omega)} = 1.08 \text{ mA}$$

The worse-case collector current is

$$i_{C,\text{min}} = \beta_{\text{min}} i_{B,\text{min}} = 19.44 \text{ mA}$$

The portion of collector current that flows through R_C is

$$i_{C-R_C} = \frac{5 \text{ V} - 0.2 \text{ V}}{(0.8)(2 \text{ k}\Omega)} = 3.00 \text{ mA}$$

The portion of i_C remaining to sink loads is

$$i_{\text{Sink}} = 19.44 \text{ mA} - 3 \text{ mA} = 16.44 \text{ mA}$$

Then the maximum number of loads is

$$n = \frac{16.44 \text{ mA}}{2.63 \text{ mA}} = \boxed{6.25 \rightarrow 6 \text{ loads}}$$

Concentrate 4

(a) Since inductance current cannot change instantaneously, the inductance current flowing just after the switching is zero. When the switch closes, the 200 V across the capacitor will ionize the lamp, which will absorb 50 V, leaving 150 V for the 2-Ω resistor, so the initial lamp current is 75 A.

The lamp will extinguish when its current drops to zero.

As long as the lamp is illuminated, it will have the 50-V drop, so that

$$i_R = \frac{v_C - 50 \text{ V}}{R}$$
$$\frac{dv_C}{dt} = -\frac{i_R}{C} = \frac{50 \text{ V} - v_C}{RC}$$
$$RC \frac{dv_C}{dt} + v_C = 50 \text{ V}$$

Solving the differential equation,

$$v_C = 50 \text{ V} + (200 \text{ V} - 50 \text{ V})e^{\frac{-t}{RC}}$$

$$= 50 \text{ V} + (150 \text{ V})e^{-25t}$$

$$i_C = (0.2 \text{ F})(-25 \text{ s}^{-1})(150 \text{ V})e^{-25t}$$

$$= 75e^{-25t}\text{A}$$

At the same time the capacitor current is decreased, the inductor current increases. With 50 V across the inductor (lamp illuminated),

$$L\frac{di_L}{dt} = (1.0 \text{ H})\frac{di_L}{dt} = 50 \text{ V}$$

$$i_L = 50t + i_0$$

$$i_0 = 0 \text{ A}$$

$$i_L = 50t \text{ A}$$

The lamp extinguishes when $i_L = -i_C$ or

$$50t = 75e^{-25t}$$

$$t = 1.5e^{-25t}$$

$$e^{25t} = \frac{1.5}{t}$$

$$25t = \ln\left(\frac{1.5}{t}\right)$$

$$t = \frac{1}{25}\ln\left(\frac{1.5}{t}\right)$$

The iterations are made by calculating the next t from the present t. Starting with $t = 1$,

$$t = 0.0162, 0.1811, 0.0846, 0.1150, 0.1027, 0.1072,$$

$$0.1055, 0.1062, 0.1059, 0.1060, 0.1060, \ldots$$

Check $1.5e^{(-25)(0.1060)} = 0.1060$

(a) $t = \boxed{0 \text{ s}}$

(b) $t = \boxed{0.1060 \text{ s}}$

Concentrate 5

The UJT fires during the positive half-cycle of v_S. Thereafter, it begins to charge again and may or may not fire during the same positive half-cycle. Extra firings have no effect because the SCR is turned on by the first pulse, and remains on until v_S reverses polarity at the beginnning of the negative half-cycle.

During the negative half-cycle the UJT cannot fire. The capacitance will charge toward its steady-state response with a time constant.

$$\tau = (100 \text{ k}\Omega)(10^{-8}) \text{ F}$$

$$= 10^{-3} \text{ s} = 1 \text{ ms}$$

The duration of the half-cycle is $\left(\frac{1}{2}\right)\left(\frac{1}{60} \text{ s}\right) = 8.33$ ms, so the transient will be completed, and the steady state is found.

$$V_c = \frac{\frac{1}{j\omega C}}{R + \frac{1}{j\omega C}}V_s = \frac{V_s}{1 + j\omega RC}$$

$$= \frac{V_c}{\sqrt{1 + (\omega\tau)^2}}\angle -\tan^{-1}\omega\tau$$

$$\omega\tau = 377 \times 10^{-3} \text{ rad}$$

$$v_C = \frac{120\sqrt{2} \text{ V}}{\sqrt{1 + (0.377)^2}}\sin(\omega t - 20.66°)$$

$$= (159 \text{ V})\sin(377t - 20.66°)$$

When $v_C = (36 \text{ V})[R_1/(R_1 + R_2)] = 24$ V, the UJT will fire. The firing angle where $377t$ is θ_f is

$$\theta_f - 20.66° = \sin^{-1}\left(\frac{24}{159}\right)$$

$$\theta_f - 20.66° = 8.68°$$

$$\theta_f = \boxed{29.3°}$$

Concentrate 6

The load line must only intersect the negative resistance region, which has end points $(1 \text{ mA}, 28 \text{ V})$ and $(10 \text{ mA}, 9 \text{ V})$.

The DC load-line equation is $v_D = 48 \text{ V} - R_s i_D$. One point on the load line is $(0 \text{ mA}, 48 \text{ V})$.

A load line through $(1 \text{ mA}, 28 \text{ V})$ is

$$-R_s = \frac{v_D - 48 \text{ V}}{i_D} = \frac{28 \text{ V} - 48 \text{ V}}{0.001 \text{ A}} = -20 \text{ k}\Omega$$

$$v_D = 48 \text{ V} - (20 \text{ k}\Omega)i_D$$

The load line through $(10 \text{ mA}, 9 \text{ V})$ is

$$\frac{v_D - 48 \text{ V}}{i_D} = \frac{9 \text{ V} - 48 \text{ V}}{0.010 \text{ A}} = -3.9 \text{ k}\Omega = -R_s$$

Any value of R in this range will result in oscillation: $3.9 \text{ k}\Omega < R_s < 20 \text{ k}\Omega$.

The left-hand positive resistance region has the equation

$$\frac{v_D}{i_D} = \frac{28 \text{ V}}{0.001 \text{ A}}$$

$$v_D = (28 \text{ k}\Omega)i_D \text{ for } 28 \text{ k}\Omega$$

The right-hand positive resistance region has the equation

$$\frac{v_D - 9\text{ V}}{i_D - 0.01\text{ A}} = \frac{28\text{ V} - 9\text{ V}}{0.2\text{ A} - 0.01\text{ A}} = \frac{19\text{ V}}{0.19\text{ A}}$$

$$= 100\ \Omega$$

$$v_D - 9\text{ V} = (100\ \Omega)i_D - 1\text{ V}$$

$$v_D = 8\text{ V} + (100\ \Omega)i_D \text{ (for 8 V in series}$$
$$\text{with } 100\ \Omega)$$

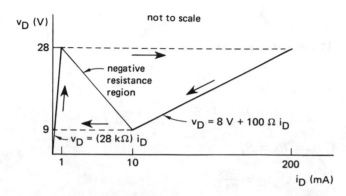

The operation will be in the left branch until the negative resistance region is reached, when there will be a jump (at constant voltage because of C) to the right branch, where the voltage will fall until the negative resistance region is reached. Then, a jump to the left branch occurs at constant voltage.

On the left branch, the starting voltage is 9 V, and the switch to the right branch occurs when the voltage reaches 28 V.

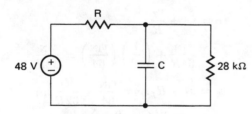

left branch circuit

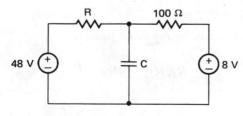

right branch circuit

Since $3.9\text{ k}\Omega < R < 20\text{ k}\Omega$, choose

$$\boxed{R = 5\text{ k}\Omega}$$

Then the Thevenin circuit seen by the capacitor for the left branch is

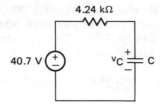

Beginning at $t = 0$ s,

$$v_C = 40.7\text{ V} + (9\text{ V} - 40.7\text{ V})e^{\frac{-t}{\tau_L}}$$

$$\tau_L = (4.24 \times 10^3)C$$

This ends at $v_C = 28\text{ V} = 40.7\text{ V} - (31.7\text{ V})e^{\frac{-t_1}{\tau_L}}$

$$\frac{t_1}{\tau_L} = \ln\left(\frac{31.7\text{ V}}{40.7\text{ V} - 28\text{ V}}\right)$$

$$t_1 = 0.9147\tau_L = 3878C$$

The operation then jumps to the right branch, beginning at 28 V.

The Thevenin equivalent seen by C is

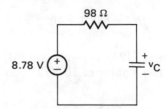

$$v_C = 8.78\text{ V} + (28\text{ V} - 8.78\text{ V})e^{\frac{-t'}{\tau_R}}$$

$$t' = t - t_1$$

$$\tau_R = 98C$$

Switching back to the left branch occurs when

$$v_C = 9\text{ V} = 8.78\text{ V} + (19.22\text{ V})e^{\frac{-t'}{\tau_R}}$$

$$\frac{t'}{\tau_R} = \ln\left(\frac{19.22\text{ V}}{9\text{ V} - 8.78\text{ V}}\right) = 4.47$$

$$t' = 4.47\tau_R = 438.1C$$

$$T - t_1 = 438.1C$$

$$T = 4316C = \frac{1}{400}\text{ s}$$

$$\boxed{C = 580\text{ nF}}$$

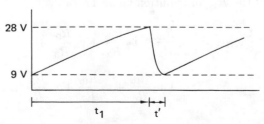

Concentrate 7

In 1 ms, a 3-mHz clock goes through 3000 clock pulses. The closest binary number less than 3000 is 2048, so the full count will be 2048. This is obtained with an 11-bit counter with place values.

$$2^{10} + 2^9 + 2^8 + 2^7 + 2^6 + 2^5 + 2^4 + 2^3 + 2^2 + 2^1 + 1 = 2^{11} - 1$$

The duration of a full count is

$$\frac{2^{11} \text{ counts}}{3 \times 10^6 \, \dfrac{\text{counts}}{\text{s}}} = 0.6827 \text{ ms}$$

$$\frac{v_{\text{Full Range}}}{RC} \int_0^{682.7\mu s} dt = v_{\max}$$

$$RC = \left(\frac{v_{\text{Full Range}}}{v_{\max}} \right) (682.7 \times 10^{-6} \text{ s})$$

For $|v_{\text{Full Range}}| = |v_{\max}| = 10$ V,

$$RC = 682.7 \times 10^{-6} \text{ s}$$

The accuracy is $\pm 1/2$ least significant bit, and the least significant bit has a value of $10 \text{ V}/2^{11}$, so the accuracy is

$$\pm \frac{1}{2} \text{ least significant bit} = \left(\frac{1}{2} \right) \left(\frac{10 \text{ V}}{2^{11}} \right)$$

$$= \frac{10 \text{ V}}{2^{12}} = \boxed{2.44 \text{ mV}}$$

Concentrate 8

The resistors R_1 through R_8 are either connected to ground directly at the positive terminal of the opamp, or connected to ground effectively via the negative terminal. In either case, the impedance of the input circuit remains unchanged by the switch positions.

The overall gain, with all switches to the left, is to be 2, with the R_1 contribution to be 1.

$$-v_{\text{OUT}} = v_{\text{IN}} \frac{R_{\text{fb}}}{R_1} + v_2 \frac{R_{\text{fb}}}{R_2} + v_3 \frac{R_{\text{fb}}}{R_3} + \dots$$

$$\dots + v_6 \frac{R_{\text{fb}}}{R_6} + v_7 \frac{R_{\text{fb}}}{R_7} + v_8 \frac{R_{\text{fb}}}{R_8}$$

The most straightforward solution is to make $R_1 = R_2 = \dots = R_7 = R_8 = R_{\text{fb}}$, and then design the circuit so that

$$v_2 = \frac{v_{\text{IN}}}{2}$$

$$v_3 = \frac{v_{\text{IN}}}{4}$$

$$v_4 = \frac{v_{\text{IN}}}{8}$$

$$\vdots$$

$$v_8 = \frac{v_{\text{IN}}}{128}$$

At the least significant bit position,

$$v_8 = \frac{v_{\text{IN}}}{128}$$

$$i_G = \left(\frac{v_{\text{IN}}}{128} \right) \left(\frac{1}{R_8} + \frac{1}{R_9} \right)$$

If $R_8 = R_9 = R$,

$$i_G = \frac{v_{\text{IN}}}{64R}$$

$$v_7 = v_8 + R_g i_G = \frac{v_{\text{IN}}}{128} + \frac{2 R_g v_{\text{IN}}}{128 R}$$

$$v_7 = \left(\frac{v_{\text{IN}}}{128} \right) \left(1 + \frac{2 R_g}{R} \right)$$

$$v_7 \to \frac{v_{\text{IN}}}{64}$$

$$R_g = \frac{R}{2}$$

Then,

$$i_F = i_G + \frac{v_7}{R}$$

$$= \frac{v_{\text{IN}}}{64R} + \left(\frac{1}{R} \right) \left(\frac{v_{\text{IN}}}{64} \right) = \frac{v_{\text{IN}}}{32R}$$

$$v_6 = v_7 + R_f i_F = \frac{v_{\text{IN}}}{64} + \frac{R_f}{32R} v_{\text{IN}}$$

$$= \left(\frac{v_{\text{IN}}}{64} \right) \left(1 + \frac{2 R_f}{R} \right) \to \frac{v_{\text{IN}}}{32}$$

Then $R_f = R/2 = R_g$.

This process can be repeated to show

$$R_g, R_f, \dots, R_a = \frac{R}{2}$$

$$R_a = R_b = R_c = R_d = R_e = R_f = \boxed{\frac{R_{\text{fb}}}{2}}$$

$$R_1 = R_2 = R_3 = R_4 = R_5 = R_6 = R_7 = R_8 = \boxed{R_{\text{fb}}}$$

Concentrate 9

Following Ex. 10.4, assume that the nominal zener voltage is obtained at the keep-alive current.

$$v_{OUT} = V_{Z0} + R_Z I_{ZK}$$
$$5.6 \text{ V} = V_{Z0} + (11 \ \Omega)(0.001 \text{ A})$$
$$V_{Z0} = 5.589 \text{ V}$$

The initial design is set with the minimum input voltage supplying exactly the keep-alive current.

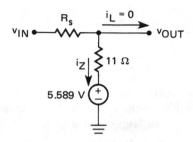

reference circuit

With $v_{IN} = 30$ V and $i_Z = I_{ZK} = 0.001$ A, the output voltage is 5.6 V and the necessary value for R_s is

$$R_s = \frac{30 \text{ V} - 5.6 \text{ V}}{0.001 \text{ A}} = \boxed{24.4 \text{ k}\Omega}$$

When the input voltage becomes 40 V, the output voltage becomes

$$v_{OUT} = \frac{(40 \text{ V})(11 \ \Omega) + (5.589 \text{ V})(24.4 \text{ k}\Omega)}{11 \ \Omega + 24.4 \text{ k}\Omega}$$
$$= 5.6045 \text{ V}$$

The resulting voltage regulation of the opamp will follow that of the reference circuit, which is found to be

$$\text{regulation} = \left(\frac{5.6045 \text{ V} - 5.6 \text{ V}}{5.6 \text{ V}}\right)(100\%) = \boxed{0.08\%}$$

The improvement of this regulation, while clearly unnecessary, is done with a two-stage regulator reference circuit as shown in the following figure. For the 1-W zener diode, the voltage V_{Z01} is found.

$$10 \text{ V} = V_{Z01} + (7 \ \Omega)(0.025 \text{ A})$$
$$V_{Z01} = 9.825 \text{ V}$$

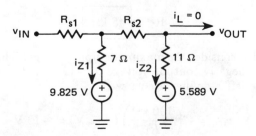

improved regulator reference circuit

For this circuit, the series resistances are designed with the minimum input voltage and both diode currents at the keep-alive value.

$$v_{Z1} = 10 \text{ V}$$
$$v_{Z2} = 5.6 \text{ V}$$
$$R_{s2} = \frac{10 \text{ V} - 5.6 \text{ V}}{0.001 \text{ A}} = \boxed{4.4 \text{ k}\Omega}$$
$$R_{s1} = \frac{30 \text{ V} - 10 \text{ V}}{0.025 \text{ A}} = \boxed{800 \ \Omega}$$

The regulation is determined by first finding the output voltage when the input voltage is 40 V. The Thevenin equivalent circuit seen to the left of R_{s2} is

$$v_{Th} = \frac{(40 \text{ V})(7 \ \Omega) + (9.825 \text{ V})(800 \ \Omega)}{7 \ \Omega + 800 \ \Omega} = 10.087 \text{ V}$$
$$R_{Th} = \frac{(7 \ \Omega)(800 \ \Omega)}{7 \ \Omega + 800 \ \Omega} = 6.9 \ \Omega$$

The output voltage is found.

$$v_{OUT} = \frac{(10.087 \text{ V})(11 \ \Omega) + (5.589 \text{ V})(4406.9 \ \Omega)}{11 \ \Omega + 4406.9 \ \Omega}$$
$$= 5.6021 \text{ V}$$

The resulting regulation is

$$\text{regulation} = \left(\frac{5.6021 \text{ V} - 5.6 \text{ V}}{5.6 \text{ V}}\right)(100\%) = \boxed{0.038\%}$$

This reference circuit has improved the regulation by a factor of about one-half.

Concentrate 10

Before the trigger, assume steady state, so T1 is off and T2 is on with $v_{BE2} = 0.6$ V. Then C_1 is charged to 15.4 V with the left plate positive. C_2 is discharged.

When the trigger occurs ($t = 0$ s), T1 turns on so v_{CE1} goes to 0.2 V and v_{BE2} goes to 0.2 V$-V_{C1} = -15.2$ V. This turns T2 off so that v_{CE2} rises, coupled to v_{BE1} to keep T1 on.

I_{BE2} starts at $(16 \text{ V} - 0.6 \text{ V})/1 \text{ k}\Omega$ or 15.4 mA, and as C_2 charges, it will drop toward 15.4 V/2 kΩ = 7.7 mA. In any case, it will be sufficient to hold T1 on as long as T2 stays off.

The determination of the duration of the pulse will be the time to charge V_{C1} enough so that V_{BE2} reaches +0.6 V. C_1 is charging toward 16 V $-$ 0.2 V = 15.8 V with the right plate positive, through R_2 for a time constant of $C_1 R_2 = 10^{-6} \times 10^3$ s.

$$v_{C1} = 15.8 \text{ V} + (-15.4 \text{ V} - 15.8 \text{ V})e^{\frac{-t}{\tau}}$$
$$= 15.8 \text{ V} - (31.2 \text{ V})e^{-10^3 t}$$
$$v_{BE2} = 0.2 \text{ V} + v_{C2}$$
$$= 16 \text{ V} - (31.2 \text{ V})e^{-10^3 t}$$

The pulse ends when $V_{BE2} = 0.6$ V or

$$e^{-10^3 t} = \frac{0.6\text{ V} - 16\text{ V}}{-31.2\text{ V}}$$

$$t = 10^{-3} \ln\left(\frac{31.2\text{ V}}{15.4\text{ V}}\right) = 706 \times 10^{-6}\text{ s}$$

$$\Delta t_{on} = 706\ \mu s$$

When the pulse has ended, the capacitors have to reach steady state before another trigger occurs. Both capacitors see 1000 Ω in this situation. C_1 charges toward 15.4 V with the left plate positive through R_1, and C_2 is discharging through R_4, both with time constants of 1 ms. To reach steady steady, the time should be four or five time constants. Taking five time constants, the minimum period is

$$5 \times 10^{-3}\text{ s} + 0.706 \times 10^{-3}\text{ s} = T_{min}$$

$$T_{min} = 5.706\text{ ms}$$

$$\boxed{f_{max} = 175\text{ Hz}}$$

The output can be taken from the collector of either T1 or T2.

v_{CE1} is at 16 V until the trigger arrives, whereupon it drops to 0.2 V and remains there until T2 returns to its on state. Then v_{CE1} charges back to 16 V with a time constant of 1 ms.

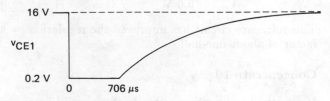

v_{CE2} is at 0.2 V until the trigger arrives, whereupon it is determined by the relation

$$v_{CE2} = v_{BE1} + v_{C2}$$

v_{C2} is charging toward half the difference between the 16-V power supply voltage and v_{BE1}, with a time constant of 500 μs because it sees two 1-kΩ resistors in parallel. Thus while T2 is off,

$$v_{CE2} = 0.6\text{ V} + (7.7\text{ V})(1 - e^{2000t})$$

At $t = 706\ \mu s$, $v_{CE2} = 6.42$ V.

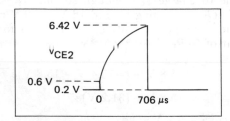

v_{CE2} is the usual output.

Timed 1

First consider the left-hand amplifier. With $v_{in} > 0$ V, the upper diode functions as a precision diode, so the amplifier output is

$$v_{OUT,left} = -\frac{R_1}{100\text{ k}\Omega} v_{IN}$$

$v_{OUT,left}$ appears at the junction of R_1 and R_2.

Then, by summing currents at the negative input of the right-hand amplifier,

$$\left(-\frac{R_1}{100\text{ k}\Omega}\right)\left(\frac{v_{IN}}{R_2}\right) + \frac{v_{IN}}{R_3} + \frac{v_{OUT}}{100\text{ k}\Omega} = 0$$

$$v_{OUT} = v_{IN}\left(\frac{R_1}{R_2} - \frac{100\text{ k}\Omega}{R_3}\right)$$

Next, consider the case for $v_{IN} < 0$ V. $v_{OUT,left}$ is clamped to 0 V by the lower diode, so there is no input voltage at the junction of R_1 and R_2.

Then, the output voltage is

$$v_{OUT} = -\frac{100\text{ k}\Omega}{R_3} v_{IN}$$

Because v_{IN} is negative, v_{OUT} is positive.

The DC meter indicates the RMS value of a sinusoid, which is related to the average by

$$v_{RMS} = \frac{\pi}{2\sqrt{2}} v_{AVG}$$

With a gain of $1 \times |v_{IN}| = v_{OUT}$, the meter would read the average value, so a gain of $\pi/2\sqrt{2} = 1.111$ is required. Then,

$$\frac{100\text{ k}\Omega}{R_3} = \frac{\pi}{2\sqrt{2}}$$

$$\boxed{R_3 = 90\text{ k}\Omega}$$

$$\frac{R_1}{R_2} - \frac{100\text{ k}\Omega}{R_3} = \frac{\pi}{2\sqrt{2}}$$

$$\frac{R_1}{R_2} = \frac{\pi}{\sqrt{2}}$$

Choose $\boxed{R_1 = 100\text{ k}\Omega.}$ Then,

$$\boxed{R_2 = 45\text{ k}\Omega}$$

Finally, consider the maximum input voltage. The maximum negative output voltage of -12 V at the output of the left amplifier occurs with

$$v_{IN} = -\left(\frac{100\text{ k}\Omega}{R_1}\right)(-12\text{ V}) = +12\text{ V}$$

Also, an input of -12 V will saturate the right-hand amplifier, so the maximum input magnitude is

$$\left| v_{\text{IN,max}} \right| = \frac{12 \text{ V}}{1.111} = 10.8 \text{ V}$$

This would be the peak value of the sinusoid, so its maximum RMS voltage will be

$$V_{\text{RMS,max}} = \frac{10.8 \text{ V}}{\sqrt{2}} = \boxed{7.64 \text{ V}}$$

Timed 2

With at least one input low, the collector is high, and no current flows in the collector circuit.

One or more low inputs of 0.2 V, when combined with a diode drop of 0.7 V, results in a current through the left resistor of

$$i = \frac{4 \text{ V} - 0.07 \text{ V} - 0.2 \text{ V}}{2 \text{ k}\Omega} = 1.55 \text{ mA}$$

The power for high output is

$$(4 \text{ V})(1.55 \text{ mA}) = 6.2 \text{ mW}$$

With both inputs high,

$$i_B = \frac{4 \text{ V} - (3)(0.7 \text{ V})}{2 \text{ k}\Omega} = 0.95 \text{ mA}$$

This saturates the transistor, so

$$i_C = \frac{4 \text{ V} - 0.2 \text{ V}}{2 \text{ k}\Omega} = 1.9 \text{ mA}$$

The power supply provides

$$(4 \text{ V})(1.9 \text{ mA} + 0.95 \text{ mA}) = 11.4 \text{ mW}$$

However, the transistor must absorb power from the loads, which must be calculated from a current of five times the input current for the high output. This excess collector current is

$$(5)(1.55 \text{ mA}) = 7.75 \text{ mA}$$

Assume the transistor remains saturated, then the excess transistor power can be as high as

$$P_{\text{excess}} = (7.75 \text{ mA})(0.2 \text{ V}) = 1.55 \text{ mW}$$

The maximum total power is

$$P_{\text{total}} = 1.55 \text{ mW} + 11.4 \text{ mW} = \boxed{12.95 \text{ mW}}$$

Timed 3

On each half-cycle, the breakdown diode triggers the TRIAC when its voltage reaches ± 4 V ($+$ for the positive half-cycle and $-$ for negative). For the remainder of the half-cycle, the breakdown diode (BDD) will remain on, so the capacitor is entirely discharged.

At the beginning of each half-cycle, the capacitor begins to charge toward the supply voltage. When it reaches ± 4 V, it fires the TRIAC.

Taking a positive half-cycle, for example,

$$v_S = iR + v_C$$
$$i = C\frac{dv_C}{dt}$$
$$RC = 10^5 \times 10^{-8} \text{ s}$$
$$10^{-3}\frac{dv_C}{dt} + v_C = (220\sqrt{2} \text{ V}) \sin 377t$$

This will have the solution

$$v_C = Ae^{-1000t} + B\sin(377t + \phi)$$

The sinusoidal part is the steady-state solution and is found by phasor analysis.

$$\frac{d}{dt} \to j377$$
$$V_c(j377 + 1) = V\underline{/0°}$$
$$V_c = \frac{V}{\sqrt{1 + (377)^2}}\underline{/-\tan^{-1}3.77}$$
$$V = 220\sqrt{2} \text{ V}$$
$$V_c = 291.1\underline{/-20.7°} \text{ V}$$

Since the reference was sine,

$$v_C(t) = Ae^{-1000t} + (291.1 \text{ V})\sin(377t - 20.66°)$$

Since numerical computations are required, angles must be expressed in one unit system (i.e., either degrees or radians). The angle can be written as

$$(21{,}600t - 20.66)° \text{ or } (377t - 0.36) \text{ rad}$$

The latter is chosen.

At $t = 0$ s, $v_C = 0$ V, so

$$A = (-291.1 \text{ V})\sin(-0.36) = 102.7 \text{ V}$$
$$v_C(t) = (102.7 \text{ V})e^{-1000t} + (291.1 \text{ V})\sin(\omega t - 0.36)$$

Since 0.36 rad $\approx \dfrac{1}{9}$ of a half cycle,

$$e^{\left(-\frac{1000}{377}\right)(0.36)} = 0.38$$

At $\omega t = 0.36$ rad, $v_C \approx (0.39)(102 \text{ V})$, so $v_C = 4$ V near $\omega t \approx 0.36/4$ or about 0.25 ms.

Checking at $t_1 = 0.25$ ms,

$$v_C = 3.53 \text{ V}$$

At $t_2 = 0.3$ ms,
$$v_C = 4.937 \text{ V}$$

Interpolating,

$$\frac{t_3 - t_1}{t_2 - t_1} = \frac{4 \text{ V} - v_{C1}}{v_{C2} - v_{C1}}$$

$$t_3 = 0.2667 \text{ ms}$$

$$v_{C3} = 3.976 \text{ V}$$

Interpolating,

$$\frac{t_4 - 0.2667 \text{ ms}}{2.667 \text{ ms} - 0.25 \text{ ms}} = \frac{4 \text{ ms} - 3.976 \text{ ms}}{3.976 \text{ ms} - 3.53 \text{ ms}}$$

(a) $t_4 = 0.2676$ ms
$$v_{C4} = 4.0004 \text{ V}$$

The firing angle is

$$377t_4 = 0.1009 \text{ rad} = \boxed{5.78^\circ}$$

(b) $$q = Cv = 4 \times 10^{-8} \text{ C}$$
$$(I_{GT})(50 \text{ }\mu s) = Q_{GT}$$
$$(50 \times 10^{-6})I_{GT} \leq 4 \times 10^{-8} \text{ C}$$

$$I_{GT} \leq \boxed{800 \text{ }\mu A}$$

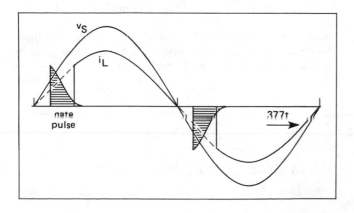

Timed 4

The negative resistance region is the straight line between $(0.4, 0.1)$ and $(0.1, 0.4)$ with i_D in mA.

$$\frac{v_D - 0.4 \text{ V}}{i_D - 0.1 \text{ mA}} = \frac{0.1 \text{ V} - 0.4 \text{ V}}{0.4 \text{ mA} - 0.1 \text{ mA}} = -1$$
$$v_D = 0.5 \text{ V} - i_D \quad (i_D \text{ in mA})$$

The DC load-line equation is

$$v_D = 0.4 \text{ V} - 0.6 i_D$$

They intersect at

$$i_D = 0.25 \text{ mA}$$
$$v_D = 0.25 \text{ V}$$

This is in the negative resistance region, so the circuit will oscillate.

When operation reaches the end of a positive resistance region, it will jump to the other branch at constant current because the inductor holds the current.

In the left branch, the operation begins with $i_D = 0.1$ mA and ends with $i_D = 0.4$ mA. During left branch operation, the diode acts as a resistor.

$$r_{d1} = \frac{0.1 \text{ V}}{0.4 \text{ mA}} = 0.25 \text{ k}\Omega$$

Then Kirchhoff's voltage equation is

$$0.4 \text{ V} = (0.25 \text{ k}\Omega + 0.6 \text{ k}\Omega)i + (1.5 \text{ H})\frac{di}{dt} \text{ (for } i \text{ in A)}$$

$$\left(\frac{1 \text{ s}}{567}\right)\left(\frac{di_D}{dt}\right) + i_D = 0.4706 \times 10^{-3} \text{ A}$$

$$= 0.4706 \text{ mA}$$

Then (i_D in mA),

$$i_D = 0.4706 \text{ mA} + (0.1 \text{ mA} - 0.4706 \text{ mA})e^{-567t}$$

Branch 1 operation is complete at $i_D = 0.4$ mA.

$$t_1 = \frac{1}{567}\ln\left(\frac{0.4706 \text{ mA} - 0.1 \text{ mA}}{0.4706 \text{ mA} - 0.4 \text{ mA}}\right)$$

$$= 2.92 \text{ ms}$$

The right branch operation begins at $i_D = 0.4$ mA. The branch equation is

$$\text{points } (v_D, i_D) = (0.4, 0.1) \text{ and } (0.8, 0.4)$$

$$\frac{v_D - 0.4 \text{ V}}{i_D - 0.1 \text{ mA}} = \frac{0.8 \text{ V} - 0.4 \text{ V}}{0.4 \text{ mA} - 0.1 \text{ mA}} = \frac{4}{3} \text{ k}\Omega$$

$$v_D = 0.4 \text{ V} + \left(\frac{4}{3} \text{ k}\Omega\right)i_D - \frac{0.4}{3} \text{ V}$$

$$= 0.2667 \text{ V} + 1.333 i_D \text{ (mA)}$$

Then the Kirchhoff voltage law equation is

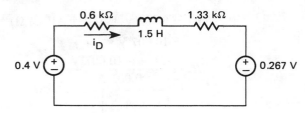

$$0.4 \text{ V} - 0.2667 \text{ V} = (1.93 \text{ k}\Omega)i_D + 1.5\frac{di_D}{dt}$$

$$\left(\frac{1 \text{ s}}{1289}\right)\left(\frac{di_D}{dt}\right) + i_D = 0.069 \text{ mA}$$

This is solved to give

$$i_D = 0.069 \text{ mA} + (0.4 \text{ mA} - 0.069 \text{ mA})e^{-1289t'}$$

(beginning at $t' = 0$ s, ending when $i_D = 0.1$ mA)

$$t' = \left(\frac{1 \text{ s}}{1289}\right)\ln\left(\frac{0.4 \text{ mA} - 0.069 \text{ mA}}{0.1 \text{ mA} - 0.069 \text{ mA}}\right) = 1.84 \text{ ms}$$

(a) $T = t_1 + t' = \boxed{4.78 \text{ ms}}$

(b)

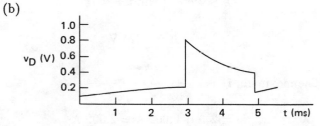

(c)

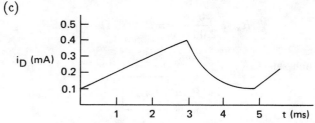

Timed 5

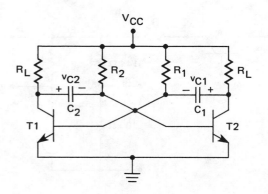

Beginning with T1 off and T2 on, v_{C2} charges toward $V_{CC} - 0.7$ V, v_{C1} charges toward $-(V_{CC} - 0.2 \text{ V})$.

When v_{C1} charges to a certain level, it will turn T1 on, which requires that $v_{B1} = 0.6 \text{ V} = v_{CE2} - v_{C1}$ or

$$v_{C1} = v_{CE} - 0.6 \text{ V} = 0.2 \text{ V} - 0.6 \text{ V} = -0.4 \text{ V}$$

When T1 turns on, $v_{CE1} \rightarrow 0.2$ V, so $v_{B2} = 0.2 \text{ V} - v_{C2}$, which turns T2 off.

Then the roles of the two transistors are reversed from the starting point. (Note: It is assumed transistors become active when the base-emitter voltage is 0.6 V, but are 0.7 V when fully on.)

Taking $t = 0$ s as the time when T2 turned on (which quickly turned T1 off),

$$v_{C2} = (V_{CC} - 0.7 \text{ V}) + (v_{C20} - V_{CC} + 0.7 \text{ V})e^{\frac{-t}{R_L C_2}}$$

$$v_{C1} = (V_{CC} - 0.2 \text{ V}) + (v_{C10} + V_{CC} - 0.2 \text{ V})e^{\frac{-t}{R_1 C_1}}$$

From the given waveform taken from a transistor collector, the off-transistor will quickly reach V_{CC}, so that $v_{C10} = V_{CC} - 0.7$ V.

T1 turns on at t_a, when $v_{C1} = -0.4$ V.

$$-0.4 \text{ V} = -(V_{CC} - 0.2 \text{ V}) + (2V_{CC} - 0.9 \text{ V})e^{\frac{-t_a}{R_1 C_1}}$$

$$\frac{t_a}{R_1 C_1} = \ln\left(\frac{2V_{CC} - 0.9 \text{ V}}{V_{CC} - 0.6 \text{ V}}\right)$$

$$= \ln 2 + \ln\left(\frac{V_{CC} - 0.45 \text{ V}}{V_{CC} - 0.6 \text{ V}}\right)$$

For $V_{CC} = 5$ V,

$$\ln\left(\frac{V_{CC} - 0.45 \text{ V}}{V_{CC} - 0.6 \text{ V}}\right) = 0.033$$

For $V_{CC} = 15$ V,

$$\ln\left(\frac{V_{CC} - 0.45 \text{ V}}{V_{CC} - 0.6 \text{ V}}\right) = 0.010$$

$\ln 2 = 0.693$, so use a value of

$$\ln\left(\frac{V_{CC} - 0.45 \text{ V}}{V_{CC} - 0.6 \text{ V}}\right) \approx 0.02$$

$$V_{CC} = \boxed{8 \text{ V}}$$

$$\frac{t_a}{R_1 C_1} = 0.71$$

A similar development for the period when T1 is on and T2 is off yields

$$\frac{t_b}{R_2 C_2} = 0.71$$

Arbitrarily taking $t_a = 248$ μs and $t_b = 94$ μs,

$$R_1 C_1 = 349.3 \times 10^{-6} \text{ s}$$
$$R_2 C_2 = 132.4 \times 10^{-6} \text{ s}$$
$$C_1 = C_2 = \boxed{0.01 \ \mu\text{F}}$$
$$R_1 = \boxed{34.9 \text{ k}\Omega \rightarrow 35 \text{ k}\Omega}$$
$$R_2 = \boxed{13.2 \text{ k}\Omega}$$
$$R_L = \boxed{1 \text{ k}\Omega}$$

Timed 6

If the opamp came on with zero or negative output, the transistor would never turn on. One way to overcome this problem is to connect a starting resistor from v_{UN} to the top of the zener diode, which is connected to the positive terminal. This resistor should be large compared with R_r, but small compared with R_1.

Another method would be to put a resistor from the collector to the emitter of the transistor, which would also provide more voltage to the opamp positive terminal than the negative terminal, provided a current less than I_{ZK} was then provided to the zener diode, so that

$$R_{\text{ce}} + R_r > \frac{v_{\text{UN,max}}}{I_{\text{ZK}}}$$

This second technique is preferred, as it does not interfere with the regulator design. For that reason it is selected.

The maximum zener diode current is

$$\sim \frac{500 \text{ mW}}{10 \text{ V}} = 50 \text{ mA}$$

Because it was not specified, it is assumed the current corresponding with $v_D = 10$ V is $I_{\text{ZK}}(0.25 \text{ mA})$.

$$v_D = 10 \text{ V} = V_{\text{ZO}} + R_z(0.25 \text{ mA})$$
$$V_{\text{ZO}} = 10 \text{ V} - (0.25 \times 10^{-3} \text{ A})(8.5 \ \Omega)$$
$$= 9.998 \text{ V}$$

Then for an output voltage of 24 V, with $i_Z = 1.0$ mA,

$$v_Z = 9.998 \text{ V} + (0.001 \text{ A})(8.5 \ \Omega)$$
$$= 10.007 \text{ V}$$
$$R_r = \frac{24 \text{ V} - 10.007 \text{ V}}{0.001 \text{ A}}$$
$$= \boxed{13,993 \ \Omega}$$
$$\left(\frac{R_2}{R_1 + R_2}\right)(24 \text{ V}) = 10 \text{ V}$$
$$14R_2 = 10R_1$$
$$R_2 = \boxed{10 \text{ k}\Omega}$$
$$R_1 = \boxed{14 \text{ k}\Omega}$$

The current through R_1 and R_2 is 1 mA.

To select R_s, the minimum drop, v_{CE}, to ensure that the transistor operates in its linear zone is 1 V. At maximum load current and minimum v_{UN}, for $v_{\text{REG}} = 24$ V,

$$V_E \leq 29 \text{ V} \geq v_{\text{REG}} + R_s i_S$$
$$R_s \leq \frac{29 \text{ V} - 24 \text{ V}}{i_S}$$

The maximum i_S is

$$i_S = 2 \text{ A} + 0.002 \text{ A} = 2.002 \text{ A}$$
$$R_s \leq \frac{5 \text{ V}}{2.002 \text{ A}} = 2.4975 \ \Omega$$

Then select

$$R_s = \boxed{2.4 \ \Omega}$$

To determine voltage regulation, it is necessary to include the opamp gain.

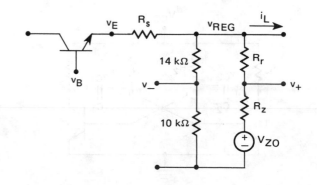

$$v_B = A(v_+ - v_-)$$

$$v_+ = \frac{v_{REG} r_Z + V_{ZO} R_r}{R_r + r_Z}$$

$$= \left(\frac{13{,}993\ \Omega}{14{,}001\ \Omega}\right)(9.998\ \mathrm{V}) + \frac{8.5\ \Omega}{14{,}001\ \Omega} v_{REG}$$

$$v_- = \frac{10\ \Omega}{24\ \Omega} v_{REG}$$

$$v_B = A(9.992\ \mathrm{V} - 0.4161\ v_{REG})$$

$$v_E = v_B - 0.7\ \mathrm{V} = v_{REG} + i_S R_s$$

$$i_S = i_L + \frac{v_{REG}}{24\ \mathrm{k}\Omega} + \frac{v_{REG} - V_{ZO}}{14{,}001\ \Omega}$$

$$v_B = 0.7\ \mathrm{V} + (2.4\ \Omega) i_L + (2.4\ \Omega)\frac{v_{REG}}{24\ \mathrm{k}\Omega}$$

$$+ (2.4\ \Omega)\frac{v_{REG} - v_{ZO}}{14{,}001\ \Omega} + v_{REG}$$

$$= (1.0003) v_{REG} + (2.4\ \Omega) i_L + 0.698\ \mathrm{V}$$

Taking $A = 10^5$,

$$9.992\ \mathrm{V} - 0.4161 v_{REG} = (1.0003 \times 10^{-5}) v_{REG}$$
$$+ (2.4 \times 10^{-5}) i_L$$
$$+ 0.698 \times 10^{-5}\ \mathrm{V}$$

$$v_{REG} = 24.0134 - 0.00023 i_L$$

The regulation is due to i_L, so

$$\mathrm{regulation} = \left[\frac{(2\ \mathrm{A})(0.00023\ \Omega)}{24\ \mathrm{V}}\right](100\%) = \boxed{0.002\%}$$

Timed 7

The zener diode has a maximum current of

$$\frac{500\ \mathrm{mW}}{10\ \mathrm{V}} = 50\ \mathrm{mA}$$

It is assumed the 10 V diode voltage is obtained with $I_{ZK}(0.25\ \mathrm{mA})$. At $i_Z = 0.25\ \mathrm{mA}$,

$$v_Z = 10\ \mathrm{V}$$

Because the load voltage should be 20 V, (i.e., $R_1 = R_2$), and the maximum load current 5 A, the current through R_r and $R_1 - R_2$ will be negligible except when $i_L = 0$.

This should be considered to be a constant.

To maintain regulation, the transistor must have a minimum $v_{CE} \geq 1$ V. At the highest load current,

$$v_E = 20\ \mathrm{V} + (2\ \Omega)(5\ \mathrm{A}) = 30\ \mathrm{V}$$

$$v_{C,\mathrm{min}} = 31\ \mathrm{V}$$

The capacitor charges to $48\ \mathrm{V} - 0.7\ \mathrm{V}$ while the rectifier conducts and then discharges.

$$C\frac{dv_C}{dt} + i_L = 0$$

$$\frac{dv_C}{dt} = -\frac{1}{C}(5.0\ \mathrm{A})\ \text{(in the worst case)}$$

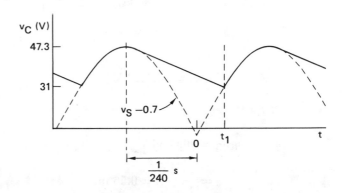

$$v_S = 48 \sin 377 t$$

$$47.3\ \mathrm{V} - \left(\frac{5.0\ \mathrm{A}}{C}\right)\left(t_1 + \frac{1}{240}\ \mathrm{s}\right) = 31\ \mathrm{V}$$

$$48 \sin 377 t_1 = 31\ \mathrm{V} + 0.7\ \mathrm{V}$$

From this,

$$t_1 = 1.91\ \mathrm{ms}$$

$$C = \boxed{0.00186\ \mathrm{F}}$$

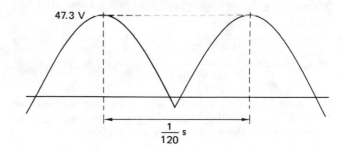

For no load, the drain on the capacitor is simply the zener current and the current through R_1 and R_2.

Assuming the diode conducts a negligible time,

$$\Delta v_C = \left(\frac{2}{240}\ \mathrm{s}\right)\left(\frac{i_Z + i_{R1}}{C}\right)$$

This is the no-load peak-to-peak ripple of v_C. However, the output ripple is needed.

First the regulator circuit must be designed. Set

$$i_Z = 0.25\ \mathrm{mA\ at}\ v_C = 31\ \mathrm{V}$$

This is the condition with $i_L = 5$ A and $v_{REG} = 20$ V.

$$v_Z = 10 \text{ V} = V_{ZO} + (0.25 \times 10^{-3} \text{ A})(8.5 \text{ } \Omega)$$

$$V_{ZO} = 9.998 \text{ V}$$

$$R_s = \frac{31 \text{ V} - 10 \text{ V}}{0.25 \text{ mA}} = 84 \text{ k}\Omega$$

$$V_{REG} = (2)\left[\frac{(9.998 \text{ V})(84 \text{ k}\Omega) + v_C(8.5 \text{ } \Omega)}{84 \text{ k}\Omega}\right]$$

At $v_C = 31$ V,

$$V_{REG} = 20.0023 \text{ V}$$

At $v_C = 47.3$ V,

$$v_{REG} = 20.0056 \text{ V}$$

$$i_Z = \frac{47.3 \text{ V}}{84 \text{ k}\Omega} = 0.56 \text{ mA}$$

(Full-load ripple is 3.3 mV peak to peak.)

With no load, the capacitor is discharged by i_Z and the current through R_1 and R_2, which is called i_{R1}. Assuming that i_{R1} is 1 mA, the discharging current will be about 0.56 mA + 1 mA = 1.56 mA.

Because the voltage drops very little in this no-load condition, the necessary charging time is a negligible part of the cycle, and the discharging time can be assigned the full half-cycle time (1/120 s). The drop in capacitance voltage that occurs under no load is approximated by

$$\Delta v_C = \frac{(1.56 \text{ mA})\left(\frac{1}{120} \text{ s}\right)}{0.00186 \text{ F}} = 7.0 \text{ mV}$$

v_C drops from 47.3 V to 47.293 V and then is recharged to 47.3 V each half cycle of the source voltage. At the lower voltage, the output is then calculated.

$$v_{REG} = \frac{(9.998 \text{ V})(84 \text{ k}\Omega) + (47.293 \text{ V})(8.5 \text{ } \Omega)}{84 \text{ k}\Omega}$$

$$= 20.0056 \text{ V}$$

There is no change of output voltage within the accuracy of calculations made here.

$$\text{no-load ripple} = \boxed{0 \text{ V}}$$

Carrying more significant figures, a ripple of about 1 μV will occur, which stretches the modeling of the circuit beyond credibility.

Timed 8

Assume T1 is off and T2 is on, so $v_{B2} = 0.7$ V, $v_{CE2} = 0.2$ V.

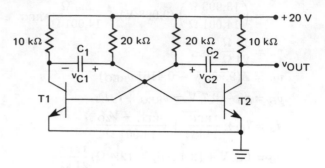

C_1 is charging toward $-(20 \text{ V} - 0.7 \text{ V}) = -19.3$ V, with a time constant of $10^4 C = 1$ ms.

$$v_{C1} = -19.3 \text{ V} + (v_A + 19.3 \text{ V})e^{-1000t}$$

v_A is the initial voltage value of v_{C1}. The right-hand capacitor, C_2, is charging toward $20 \text{ V} - 0.2 \text{ V} = 19.8$ V with a time constant of 2 ms.

$$v_{C2} = 19.8 \text{ V} + (v_B - 19.8 \text{ V})e^{-500t}$$

v_B is the initial voltage value of v_{C2}.

When v_{C2} reaches 0.4 V, T1 will turn on, which will turn T2 off. At this time, the roles of the capacitors are reversed, so

$$v_{C2} = 0.4 \text{ V} = v_A$$
$$v_A = 19.8 \text{ V} + (v_B - 19.8 \text{ V})e^{-500t_1}$$
$$v_{C1} = v_B$$
$$= -19.3 \text{ V} + (0.4 \text{ V} + 19.3 \text{ V})e^{-1000t_1}$$
$$e^{-1000t_1} = (e^{-500t_1})^2$$

From this,

$$\frac{v_B - 19.8 \text{ V}}{-19.4 \text{ V}} = e^{500t}$$

$$\frac{v_B + 19.3 \text{ V}}{19.7 \text{ V}} = e^{-1000t}$$

$$v_B = (19.7 \text{ V})\left(\frac{19.4 \text{ V}}{19.8 \text{ V} - v_B}\right)^2 - 19.3 \text{ V}$$

This is iterated.

$$v_B = -10 \text{ V}$$
$$= -11 \text{ V}, -11.5 \text{ V}, -12 \text{ V}, -11.8 \text{ V}, -11.95 \text{ V},$$
$$- 11.94 \text{ V}, -11.94 \text{ V}$$
$$= -11.94 \text{ V}$$

Then,

$$500t_1 = \ln\left(\frac{19.8\text{ V} + 11.94\text{ V}}{19.4\text{ V}}\right)\text{s}$$

$$t_1 = 0.985\text{ ms}$$

$$v_{\text{OUT}} = v_{CE2} = 0.2\text{ V for } 0 \le t < t_1$$

$$= 0.7\text{ V} - v_{C2} \text{ for } t_1 \le t < 2t_1$$

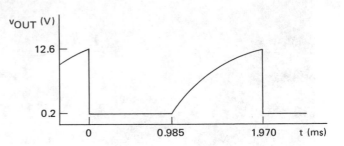

For $t_1 \le t < 2t_1$,

$$v_{\text{OUT}} = 0.7\text{ V} + 19.3\text{ V} - (0.4\text{ V} + 19.3\text{ V})e^{-1000(t-t_1)}$$

$$= 20\text{ V} - (19.7\text{ V})e^{-1000(t-t_1)}$$

$$f - \frac{1000}{1.97\text{ s}} = \boxed{508\text{ Hz}}$$

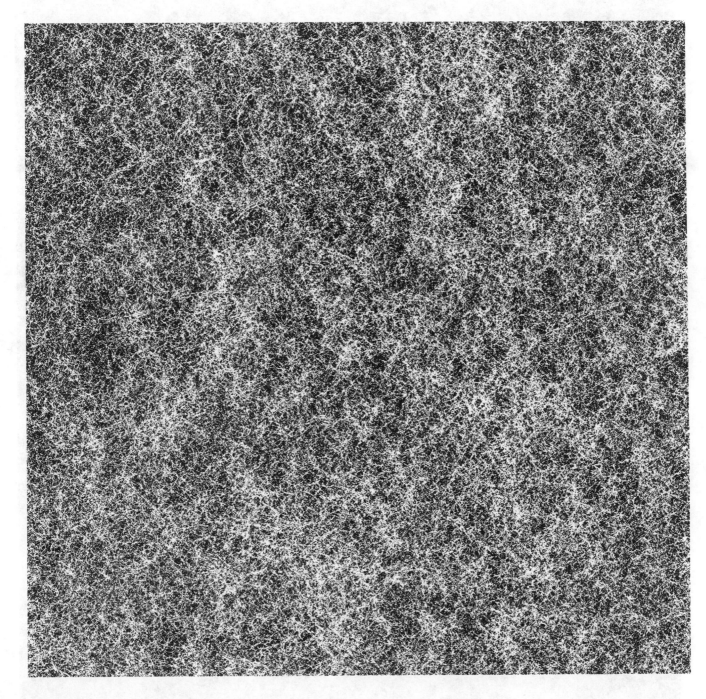

PROFESSIONAL PUBLICATIONS, INC.   ●   Belmont, CA

DIGITAL LOGIC

Warmup 1

$$D = \overline{(A \cdot B) \cdot (B + C)}$$

A B C	A·B	B+C	$\overline{D}$	D
0 0 0	0	0	0	1
0 0 1	0	1	0	1
0 1 0	0	1	0	1
0 1 1	0	1	0	1
1 0 0	0	0	0	1
1 0 1	0	1	0	1
1 1 0	1	1	1	0
1 1 1	1	1	1	0

Warmup 2

SOP:

$$D = \boxed{\begin{array}{l} \overline{A}\cdot\overline{B}\cdot\overline{C} + \overline{A}\cdot\overline{B}\cdot C + \overline{A}\cdot B\cdot\overline{C} \\ + \overline{A}\cdot B\cdot C + A\cdot\overline{B}\cdot\overline{C} + A\cdot\overline{B}\cdot C \end{array}}$$

POS:

$$\overline{D} = A\cdot B\cdot\overline{C} + A\cdot B\cdot C$$

$$D = \overline{A\cdot B\cdot\overline{C} + A\cdot B\cdot C}$$

$$= \boxed{(\overline{A} + \overline{B}C)\cdot(\overline{A} + \overline{B} + \overline{C})}$$

Warmup 3

$$\overline{D} = A\cdot B(\overline{C} + C) = A\cdot B$$

$$D = \boxed{\overline{A\cdot B} \quad \text{NAND}}$$

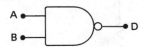

Warmup 4

Karnaugh maps:

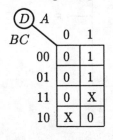

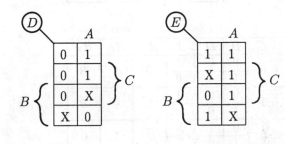

Veitch diagrams:

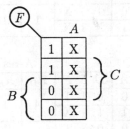

Warmup 5

$$D = A\cdot\overline{B}$$
$$\overline{E} = \overline{A}\cdot C$$
$$E = A + \overline{C}$$
$$F = \overline{B}$$

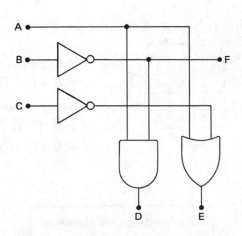

PROFESSIONAL PUBLICATIONS, INC. ● Belmont, CA

Warmup 6

C-residues

$A\ B$	C	$D\ E\ F$	R_D	R_E	R_F
0 0	0	0 1 1	0	1	1
	1	0 X 1			
0 1	0	X 1 0	0	$\overline{C}$	0
	1	0 0 0			
1 0	0	1 1 X	1	1	X
	1	1 1 X			
1 1	0	0 X X	0	1	X
	1	X 1 X			

B-residues

$A\ C$	B	$D\ E\ F$	R_D	R_E	R_F
0 0	0	0 1 1	0	1	$\overline{B}$
	1	X 1 0			
0 1	0	0 X 1	0	0	$\overline{B}$
	1	0 0 0			
1 0	0	1 1 X	$\overline{B}$	1	0
	1	0 X X			
1 1	0	1 1 X	1	1	0
	1	X 1 X			

A-residues

$B\ C$	A	$D\ E\ F$	R_D	R_E	R_F
0 0	0	0 1 1	A	1	1
	1	1 1 X			
0 1	0	0 X 1	A	1	1
	1	1 1 X			
1 0	0	X 1 0	0	1	0
	1	0 X X			
1 1	0	0 0 0	0	A	0
	1	X 1 X			

Warmup 7

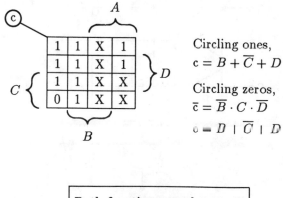

Circling ones,
$$c = B + \overline{C} + D$$

Circling zeros,
$$\overline{c} = \overline{B} \cdot C \cdot \overline{D}$$
$$c = D + \overline{C} + D$$

Both functions are the same.

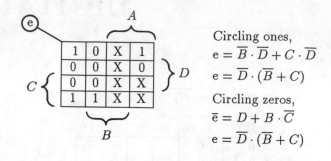

Circling ones,
$$e = \overline{B} \cdot \overline{D} + C \cdot \overline{D}$$
$$e = \overline{D} \cdot (\overline{B} + C)$$

Circling zeros,
$$\overline{e} = D + B \cdot \overline{C}$$
$$e = \overline{D} \cdot (\overline{B} + C)$$

Again, both functions are the same.

Warmup 8

ABC	D	F	res
0 0 0	0	1	$\overline{D}$
	1	0	
0 0 1	0	0	0
	1	0	
0 1 0	0	1	1
	1	1	
0 1 1	0	1	$\overline{D}$
	1	0	
1 0 0	0	1	1
	1	1	
1 0 1	0	X	0
	1	X	
1 1 0	0	X	0
	1	X	
1 1 1	0	X	0
	1	X	

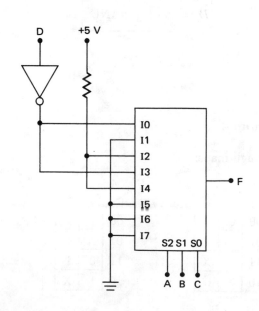

Warmup 9

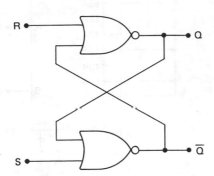

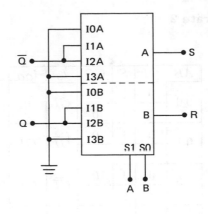

With R low and S high for some time, Q is high and $\overline{Q}$ is low. If R goes high while S remains high, Q will go low.

The lower gate output will also be low because it has S high. Then Q and $\overline{Q}$ are both low, which is not permitted (by definition), so it is not permitted to have both inputs high.

> It makes no difference that one gate is faster than the other.

Warmup 10

S-R transition table:

$Q \rightarrow Q^+$		S	R
0	0	0	X
0	1	1	0
1	1	X	0
1	0	0	1

Because both Q and Q^+ are available, the most convenient design uses a dual 4:1 multiplexer with Q residues.

A	B	Q	Q^+	S	R	I_S	I_R
0	0	0	0	0	X	0	0
		1	1	X	0		
0	1	0	1	1	0	$\overline{Q}$	Q
		1	0	0	1		
1	0	0	1	1	0	$\overline{Q}$	Q
		1	0	0	1		
1	1	0	0	0	X	0	0
		1	1	X	0		

Concentrate 1

$$R_1 = Q_2 \cdot \overline{Q}_3$$
$$S_1 = \overline{Q}_2 \cdot Q_3$$
$$K_2 = Q_1 + Q_3$$
$$J_2 = Q_1 + \overline{Q}_3$$
$$D_3 = Q_2 \oplus Q_3$$

Q_1	Q_2	Q_3	R_1	S_1	K_2	J_2	D_3	Q_1^+	Q_2^+	Q_3^+
0	0	0	0	0	0	1	0	0	1	0
0	0	1	0	1	1	0	1	1	0	1
0	1	0	1	0	0	1	1	0	1	1
0	1	1	0	0	1	0	0	0	0	0
1	0	0	0	0	1	1	0	1	1	0
1	0	1	0	1	1	1	1	1	1	1
1	1	0	1	0	1	1	1	0	0	1
1	1	1	0	0	1	1	0	1	0	0

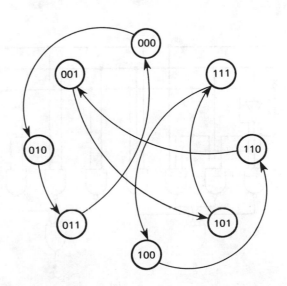

Concentrate 2

AB	CI	S	CO	I_S	I_{CO}
0 0	0	0	0	CI	0
	1	1	0		
0 1	0	1	0	$\overline{CI}$	CI
	1	0	1		
1 0	0	1	0	$\overline{CI}$	CI
	1	0	1		
1 1	0	0	1	CI	1
	1	1	1		

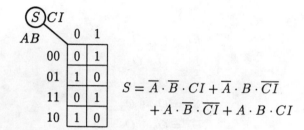

$$S = \overline{A} \cdot \overline{B} \cdot CI + \overline{A} \cdot B \cdot \overline{CI}$$
$$+ A \cdot \overline{B} \cdot \overline{CI} + A \cdot B \cdot CI$$

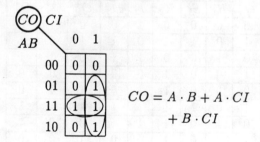

$$CO = A \cdot B + A \cdot CI$$
$$+ B \cdot CI$$

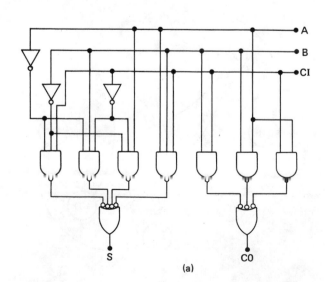

(a)

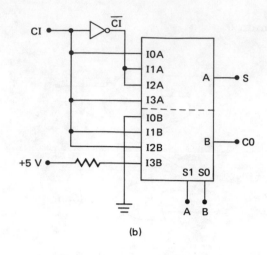

(b)

Concentrate 3

The next state output will be one of four inputs, which indicates the use of a 4:1 data selector.

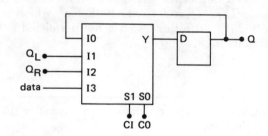

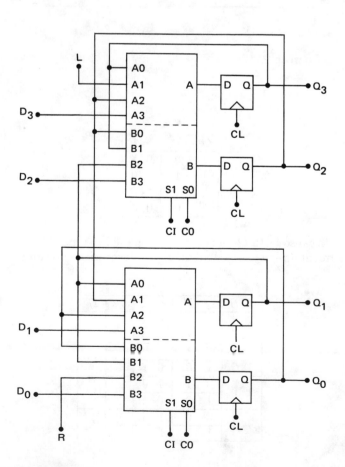

Concentrate 4

$$K_A = \overline{B}$$
$$K_B = A$$
$$K_C = B$$
$$J_A = \overline{B + C} = B \cdot \overline{C}$$
$$J_B = C$$
$$J_C = \overline{A + B} = \overline{A} \cdot \overline{B}$$

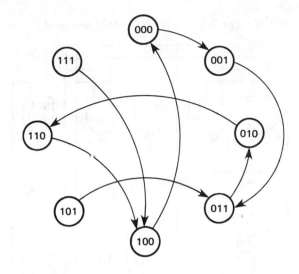

J	K	Q	Q^+
0	0	0	0
0	0	1	1
0	1	0	0
0	1	1	0
1	0	0	1
1	0	1	1
1	1	0	1
1	1	1	0

$$J\text{-}K: \quad Q^+ = Q \cdot \overline{K} + \overline{Q} \cdot J$$

$$A^+ = A \cdot B + \overline{A}B\overline{C}$$

$$= (110) \text{ OR } (111) \text{ OR } (010)$$

$$B^+ = \overline{A} \cdot B + \overline{B}C$$

$$= (010) \text{ OR } (011) \text{ OR } (001) \text{ OR } (101)$$

$$C^+ = \overline{B}C + \overline{A} \cdot \overline{B} \cdot \overline{C}$$

$$= (000) \text{ OR } (001) \text{ OR } (101)$$

A B C	$A^+B^+C^+$
0 0 0	0 0 1
0 0 1	0 1 1
0 1 0	1 1 0
0 1 1	0 1 0
1 0 0	0 0 0
1 0 1	0 1 1
1 1 0	1 0 0
1 1 1	1 0 0

Concentrate 5

From the timing diagram, the sequence triggered by the rising clock edge is

$$ABC$$
$$\rightarrow 000 \rightarrow 100 \rightarrow 110 \rightarrow 011 \rightarrow 001$$
$$111 \leftarrow 101 \leftarrow$$

The next state table is

A B C	$A^+B^+C^+$	$T_AT_BT_C$
0 0 0	1 0 0	1 0 0
0 0 1	1 0 1	1 0 0
0 1 0	- - -	- - -
0 1 1	0 0 1	0 1 0
1 0 0	1 1 0	0 1 0
1 0 1	1 1 1	0 1 0
1 1 0	0 1 1	1 0 1
1 1 1	0 0 0	1 1 1

From this,

$$T_A = \overline{A} \cdot \overline{B} + A \cdot B$$
$$T_B = A \cdot \overline{B} + BC$$
$$T_C = A \cdot B$$

This requires six 2-input NAND gates.

Something must be done about the 010 state since it will allow a startup problem of a hang-up state. This can be done by adding a term $B \cdot \overline{C}$ to T_C.

$$T_C = A \cdot B + B \cdot \overline{C}$$

A total of eight 2-input NAND gates are used.

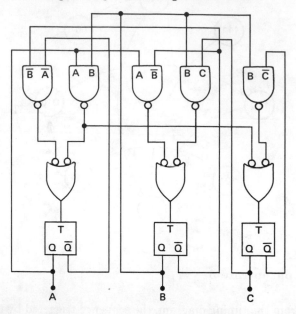

Concentrate 6

For convenicence, express the flip-flop transition table in levels.

Q	Q^+	R	S	K	J	D
$L \to L$		X	L	X	L	L
$L \to H$		L	H	X	H	H
$H \to H$		L	X	L	X	H
$H \to L$		H	L	H	X	L

M	N	Q	Q^+	R	S	K	J	D
L	L	L	H	L	H	X	H	H
L	L	H	H	L	X	L	X	H
L	H	L	L	X	L	X	L	L
L	H	H	L	H	L	H	X	L
H	L	L	L	X	L	X	L	L
H	L	H	L	H	L	H	X	L
H	H	L	H	L	H	X	H	H
H	H	H	H	L	X	L	X	H

$\widehat{R}$ MN

Q	00	01	11	10
0	L	X	L	X
1	L	H	L	H

Positive Logic:

$$R = M\overline{N} + \overline{M}N = M \oplus N$$

$\widehat{S}$ MN

Q	00	01	11	10
0	H	L	H	L
1	X	L	X	L

Positive Logic:

$$S = \overline{MN} + MN = M \odot N$$

$\widehat{K}$ MN

Q	00	01	11	10
0	X	X	X	X
1	L	H	L	H

Positive logic:

$$K = \overline{M}N + M\overline{N} = M \oplus N$$

$\widehat{J}$ MN

Q	00	01	11	10
0	H	L	H	L
1	X	X	X	X

Positive logic:

$$J = \overline{MN} + MN = M \odot N$$

$\widehat{D}$ MN

Q	00	01	11	10
0	H	L	H	L
1	H	L	H	L

$$D = \overline{MN} + MN = M \odot N$$

Then the D-flip-flop uses half the logic (only one input)

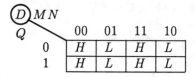

Positive logic:

MN	Q	Q^+
0 0	0	1
0 0	1	1
0 1	0	0
0 1	1	0
1 0	0	0
1 0	1	0
1 1	0	1
1 1	1	1

Concentrate 7

The outputs of the decoder are all high, except for the case when $\overline{G1}$ and $\overline{G2}$ are both low. In that case, the output with the binary address corresponding to $A3$, $A2$, $A1$, and $A0$ will go low, thus selecting a particular device.

The objective is to provide logic, using a minimum number of 2-input NAND gates, so that the decoder will be active when lines $A4$, $A5$, $A6$, and $A7$ are all high.

This can be done with two NAND gates as shown.

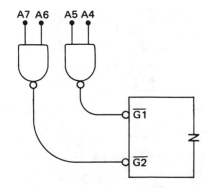

Concentrate 8

The sequence detection requires four states, but the specification that the output be available at the next clock after a sequence has been detected requires an additional flip-flop.

The most straightforward design uses eight states with the output being one of the state variables.

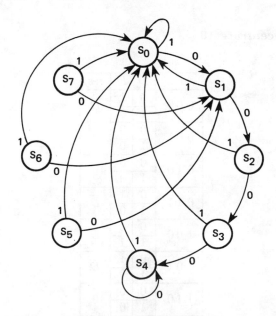

However, the design is more complex than necessary. Using four states with an additional flip-flop to provide

the output, the next period after a sequence is detected results in simpler logic.

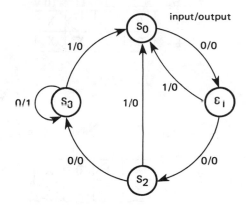

state assignment:

$$X = \text{input}$$

S	S^+ $X = 0$	S^+ $X = 1$
S_0	S_1	S_0
S_1	S_2	S_0
S_2	S_3	S_0
S_3	S_3	S_0

All states have S_0 as a next state, so that is eliminated from state assignments.

S_2 and S_3 both have S_3 as a next state and should be adjacent.

With S_2 and S_3 adjacent, only one can be adjacent to S_0. Since S_3 has a different output, it is selected to not be adjacent to S_0.

	0	1
0	S_0	S_1
1	S_2	S_3

Since J-K flip-flops use less logic, they are chosen.

$S : AB$	X	A^+B^+	$K_A J_A$	$K_B J_B$
$S_0: 0\,0$	0	0 1	X 0	X 1
	1	0 0	X 0	X 0
$S_1: 0\,1$	0	1 0	X 1	1 X
	1	0 0	X 0	1 X
$S_2: 1\,0$	0	1 1	0 X	X 1
	1	0 0	1 X	X 0
$S_3: 1\,1$	0	1 1	0 X	0 X
	1	0 0	1 X	1 X

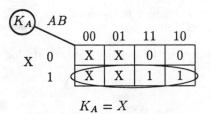

$$K_A = X$$

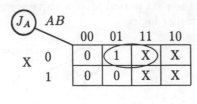

$$J_A = B\overline{X}$$

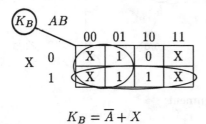

$$K_B = \overline{A} + X$$

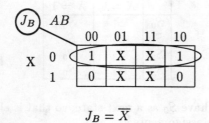

$$J_B = \overline{X}$$

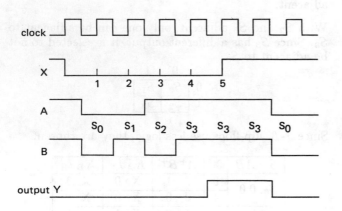

For J-K master-slave flip-flops, the condition at the rise of the clock is acted upon at the fall of the clock.

In the timing diagram shown, the rising clock before 1 saw a high input, so no matter what A and B were, A and B become low at the clock fall.

The instant marked 1 is the first zero, so S_1 occurs at the next clock fall.

After four zeros, the output rises, so its logic input is as follows.

$$J_Y = A \cdot B \cdot \overline{X}$$
$$K_Y = \overline{J}_Y$$

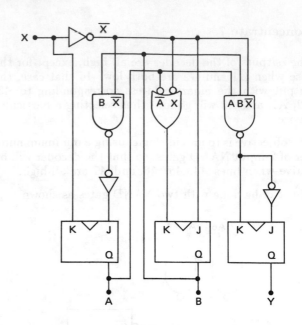

Concentrate 9

$$100_{10} = 64 + 32 + 4$$
$$= 01100100_2$$

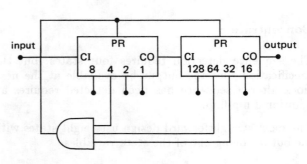

Concentrate 10

ABC	D	F	res
0 0 0	0	1	$\overline{D}$
	1	0	
0 0 1	0	0	0
	1	0	
0 1 0	0	0	0
	1	0	
0 1 1	0	1	$\overline{D}$
	1	0	
1 0 0	0	0	D
	1	1	
1 0 1	0	1	$\overline{D}$
	1	0	
1 1 0	0	0	0
	1	0	
1 1 1	0	0	D
	1	1	

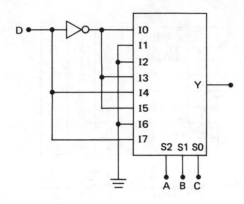

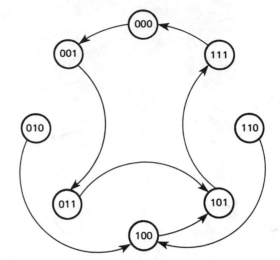

Timed 1

Timed 2

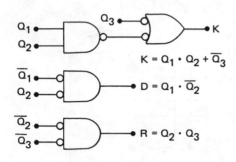

Q_2 will toggle when Q_1 falls from high to low (assuming outputs change on the falling edge of the clock).

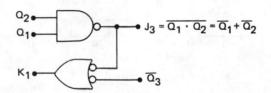

$$J = Q_2$$
$$K = Q_1 \cdot Q_2 + \overline{Q}_3$$
$$D = Q_1 \cdot \overline{Q}_2$$
$$S = \overline{Q}_2$$
$$R = Q_2 \cdot Q_3$$

$$K_1 = Q_1 \cdot Q_2 + Q_3$$
$$J_1 = Q_3$$
$$J_3 = \overline{Q}_1 + \overline{Q}_2$$
$$K_3 = 1$$

Q_3	Q_2	Q_1	K	J	D	R	S	Q_3^+	Q_2^+	Q_1^+
0	0	0	1	0	0	0	1	0	0	1
0	0	1	1	0	1	0	1	0	1	1
0	1	0	1	1	0	0	0	1	0	0
0	1	1	1	1	0	0	0	1	0	1
1	0	0	0	0	0	0	1	1	0	1
1	0	1	0	0	1	0	1	1	1	1
1	1	0	0	1	0	1	0	1	0	0
1	1	1	1	1	0	1	0	0	0	0

Q_1	Q_2	Q_3	J_1	K_1	$Q_1 \rightarrow Q_1^+$	J_3	Q_1^+	Q_2^+	Q_3^+
0	0	0	0	0	$0 \rightarrow 0$	1	0	0	1
0	0	1	1	1	$0 \rightarrow 1$	1	1	0	0
0	1	0	0	0	$0 \rightarrow 0$	1	0	1	1
0	1	1	1	1	$0 \rightarrow 1$	1	1	1	0
1	0	0	0	0	$1 \rightarrow 1$	1	1	0	1
1	0	1	1	1	$1 \rightarrow 0$	1	0	1	0
1	1	0	0	1	$1 \rightarrow 0$	0	0	0	0
1	1	1	1	1	$1 \rightarrow 0$	0	0	0	0

Q1 Q2 Q3

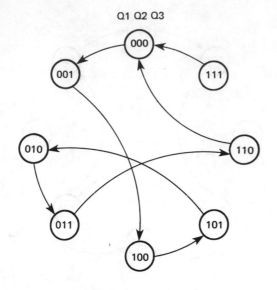

m	input			A	F	R
	D	C	B			
0	0	0	0	0	1	$\overline{A}$
1				1	0	
2	0	0	1	0	0	0
3				1	0	
4	0	1	0	0	0	A
5				1	1	
6	0	1	1	0	0	A
7				1	1	
8	1	0	0	0	0	0
9				1	0	
10	1	0	1	0	1	$\overline{A}$
11				1	0	
12	1	1	0	0	0	A
13				1	1	
14	1	1	1	0	1	1
15				1	1	

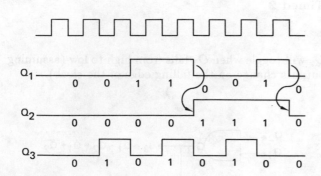

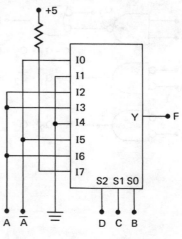

Timed 3

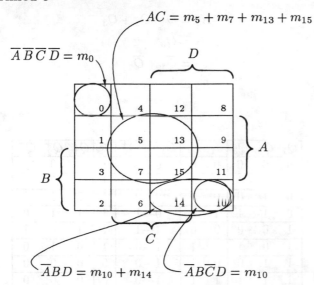

$$AC = m_5 + m_7 + m_{13} + m_{15}$$

$$\overline{A}\,\overline{B}\,\overline{C}\,\overline{D} = m_0$$

$$\overline{A}BD = m_{10} + m_{14}$$

$$\overline{A}B\overline{C}D = m_{10}$$

Timed 4

$$F = m_3 + m_6 + m_7 + m_{11} + m_{12} + m_{14} + m_{15}$$

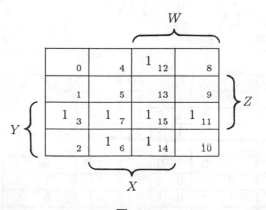

$$F = WX\overline{Z} + XY + YZ$$

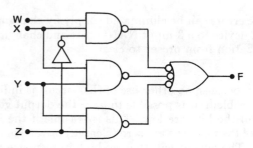

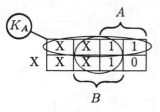

$$K_A = B + \overline{X}$$

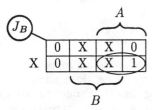

$$J_B = A \cdot X$$

Timed 5

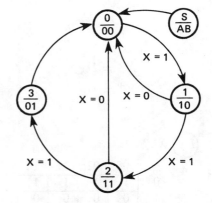

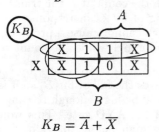

$$K_B = \overline{A} + \overline{X}$$

There are four states, so two flip-flops are required. The states are set equal to the outputs to minimize output logic.

	A	B	X	A^+	B^+	J_A	K_A	J_B	K_B
S_0	0	0	0	0	0	0	X	0	X
			1	1	0	1	X	0	X
S_1	0	1	0	0	0	0	X	X	1
			1	0	0	0	X	X	1
S_3	1	0	0	0	0	X	1	0	X
			1	1	1	X	0	1	X
S_2	1	1	0	0	0	X	1	X	1
			1	0	1	X	1	X	0

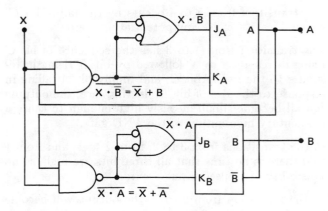

Timed 6

$$A_7 A_6 A_5 A_4 A_3 A_2 A_1 A_0 = 00101101$$

$$A_5 A_4 A_3 A_2 = 1011_2 = 11_{10}$$

Y_{11} is asserted low.

$$F = \overline{X}\,\overline{Y}_{11}\overline{A}_1 A_0$$

Desired function: 2 input gates

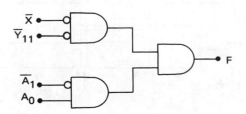

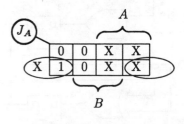

$$J_A = \overline{B} \cdot X$$

PROFESSIONAL PUBLICATIONS, INC. ● Belmont, CA

Implementation:

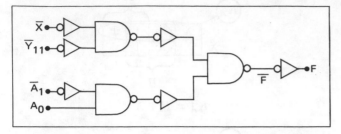

Timed 7

(a) An error can occur when more than one bit changes in response to the rising clock edge. Bit C changes at each clock rising, bit B changes in response to the rise of bit C, and bit A changes in response to bit B.

Beginning with the count at 7, the transition to 6 occurs with the falling of bit C in response to the rise of X, the input, which cannot cause a problem, as the output is supposed to be high while the count remains at 7.

The transition from 6 to 5 occurs by the rising of bit C, which initiates the fall of bit B, so it is possible that all three bits will be high enough to cause a momentary high output of the AND gate. This would be because bit B becomes high before bit A begins to go low in response to the rising of bit B.

The transition from 5 to 4 occurs by the fall of bit C, which does not cause any potential problem.

The transition from 4 to 3 has the sequence of bit C rising in response to X followed by bit B rising in response to the rise of bit C, and finally bit A falling in response to the rise of bit B. In this case, the outputs can all become simultaneously high enough to cause a momentary high output of the AND gate.

In the transitions from 3 to 2, from 2 to 1, and from 1 to 0 there is no time that all three bits are high, so no possibility of a false output occurs.

In the transition from 0 to 7, the output will become high as required.

(b) The errors, called *glitches*, are momentary high outputs that occur when all outputs are sufficiently high to cause the AND gate output to rise. These are shown schematically in the accompanying figure.

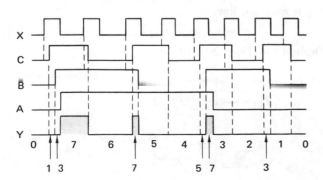

(c) The errors can be eliminated simply by changing the output device to a 3-input NAND gate and changing the initialization from preset to clear.

That is, because no other use of this circuit is indicated in the problem, it is possible to have the output go high when all the bits are low. This is feasible if the initial states of the flip-flops are zero (cleared) instead of preset to one. The output will then go high in response to the initialization and at every eighth input pulse. There is no possibility of a glitch in this mode.

Timed 8

$$X^+ = D_X$$
$$Y^+ = D_Y$$

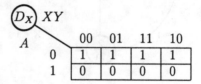

$$D_X = \overline{A}$$

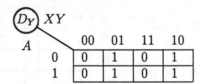

$$D_Y = \overline{X}Y + X\overline{Y} = X \oplus Y$$

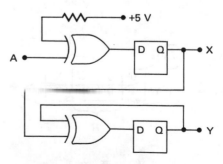

Timed 9

| | $R = 0$ |
| | $C = 0$ |

| | $R = 1$ |
| | $C = 0$ |

| | $R = 1$ |
| | $C = 1$ |

| | $R = 0$ |
| | $C = 1$ |

A positive sequence:

R	0 0 0 1 1 1 1 0 0 0 0
C	0 0 0 0 0 1 1 1 1 0 0

A negative sequence:

R	0 0 0 0 1 1 1 1 1 0 0 0 0
C	0 1 1 1 1 1 1 0 0 0 0 0 0

One solution assigns states to correspond to the four possible combinations of R and C.

$$S_0 \quad (R, C) \text{ has been } (0,0)$$
$$S_1 \quad (R, C) \text{ has been } (0,1)$$
$$S_2 \quad (R, C) \text{ has been } (1,0)$$
$$S_3 \quad (R, C) \text{ has been } (1,1)$$

The outputs are assigned to the transition between two states, say, S_1 and S_3. When the transition is from S_1 to S_3, the output is up. When the transition is from S_3 to S_1, the output is down.

The transition from S_1 to S_3 occurs when

Q_R	Q_C	R	C
0	1	1	1

$$\text{up} = \overline{Q}_R Q_C R C$$

The transition from S_3 to S_1 occurs when

Q_R	Q_C	R	C
1	1	0	1

$$\text{down} = Q_R Q_C \overline{R} C$$

The transition table is

S	Q_R	Q_C	R	C	Q_R^+	Q_C^+	up	down
0	0	0	0	0	0	0	0	0
0	0	0	0	1	0	1	0	0
0	0	0	1	0	1	0	0	0
0	0	0	1	1	X	X	0	0
1	0	1	0	0	0	0	0	0
1	0	1	0	1	0	1	0	0
1	0	1	1	0	X	X	0	0
1	0	1	1	1	1	1	1	0
2	1	0	0	0	0	0	0	0
2	1	0	0	1	X	X	0	0
2	1	0	1	0	1	0	0	0
2	1	0	1	1	1	1	0	0
3	1	1	0	0	X	X	0	0
3	1	1	0	1	0	1	0	1
3	1	1	1	0	1	0	0	0
3	1	1	1	1	1	1	0	0

From this, $D_R = R$, and $D_C = C$.

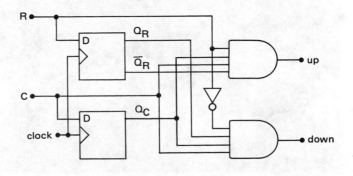

Timed 10

$$X = A + \overline{B} \cdot C$$
$$Y = \overline{A} \cdot B$$
$$Z = \overline{A} \cdot \overline{B} \cdot C$$

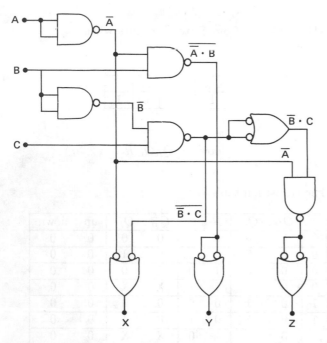

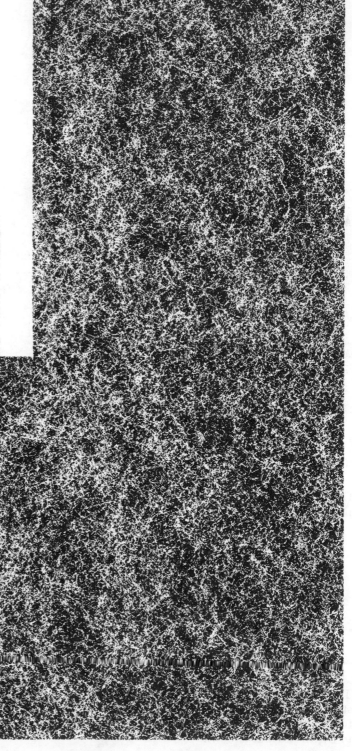

CONTROL SYSTEMS

Warmup 1

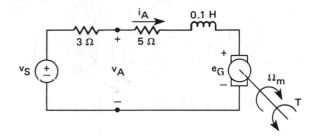

$$T = D\Omega_m + J\frac{d\Omega_m}{dt}$$

(Note: Ω_m is the mechanical angular velocity in rad/s.)

$$v_A = 5i_A + 0.1\frac{di_A}{dt} + e_G$$

Under steady-state conditions, $di_A/dt \to 0$, given

$$v_A = 24 \text{ V}$$
$$i_A = 1.6 \text{ A}$$

Then $e_G = 16$ V, given

$$\Omega_m = 160 \text{ rad/s}$$

With $e_g = K_v\Omega_m$,

$$16 \text{ V} = K_v\left(160\,\frac{\text{rad}}{\text{s}}\right)$$

$$K_v = 0.1\,\frac{\text{V}}{\text{rad/s}}$$

Torque is $T = K_T i_A$, but in MKS units, $K_T = K_v$, so in steady state, $T = D\Omega_m$ or

$$D = \frac{K_T i_A}{\Omega_m} = \frac{\left(0.1\,\frac{\text{N}\cdot\text{m}}{\text{A}}\right)(1.6 \text{ A})}{160\,\frac{\text{rad}}{\text{s}}}$$

$$= 10^{-3}\,\frac{\text{N}\cdot\text{m}}{\text{rad/s}}$$

The mechanical time constant arises in $T = D\Omega_m + J(d\Omega_m/dt)$ and can be identified in the form

$$\tau_m\frac{d\Omega_m}{dt} + \Omega_m = f(t)$$

$$\tau_m = \frac{J}{D} = 1.85 \text{ s (given)}$$

$$J = 1.85 \times 10^{-3}\,\text{N}\cdot\text{m}\cdot\text{s}^2$$

The transformed circuit equation is

$$V_s = (8 + 0.1s)I_a + E_g$$
$$E_g = 0.1\Omega_m$$

The transformed mechanical equation is

$$T = (10^{-3})(1 + 1.85s)\Omega_m$$
$$= 0.1I_a$$

Then, with

$$\frac{d\Theta_c}{dt} = \Omega_m$$
$$\Omega_m \to s\Theta_c$$

Solving,

(a) $\dfrac{\Theta_c}{V_s} = \boxed{\dfrac{5.56}{s\left(\dfrac{s}{1.26} + 1\right)\left(\dfrac{s}{79.3} + 1\right)}} = \mathbf{G}_m(s)$

From Fig. 12.2,

$$\frac{V_e}{R_f} + \frac{V_{\text{tach}}}{R_\Omega} + \frac{V_\theta}{R_\theta} + \frac{V_{\text{in}}}{R_{\text{in}}} = 0$$

$$V_{\text{tach}} = 0.5s\Theta_m$$

$$V_\theta = \frac{10}{\pi}\Theta_c$$

$$V_{\text{in}} = -\frac{10}{\pi}\Theta_{\text{in}}$$

$$V_s = V_e = \left(\frac{10}{\pi}\right)[\Theta_{\text{in}} - \Theta_c(1 + K_T s)]$$

$$K_T = \frac{50\pi}{R_\Omega}\text{N}\cdot\text{m/A}$$

$$R(s) = \Theta_{\text{in}}$$

$$C(s) = \Theta_c$$

$$E(s) = \frac{\pi}{10}V_s$$

(b)
$$E(s) = R(s) - C(s)(1 + K_T s)$$
$$C(s) = \frac{10}{\pi}Ap\mathbf{G}_m(s)E(s)$$

(c)

Warmup 2

$$\frac{10(s+2)}{s(s+20)} = \frac{\frac{s}{2}+1}{s\left(\frac{s}{20}+1\right)} = \mathbf{G}$$

$$20\log|\mathbf{G}| = 20\log\left|\frac{j\omega}{2}+1\right| - 20\log|j\omega|$$

$$- 20\log\left|\frac{j\omega}{20}+1\right|$$

$$20\log|j\omega| = 0 \text{ at } \omega = 1 \text{ rad/s}$$

(a)

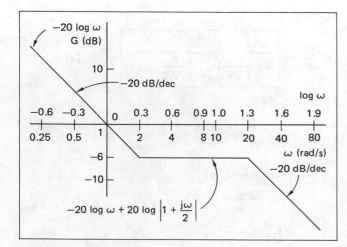

(b) $r(t) = u(t)$

$$R(s) = \frac{1}{s}$$

$$e_{ss} = \lim_{s \to o} \frac{sR(s)}{1+\mathbf{G}}$$

$$= \lim_{s \to 0} \frac{\frac{s}{s}}{1+\frac{1}{s}} = \boxed{0}$$

(c) $r(t) = tu(t)$

$$R(s) = \frac{1}{s^2}$$

$$e_{ss} = \lim_{s \to 0} \frac{s\frac{1}{s^?}}{1+\frac{1}{s}}$$

$$= \lim_{s \to 0} \frac{1}{s+1} = \boxed{1}$$

Warmup 3

$$\mathbf{G} = \frac{50s}{s^2 + 10s + 400}$$

$$= \left(\frac{1}{8}\right)\left[\frac{s}{\left(\frac{s}{20}\right)^2 + (2)\left(\frac{1}{4}\right)\left(\frac{s}{20}\right) + 1}\right]$$

$$20\log|\mathbf{G}| = 20\log\left(\frac{1}{8}\right) + 20\log\omega$$

$$- 20\log\left[\left(1 - \frac{\omega^2}{400}\right)^2 + (0.25)\left(\frac{\omega}{20}\right)^2\right]^{\frac{1}{2}}$$

Calculate the 0 dB crossing.

$$20\log\left(\frac{1}{8}\right) + 20\log\omega = 0$$

$$\log\omega = -\log\left(\frac{1}{8}\right) = \log 8$$

$$\omega = 8 \text{ rad/s}$$

(a) Asymptotic Bode diagram:

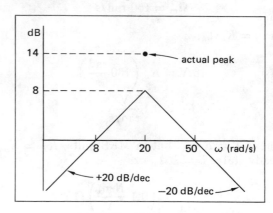

(b) $r(t) = u(t)$

$$R(s) = \frac{1}{s}$$

$$e_{ss} = \lim_{s \to 0} \frac{s\frac{1}{s}}{1+\mathbf{G}(0)} = \lim_{s \to 0} \frac{1}{1+0} = \boxed{1}$$

(c) $r(t) = tu(t)$

$$R(s) = \frac{1}{s^2}$$

$$e_{ss} = \lim_{s \to 0} \frac{s\frac{1}{s^2}}{1+0} = \lim_{s \to 0} \frac{1}{s} = \boxed{\infty}$$

Warmup 4

$$\mathbf{GH}\Big|_{s\to0} = \frac{5}{s^2}$$

$$\frac{1}{1+\mathbf{GH}}\Big|_{s\to0} = \frac{1}{1+\frac{5}{s^2}}\Big|_{s\to0} = \frac{s^2}{5}$$

Unit step:

$$R = \frac{1}{s}$$

$$e_{ss} = \lim_{s\to0}\frac{sRs}{1+\mathbf{GH}} = \lim_{s\to0}\left(\frac{s}{s}\right)\left(\frac{s^2}{5}\right) = \boxed{0}$$

Unit ramp:

$$R = \frac{1}{s^2}$$

$$e_{ss} = \lim_{s\to0}\frac{s\frac{1}{s^2}}{\frac{5}{s^2}} = \boxed{0}$$

Unit parabola:

$$R = \frac{2}{s^3}$$

$$e_{ss} = \lim_{s\to0}\left(s\frac{2}{s^3}\right)\left(\frac{s^2}{5}\right) = \boxed{\frac{2}{5}}$$

Warmup 5

(a) $(s^4 + 30s^3 + 200s^2) + (40s + 40) = 0$

s^4	1	200	40
s^3	30	40	
$-$	$-$	$-$	$-$
s^2	$198\frac{2}{3}$	40	
s^1	33.96	0	
s^0	40		

Entries below the dashed line are derived.

$$b_3 = \frac{\begin{vmatrix} 1 & 200 \\ 30 & 40 \end{vmatrix}}{-30} = 198\frac{2}{3}$$

$$b_5 = \frac{\begin{vmatrix} 1 & 40 \\ 30 & 0 \end{vmatrix}}{-30} = 40$$

$$c_3 = \frac{\begin{vmatrix} 30 & 40 \\ 198\frac{2}{3} & 40 \end{vmatrix}}{-198\frac{2}{3}} = 33.96$$

$$d_3 = \frac{\begin{vmatrix} 198\frac{2}{3} & 40 \\ 33.96 & 0 \end{vmatrix}}{-33.96} = 40$$

The system is stable.

(b) $(s^3 + s^2 + s) + (s + 8)$

s^3	1	2
s^2	1	8
$-$	$-$	$-$
s^1	-6	0
s^0	8	

Entries below the dashed line are derived.

$$c_3 = \frac{\begin{vmatrix} 1 & 2 \\ 1 & 8 \end{vmatrix}}{-1} = -6$$

$$d_3 = \frac{\begin{vmatrix} 1 & 8 \\ -6 & 0 \end{vmatrix}}{6} = 8$$

With two sign changes, the system is unstable, with two positive half-plane roots.

Warmup 6

$$G = \frac{K}{\tau s + 1} = \frac{K}{\frac{s}{4} + 1}$$

root locus $K > 0$

$$1 + G = \frac{\frac{s}{4} + 1 + K}{\frac{s}{4} + 1} = \frac{(1+K)\left[\frac{s}{(4)(1+K)} + 1\right]}{\frac{s}{4} + 1}$$

$$\frac{G}{1+G} = \left(\frac{K}{1+K}\right)\left[\frac{1}{\frac{s}{(4)(1+K)} + 1}\right]$$

$$\tau = \frac{1}{(4)(1+K)} = 0.1$$

$$K = \boxed{1.5}$$

Warmup 7

A single zero must lie on the real axis.

$$\frac{s+z}{s+p}$$

(a) $z > p$ (zero to the left of the pole):

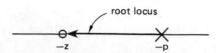

(b) $p > z$ (zero to the right of the pole):

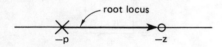

Warmup 8

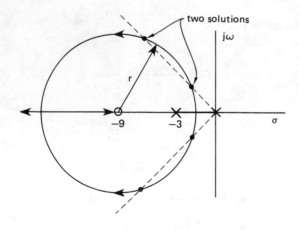

This pole-zero configuration produces a circular root locus with

$$r = \sqrt{(z-p_1)(z-p_2)} = \sqrt{(-9)(-6)}$$
$$= 3\sqrt{6} = 7.35$$

The equation of the circle is

$$(\sigma + 9)^2 + \omega^2 = r^2 = 54$$

For $\zeta = 0.707$, $\omega = -\sigma$.

$$\sigma^2 + 18\sigma + 81 + \sigma^2 = 54$$
$$\sigma^2 + 9\sigma + 13.5 = 0$$

$$\sigma = -4.5 \pm \sqrt{(4.5)^2 - 13.5}$$
$$= -1.902, -7.098$$

(a) $s = -1.902 \pm j1.902$

$$1 + \frac{K(s+9)}{s(s+3)} = 0$$
$$s^2 + (3+K)s + 9K = 0$$

$$(s + 1.902 + j1.902)(s + 1.902 - j1.902)$$
$$= s^2 + (2)(1.902s) + (2)(1.902)^2$$

Equating coefficients of s,

$$3 + K = (2)(1.902)$$
$$9K = (2)(1.902)^2$$

Both of these yield

$$K = \boxed{0.8038}$$

$$\frac{\mathbf{G}}{1 + \mathbf{GH}} = \frac{(0.8038)(s+9)}{s^2 + 3.8038s + 7.235}$$

The unit step is

$$R = \frac{1}{s}$$

The step response is

$$C(s) = \left(\frac{1}{s}\right)\left[\frac{(0.8038)(s+9)}{s^2 + 3.8038s + 7.235}\right]$$

$$= \frac{1}{s} - \frac{s+3}{s^2 + 3.8038s + 7.235}$$

$$= \frac{1}{s} - \frac{s+3}{(s+1.902)^2 + (1.902)^2}$$

$$= \frac{1}{s} - \frac{(s+1.902) + 1.0980}{(s+1.902)^2 + (1.902)^2}$$

$$= \frac{1}{s} - \frac{s+1.902}{(s+1.902)^2 + (1.902)^2}$$

$$\quad - \frac{(0.577)(1.902)}{(s+1.902)^2 + (1.902)^2}$$

$$c(t) = \boxed{1 - e^{-1.902t}(\cos 1.902t + 0.577\sin 1.902t)}$$

(b)
$$s = -7.098 \pm j7.098$$

$$(s + 7.098 + j.7098)(s + 7.098 - j7.098)$$
$$= s^2 + (2)(7.098s) + (2)(7.098)^2$$
$$= s^2 + 14.196s + 100.77$$

$$K + 3 = 14.196$$

$$K = \boxed{11.196}$$

$$C(s) = \left(\frac{1}{s}\right)\left[\frac{(11.196)(s+9)}{(s+7.098)^2 + (7.098)^2}\right]$$

$$= \frac{1}{s} - \frac{s+3}{(s+7.098)^2 + (7.098)^2}$$

$$= \frac{1}{s} - \frac{(s+7.098) - (0.577)(7.098)}{(s+7.098)^2 + (7.098)^2}$$

$$c(t) = \boxed{1 - e^{-7.098t}(\cos 7.098t - 0.577\sin 7.098t)}$$

Warmup 9

$$\frac{K(s+2)}{s^2(s+10)(s+20)}$$

The centroid is

$$\sigma = \frac{-10 - 20 + 2}{4 - 1} = -9.33$$

The angle asymptotes are

$$\frac{360n}{4-1} + 180°$$

This results in asymptotes at $-60°, +60°$ and $180°$. The asymptote at $60°$ radiates from $\sigma = -9.33$ on the negative real axis, and passes through the positive imaginary axis at
$$\omega = 9.33\tan 60° = 16.17 \text{ rad/s}$$

(a) For $s = j16.17$,

$$j^4(16.17)^4 + j^3(30)(16.17)^3$$
$$+ j^2(200)(16.17)^2 + K(j16.17 + 2) = 0$$

$$K = \frac{(16.17)^2[(16.17)^2 - 200 - j(30)(16.17)]}{2 + j16.17}$$

$$= \boxed{7847\underline{/-165.7°}}$$

(b) The Routh-Hurwitz criterion is used to find the points where the root locus crosses the imaginary axis.

$$(s^4 + 30s^3 + 200s^2) + (Ks + 2K) = 0$$

s^4	1	200	$2K$
s^3	30	K	
—	—	—	—
s^2	$\frac{6000 - K}{30}$	$2K$	
s^1	$\frac{4200 - K}{6000 - K}K$	0	
s^0	$2K$		

Entries below the dashed line are derived.

$$c_3 = \frac{\begin{vmatrix} 1 & 200 \\ 30 & K \end{vmatrix}}{-30} = \frac{6000 - K}{30}$$

$$c_1 = \frac{\begin{vmatrix} 200 & 2K \\ K & 0 \end{vmatrix}}{-K} = 2K$$

$$d_3 = \frac{\begin{vmatrix} 30 & K \\ \frac{6000 - K}{30} & 2K \end{vmatrix}}{-\frac{6000 - K}{30}}$$

$$-\frac{4200 - K}{6000 - K}K$$

The minimum value of K to cause a change of sign is

$$K = \boxed{4200}$$

(c) At $K = 4200$, for $s = j\omega$,

$$\omega^4 - j30\omega^3 - 200\omega^2 + Kj\omega + 2K = 0$$

Using the imaginary part,

$$-30\omega^3 + K\omega = 0$$
$$\omega^2 = \frac{4200}{30}$$
$$\omega = \pm\sqrt{140} = \boxed{11.83 \text{ rad/s}}$$

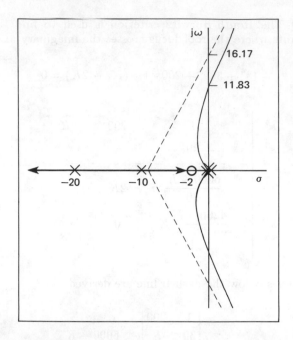

$$\frac{C}{R} = \frac{5s^2 + 16s + 25}{15s^4 + 225s^3 + 10s^2 + 16s + 25}$$

$$= \frac{\left(\dfrac{1}{3}s^2 + \dfrac{16}{15}s + \dfrac{5}{3}\right)X_1}{\left(s^4 + 15s^3 + \dfrac{2}{3}s^2 + \dfrac{16}{15}s + \dfrac{5}{3}\right)X_1}$$

$$C = \frac{1}{3}s^2 X_1 + \frac{16}{15}s X_1 + \frac{5}{3}X_1$$

$$R = s^4 X_1 + 15s^3 X_1 + \frac{2}{3}s^2 X_1 + \frac{16}{15}s X_1 + \frac{5}{3}X_1$$

$$\frac{d^4 x_1}{dt^4} = R - 15\frac{d^3 x_1}{dt^3} - \left(\frac{2}{3}\right)\frac{d^2 x_1}{dt^2} - \left(\frac{16}{15}\right)\frac{dx_1}{dt} - \frac{5}{3}x_1$$

Concentrate 1

$$\mathbf{G} = \frac{20}{s(s + 10)}$$

$$\mathbf{H} = 1 + Ks$$

$$\frac{\mathbf{G}}{1 + \mathbf{GH}} = \frac{20}{s^2 + 10s + 20Ks + 20}$$

$$s^2 + (10 + 20K)s + 20 = s^2 + 2\zeta\omega_n s + \omega_n^2$$

From this, $\omega_n = \sqrt{20}$ rad/s.

Since $\zeta = \dfrac{1}{\sqrt{2}}$ was given,

$$10 + 20K = 2\zeta\omega_n = (2)\frac{1}{\sqrt{2}}\sqrt{20} = \sqrt{40}$$

$$K = \frac{\sqrt{40} - 10}{20} = \boxed{-0.1838}$$

Warmup 10

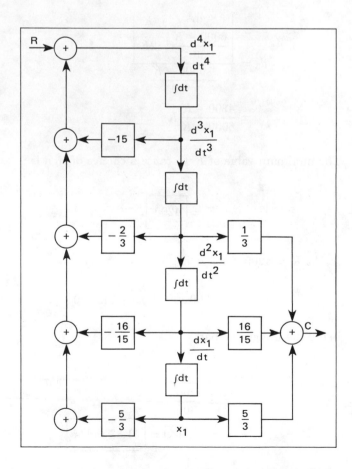

Concentrate 2

(a) $\dfrac{1 + \mathbf{GH}}{\mathbf{G}} = \dfrac{s^3 + 13s^2 + 32s + 100}{80}$

Using the Routh-Hurwitz criterion,

s^3	1	32
s^2	13	100
—	— —	— —
s^1	24.3	0
s^0	100	

Entries below the dashed line are derived.

$$c_3 = \frac{\begin{vmatrix} 1 & 32 \\ 13 & 100 \end{vmatrix}}{-13} = 24.3$$

$$d_3 = \frac{\begin{vmatrix} 13 & 100 \\ 24.3 & 0 \end{vmatrix}}{-24.3} = 100$$

The system is stable with this loop gain.

$$\frac{G}{1+GH} = \frac{80}{s^3 + 13s^2 + 32s + 100}$$

To search for a real root, start

$$s^3 + 13s^2 \rightarrow 0$$

$$s = -13$$

For $s = -13$,

$$F(s) = s^2 + 13s + 32s + 100 = -316$$

For $s = -10$,

$$F(s) \rightarrow 80$$

The change in sign indicates the root has been passed.

For $s = -11$,

$$F(s) \rightarrow -10$$

For $s = -10.9$,

$$F(s) = 0.701$$

For $s = -10.91$,

$$F(s) = -0.353$$

For $s = -10.902$,

$$F(s) = 0.0352$$

For $s = -10.906$,

$$F(s) = 0.701$$

For $s = -10.9067$,

$$F(s) = 0.0016 \rightarrow 0$$

Using long division,

$$
\begin{array}{r}
s^2 + \quad 2.0933s + \quad 9.169 \\
s + 10.9067 \overline{)\, s^3 + \quad\quad 13s^2 + \quad\quad 32s + 100} \\
s^3 + \quad 10.9067s^2 \\
\hline
2.0933s^2 + \quad\quad 32s \\
2.0933s^2 + \quad 22.831s \\
\hline
9.169s + 100 \\
9.169s + 100 \\
\end{array}
$$

$$s^2 + 2.0933s + 9.169$$

The roots are

$$s = -1.05 \pm j2.84$$

$$\frac{G}{1+GH} = \frac{80}{(s+10.9)(s^2 + 2.09s + 9.17)}$$

(b) $$\frac{G}{1+GH} = \frac{(80)(s+10)}{(s+10.9)(s^2 + 2.09s + 9.17)}$$

The stability is the same as part (a).

(c) The main difference is that the DC gain of part (b) is 10 times that of part (a).

Concentrate 3

The complex part of the root locus is a circle centered on the zero ($s = -5$) with the radius

$$r = \sqrt{(z - p_1)(z - p_2)}$$
$$= \sqrt{(-5 + 0)(-5 + 1)} = \sqrt{20}$$

At $K = 5$,

$$\frac{5s + 25}{s^2 + s} + 1 = 0$$
$$s^2 + 6s + 25 = 0$$
$$s = \boxed{-3 \pm j4}$$

At $K = 10$,

$$\frac{10s + 50}{s^2 + s} + 1 = 0$$
$$s^2 + 11s + 50 = 0$$
$$s = -5.5 \pm j4.44$$

Because the root-locus does not cross the imaginary axis, the system is unconditionally stable.

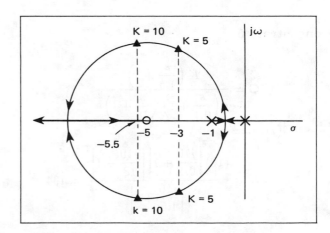

Concentrate 4

For $e(t) = \dfrac{u(t)}{100}$ V,

$$c(t) = (20)(1 - e^{-5t})u(t)\,\text{V}$$
$$C(s) = \frac{20}{s} - \frac{20}{s+5} = \frac{100}{s(s+5)}$$
$$E(s) = \frac{1}{100s}$$
$$G = \frac{C(s)}{E(s)} = \frac{10^4}{s+5}$$

Given $\left.\dfrac{G}{1+GH}\right|_{s=0} = 10$,

$$0.1\,G = 1 + GH$$
$$H = 0.1 - \frac{1}{G}$$
$$G|_{s=0} = 2 \times 10^3$$

(a) $H = \boxed{0.1}$

$$\frac{G}{1+GH} = \frac{\dfrac{10^4}{s+5}}{1 + \dfrac{10^3}{s+5}}$$
$$= \frac{10^4}{s+1005} \rightarrow \frac{10^4}{s+10^3}$$

For $R = \dfrac{1}{s}$,

$$C = \frac{10^4}{s(s+10^3)} = \frac{10}{s} - \frac{10}{s+10^3}$$

(b) $c(t) = \boxed{(10)\left(1 - e^{1000t}\right)}$

Concentrate 5

$$G = \frac{K\left(\dfrac{s}{1.5}+1\right)}{s\left(\dfrac{s}{0.1}+1\right)\left(\dfrac{s}{18}+1\right)^2}$$
$$|G(j10)| = 1$$

$$K = \frac{(10)\left|\dfrac{j10}{0.1}+1\right|\left|\dfrac{j10}{18}+1\right|^2}{\left|\dfrac{j10}{1.5}+1\right|} = 194$$

(a) $G = G_p G_c = \boxed{\dfrac{(194)\left(\dfrac{s}{1.5}+1\right)}{s\left(\dfrac{s}{0.1}+1\right)\left(\dfrac{s}{18}+1\right)^2}}$

(b) $G_c = \dfrac{G}{G_p}$

$$= \left[\frac{(194)\left(\dfrac{s}{1.5}+1\right)}{s\left(\dfrac{s}{0.1}+1\right)\left(\dfrac{s}{18}+1\right)^2}\right]\left[\frac{s(s+2)(s+10)}{20}\right]$$

$$= \boxed{\frac{(194)\left(\dfrac{s}{1.5}+1\right)\left(\dfrac{s}{2}+1\right)\left(\dfrac{s}{10}+1\right)}{\left(\dfrac{s}{0.1}+1\right)\left(\dfrac{s}{18}+1\right)^2}}$$

(c) For $r(t) = (5 + 3t)u(t)$,

$$R(s) = \frac{5}{s} + \frac{3}{s^2}$$

$$e_{ss} = \lim_{s\to0}\frac{sRs}{1+G} = \lim_{s\to0}\frac{5 + \dfrac{3}{s}}{1 + \dfrac{194}{s}}$$

$$= \frac{3}{194} = \boxed{0.0155}$$

Concentrate 6

At low frequency, the given data show a slope of -6 dB/octave (corresponding to -20 dB/dec). Then, it behaves as K/s. To evaluate K,

$$20\log K - 20\log\omega = \text{datum}$$

Taking $\omega = 0.025$ rad/s, the relation is

$$20\log K - 20\log 0.025 = 35\text{ dB}$$
$$K = 1.4059$$

The step response has the given terms e^{-t} and e^{-100t}. The denominator of G has

$$s\left(\frac{s}{1}+1\right)\left(\frac{s}{100}+1\right)$$

As the high-frequency data show a slope of -12 dB per octave, there must be a zero.

$$G = \frac{(1.4059)\left(\dfrac{s}{z}+1\right)}{s(s+1)\left(\dfrac{s}{100}+1\right)}$$

At very high frequency,

$$|G| \rightarrow \frac{1.4059\dfrac{\omega}{z}}{\omega\omega\dfrac{\omega}{100}} = \frac{140.59}{z\omega^2}$$

Then at $\omega = 1638.4$ rad/s,

$$-105.6 \text{ dB} = 20\log(140.59) - 20\log z$$
$$- 20\log(1638.4)^2$$

From this, $z = 9.98$.

(a) $\mathbf{G} = \dfrac{(1.4059)\left(\frac{s}{9.98}+1\right)}{s(s+1)\left(\frac{s}{100}+1\right)} = \boxed{\dfrac{(14.08)(s+9.98)}{s(s+1)(s+100)}}$

(b) $\underline{/\mathbf{G}} = \tan^{-1}\left(\dfrac{\omega}{9.98}\right) - 90° - \tan^{-1}\omega - \tan^{-1}\left(\dfrac{\omega}{100}\right)$

The phase angle does not reach $-180°$, so a gain margin cannot be calculated. The gain is 1 (0 dB) between 0.8 and 1.6 rad/s. Trying $\omega = 1$, $|\mathbf{G}| = 0.999 \approx 1$.

At $\omega = 1$ rad/s,

$$\underline{/\mathbf{G}} = \tan^{-1}\left(\dfrac{1}{9.98}\right) - 90° - \tan^{-1}1 - \tan^{-1}0.01$$
$$= -129.3°$$

The phase margin is

$$180 - 129.3 = \boxed{50.7°}$$

(c) For $\mathbf{H} = K$,

$$1 + \mathbf{GH} = 1 + \dfrac{14.08Ks + 140.5K}{s^3 + 101s^2 + 100s} = 0$$

$$s^3 + 101s^2 + (100 + 14.08K)s + 140.5K = 0$$

Using the Routh-Hurwitz criterion,

s^3	1	$100 + 14.08K$
s^2	101	$140.5K$
$-$	$-\ -\ -\ -\ -\ -\ -\ -$	
s^1	$100 + 12.7K$	0
s^0	$140.5K$	

Entries below the dashed line are derived.

$$c_3 = \dfrac{\begin{vmatrix} 1 & 100 + 14.08K \\ 101 & 140.5K \end{vmatrix}}{-101}$$
$$= 100 + 12.7K$$

$$c_4 = \dfrac{\begin{vmatrix} 101 & 140.5K \\ 100 + 12.7K & 0 \end{vmatrix}}{-(100 + 12.7K)}$$
$$= 140.5K$$

The system will be unstable for any $K < 0$; otherwise it is unconditionally stable (for $K > 0$).

Concentrate 7

$$G = \dfrac{10^5}{\left(\frac{s}{10}+1\right)\left(\frac{s}{10^6}+1\right)\left(\frac{s}{10^7}+1\right)}$$

$$= \dfrac{10^5}{\frac{s^3}{10^{14}} + \frac{1.1s^2}{10^7} + \frac{s}{10} + 1}$$

(a) $1 + \mathbf{GH} = 0$

$$\mathbf{H} = \dfrac{1}{K}$$

$$10^{-14}s^3 + (1.1 \times 10^{-7})s^2 + 10^{-1}s + 1 + 10^5\mathbf{H} = 0$$

Using the Routh-Hurwitz criterion,

s^3	10^{-14}	10^{-1}
s^2	1.1×10^{-7}	$1 + 10^5\mathbf{H}$
$-$	$-\ -\ -\ -\ -\ -\ -\ -$	
s^1	$(10^{-1})\left(1 - \dfrac{\mathbf{H}}{11}\right)$	0
s^0	$1 + 10^5\mathbf{H}$	

Entries below the dashed line are derived.

$$b_2 = \dfrac{\begin{vmatrix} 10^{-14} & 10^{-1} \\ 1.1 \times 10^{-7} & 1 + 10^5\mathbf{H} \end{vmatrix}}{-1.1 \times 10^{-7}}$$

$$= \dfrac{10^{-14} + 10^{-9}\mathbf{H} - 1.1 \times 10^{-8}}{-1.1 \times 10^{-8}}$$

$$= (10^{-1})\left(1 - \dfrac{\mathbf{H}}{11}\right)$$

The amplifier is stable for $\mathbf{H} < 11$ or $K > \frac{1}{11}$. Physically, $K > 1$ (resistance must be positive), so it is impossible to make the amplifier unstable.

(b) At $K = \frac{1}{11}$, $s = j\omega$ (i.e., the root locus would be at the imaginary axis).

$$(10^{-14})(j\omega)^3 + (1.1 \times 10^{-7})(j\omega)^2$$
$$+10^{-1}j\omega + 1 + (11 \times 10^5) = 0$$

The real and imaginary parts must both vanish.

$$-10^{-14}j\omega^3 + 10^{-1}j\omega = 0$$
$$\omega^2 = 10^{13}$$
$$-(1.1 \times 10^7)\omega^2 + 11 \times 10^5 = 0$$
$$\omega^2 = 10^{13}$$

$$\omega = 10^{6.5} = \boxed{3.162 \times 10^6 \text{ rad/s or 503 kHz}}$$

Concentrate 8

$$\mathbf{G}(s) = \frac{e^{-s}}{s}$$

$$\mathbf{G}(j\omega) = \frac{e^{-j\omega}}{j\omega}$$

$$\underline{/\mathbf{G}(j\omega)} = -90° - \frac{180°}{\pi}\omega$$

($\underline{/}$ in degress; ω in rad/s)

For $\underline{/\mathbf{G}} = -180° = (-90°)\left(1 + \frac{2}{\pi}\omega\right)$,

$$\omega = \frac{\pi}{2} \text{ rad/s}$$

$$\mathbf{GH} = \frac{Ke^{-s}}{s}$$

$$|\mathbf{GH}| = \frac{K}{\omega}$$

(a) For $|\mathbf{GH}| = 1$,

$$K = \boxed{\frac{\pi}{2}}$$

(b) With $K = \frac{\pi}{4}$,

$$\mathbf{GH} = \left(\frac{\pi}{4}\right)\left(\frac{e^{-s}}{s}\right)$$

$$\mathbf{GH}(j\omega) = \left(\frac{\pi}{4}\right)\left(\frac{e^{-j\omega}}{j\omega}\right)$$

At $|\mathbf{GH}| = 1$,

$$\omega = \frac{\pi}{4}$$

$$\underline{/\mathbf{GH}} = (-90°)\left[1 + \left(\frac{2}{\pi}\right)\left(\frac{\pi}{4}\right)\right] = -135°$$

The phase margin is $180° - 135° = \boxed{45°}$.

With $\underline{/\mathbf{GH}} = 180°$,

$$-180° = (-90°)\left(1 + \frac{2}{\pi}\omega\right)$$

$$\omega = \frac{\pi}{2}$$

$$|\mathbf{GH}| = \left(\frac{\pi}{4}\right)\left(\frac{1}{\frac{\pi}{2}}\right) = \frac{1}{2}$$

$$\frac{1}{2} \to 20\log(0.5) = -6 \text{ dB}$$

The gain margin is $\boxed{6 \text{ dB}}$.

Concentrate 9

$\omega\frac{\text{rad}}{\text{s}}$	0	1	10	100	400
$\mathbf{GH}_{\text{dB}}$	60	60	59.9	17.3	−16.4
$\underline{/\mathbf{GH}}$	0°	−6.3°	−96°	−219°	−255°

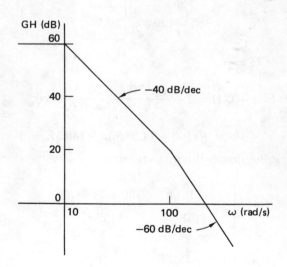

The purpose of the compensator is to lower the gain so that when the compensated system has 0 dB gain, its phase angle will be −135°.

The compensator will roll off at −20 dB/dec, so it must have its corner well below 10 rad/s.

The compensator will contribute 90° phase lag at the compensated 0-dB frequency, so that frequency must be where the uncompensated system has a phase shift of −45°,

$\omega\frac{\text{rad}}{\text{s}}$	2	5	6	5.9	5.85
$\mathbf{GH}_{\text{dB}}$	60.1	60.9	61.1	61.1	61.1
$\underline{/\mathbf{GH}}$	−12.9°	−36.6°	46.5°	45.5°	45°

The compensator must provide 61.1 dB of attenuation at $\omega = 5.85$ rad/s.

$$\frac{1}{|1 + j5.85\tau|} = 10^{-\frac{61.1}{20}}$$

$$1 + (5.85\tau)^2 = \left(10^{\frac{61.1}{20}}\right)^2 = 10^{6.11}$$

$$5.85\tau = 1135$$

$$\tau = \boxed{194 \text{ s}}$$

Concentrate 10

The complex poles with damping ratio ζ are

$$\left(\frac{s}{\omega_p}\right)^2 + 2\zeta\left(\frac{s}{\omega_p}\right) + 1$$

The integrator is $\frac{1}{s}$. There is a zero at $|s| = 2$
The complex poles are at $|s| = 8$.
Another pole is at $|s| = 80$.

(a) $$\mathbf{G} = \frac{K\left(\frac{s}{2} + 1\right)}{s\left[\left(\frac{s}{8}\right)^2 + (2)(0.25)\left(\frac{s}{8}\right) + 1\right]\left(\frac{s}{80} + 1\right)}$$

At $\omega = 10$ rad/s,

$$|\mathbf{G}| = 1$$

$$K = \frac{(10)\left|1 - \left(\frac{10}{8}\right)^2 + j\frac{10}{16}\right|\left|j\frac{10}{80} + 1\right|}{\left|j\frac{10}{2} + 1\right|}$$

$$= 1.662$$

$$\boxed{\mathbf{G} = \frac{(1.662)\left(\frac{s}{2} + 1\right)}{s\left[\left(\frac{s}{8}\right)^2 + \left(\frac{1}{2}\right)\left(\frac{s}{8}\right) + 1\right]\left(\frac{s}{80} + 1\right)}}$$

(b)   For simple poles and zeros, the maximum deviation is ±3 dB at the corner frequency. For $\zeta = 0.25$, the maximum deviation is 6.3 dB at 93% of the corner.

$$\omega_{max} = (0.93)(8) = \boxed{7.44 \text{ rad/s}}$$

(c) $$\underline{/\mathbf{G}} = \tan^{-1}\left(\frac{\omega}{2}\right) - 90° - \tan^{-1}\left(\frac{\omega}{80}\right)$$

$$- \tan^{-1}\left[\frac{\frac{\omega}{16}}{1 - \left(\frac{\omega}{8}\right)^2}\right]$$

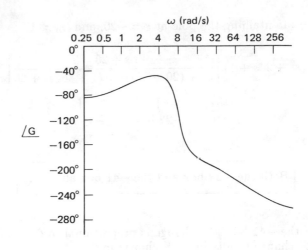

Timed 1

$$R = (s^4 + 22s^3 + 41s^2 + 20s)X$$

$$C = (s^2 + 400)X$$

$$\frac{C}{R} = \frac{s^2 + 400}{s(s^3 + 22s^2 + 41s + 20)}$$

For critical damping at $\omega = 1$,

$$(s + 1)^2 = s^2 + 2s + 1$$

Dividing the denominator,

$$\begin{array}{r} s \;+\; 20 \\ s^2 + 2s + 1 \overline{)\,s^3 \;+\; 22s^2 \;+\; 41s \;+\; 20} \\ \underline{s^3 \;+\; 2s^2 \;+\; s } \\ 20s^2 \;+\; 40s \;+\; 20 \\ \underline{20s^2 \;+\; 40s \;+\; 20} \\ 0 \end{array}$$

(a) $$\frac{C}{R} = \boxed{\frac{(s + j20)(s - j20)}{s(s + 1)^2(s + 20)} = \mathbf{G}_c}$$

(b) $$\mathbf{G} = \frac{\mathbf{G}_c}{1 - \mathbf{G}_c}$$

$$= \frac{s^2 + 400}{s(s + 1)^2(s + 20) - s^2 - 400}$$

$$= \frac{s^2 + 400}{s^4 + 22s^3 + 41s^2 + 20s - s^2 - 400}$$

$$= \boxed{\frac{s^2 + 400}{s^4 + 22s^3 + 40s^2 + 20s - 400}}$$

This is unstable because of the sign change in the denominator.

(c) Maintaining the pole at $s = -20$, and $\omega_n = 1$,

$$(s^2 + 2\zeta s + 1)\left[\frac{s + 20}{s^3 + (20 + 2\zeta)s^2 + (1 + 40\zeta)s + 20}\right]$$

$$\uparrow \qquad\qquad \uparrow$$
$$-22 \text{ box} \qquad -41 \text{ box}$$

> Both the -22 box and the -41 box affect ζ.

In the -41 box, the change is proportional to ζ, i.e., a 1% change results in a 1% change in ζ.

For the -22 box, a small charge results in a large charge in ζ.

Timed 2

$$(s^3 + 16s^2 + 81s + 126) + K = 0$$

Using the Routh-Hurwitz criterion,

$$
\begin{array}{c|cc}
s^3 & 1 & 81 \\
\hline
s^2 & 16 & 126 + K \\
s^1 & \dfrac{1170 - K}{16} & \\
s^0 & 126 + K &
\end{array}
$$

Entries below the dashed line are derived.

$$c_3 = \frac{\begin{vmatrix} 1 & 81 \\ 16 & 126 + K \end{vmatrix}}{-16}$$
$$= \frac{1170 - K}{16}$$

(a) The range is

> $1170 - K > 0$
> $126 + K > 0$

(b) A stable system will result from

> $-126 < K < 1170$

Timed 3

Begin by reducing the inner loop.

$$\frac{\dfrac{100}{s(s + 10)}}{1 + \dfrac{100}{s(s + 10)}} = \frac{100}{s^2 + 10s + 100}$$

$$GH = \mathbf{G} = \frac{\dfrac{1000K}{100}}{\left(\dfrac{s}{10}\right)^2 + \dfrac{s}{10} + 1}$$

$$\omega_n = 10 \text{ rad/s}$$
$$2\zeta\omega_n = 10 \text{ rad/s}$$
$$\zeta = 0.5$$

The roots are

$$s = -5 \pm \sqrt{25 - 100}$$
$$= -5 \pm j\sqrt{75}$$
$$= -5 \pm j8.66 = 10\underline{/\pm 120°}$$

The root loci are

$$G = \frac{GH \ \text{unity}}{1 \angle 9 \text{ } H \ \text{feedback}}$$

$$s^2 + 10s + 100 + 1000K = 0$$

$$s = -5 \pm \sqrt{25 - 100 - 1000K}$$
$$= -5 \pm j\sqrt{75 + 1000K} = -5 \pm j\omega_r$$

K	0.05	0.10	0.15	0.20	0.25
ω_r	11.2	13.2	15	16.6	18

(a)

(b)

> The system is unconditionally stable for positive K. For negative K, it is unstable for
> $$1000K + 75 \leq -25$$
> $$K \leq -0.1$$

(c)
$$e_{ss} = \lim_{s \to 0} \frac{sR(s)}{1+\mathbf{G}}$$

$$R(s) = \frac{1}{s}$$

$$\lim_{s \to 0} \mathbf{G}(s) = 10K$$

$$e_{ss} = \boxed{\frac{1}{1+10K}}$$

Timed 4

The root locus is

$$s^3 + 2s^2 + 4s + K = 0$$

At $K = 0$ (open-loop poles),

$$s(s^2 + 2s + 4) = 0$$

$$s_0 = 0$$

$$s^2 + 2s + 4 = 0$$

$$s_{1,2} = \frac{-2}{2} \pm \sqrt{1-4} = -1 \pm j\sqrt{3}$$

(a)

> There are no break-away points because there is only one pole on the real axis.

(b) Use the Routh-Hurwitz criterion to find K for instability.

$$s^3 + 2s^2 + 4s + K = 0$$

s^3	1	4
s^2	2	K
$-$	$-$	$-$
s^1	$\dfrac{8-K}{2}$	
s^0	K	

Entries below the dashed line are derived.

$$c_3 = \frac{\begin{vmatrix} 1 & 4 \\ 2 & K \end{vmatrix}}{-2} = \frac{K-8}{-2}$$

This crosses the imagining axis where $K = \boxed{8.}$

$$s^3 + 2s^2 + 4s + 8 = (s^2 + \omega^2)(s+p)$$

Using long division,

$$
\begin{array}{r}
s \quad + \quad 2 \\
s^2+\omega^2\overline{)s^3 \quad + \quad 4s \quad + \quad 2(s^2+4)} \\
\underline{s^3 \quad + \quad \omega^2 s \qquad 2s^2 + 2\omega^2} \\
(4-\omega^2)s \qquad 8 - 2\omega^2
\end{array}
$$

To have no remainder, $\omega = \boxed{2 \text{ rad/s}}$

$$s^3 + 2s^2 + 4s + 8 = (s^2 + 4)(s + 2)$$

The root locus is

$$\text{centroid}: \frac{-1-1}{3} = -\frac{2}{3}$$

The angle asymptotes are $180°$ and $\pm 60°$. The angle of emergence is

$$180° + 120° + 90° = 390°$$

$$\theta = 390° - 360° = 30°$$

(c)

> For positive K, the locus does not intersect the $\zeta = 0.707$ line.

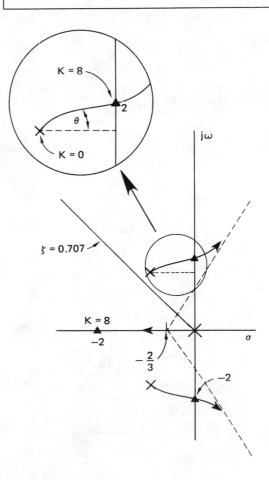

Timed 5

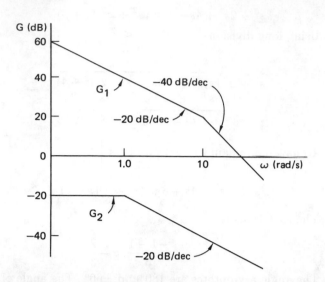

The high-frequency information shows $\mathbf{G}_1$ has two more poles than zeros, and $\mathbf{G}_2$ has one more pole than zeros. This indicates a minimum phase system, i.e., no zeros in the right-half plane. The asymptotes then define the system.

(a) $\mathbf{G}_1 = \dfrac{K_1}{s(s+10)}$

The asymptotes meet at $s = 10$. Using the low-frequency asymptote,

$$\left| \frac{K_1}{10j\omega} \right|_{\omega=10} = 10$$

$$K_1 = 1000$$

$$\mathbf{G}_1 = \boxed{\frac{1000}{s(s+10)}}$$

$$\mathbf{G}_2 = \frac{K_2}{s+1.0}$$

$$\mathbf{G}_2 \big|_{s=0} = 0.1$$

$$K_2 = 0.1$$

$$\mathbf{G}_2 = \boxed{\frac{0.1}{s+10}}$$

$$\mathbf{G}_1\mathbf{G}_2 = \boxed{\frac{100}{s(s+1)(s+10)}}$$

(b) $s^3 + 11s^2 + 10s + 100 = 0$

s^3	1	10
s^2	11	100
$-$	$-$	$-$
s^1	$\dfrac{10}{11}$	
s^0	100	

Entries below the dashed line are derived.

$$c_3 = \frac{\begin{vmatrix} 1 & 10 \\ 11 & 100 \end{vmatrix}}{-11}$$

$$= \frac{100 - 110}{-11} = \frac{10}{11}$$

With no sign changes, the system is stable.

Timed 6

The data show a pair of integrators, a zero near $\omega = 0.5$ to 1 rad/s, and a pair of poles around $\omega = 16$ to 32 rad/s.

The integrators provide $-180°$. The zero will cause a change to about $-135°$ at the value of the zero. The pair of poles will cause a phase shift of 90° at the frequency of the poles.

The angles are

$$\angle \mathbf{G} = -180° + \tan^{-1}\left(\frac{\omega}{z}\right) - 2\tan^{-1}\left(\frac{\omega}{p}\right)$$

Estimating $p \approx 21$ and taking $\omega = \dfrac{1}{4}$ rad/s,

$$\angle \mathbf{G} = -180 + \tan^{-1}\left(\frac{0.25}{z}\right) - 2\tan^{-1}\left(\frac{0.25}{21}\right)$$

$$= -167.4°$$

From this,

$$\tan^{-1}\left(\frac{0.25}{z}\right) = 13.96°$$

$$z = \frac{0.25}{\tan 13.96°} = 1.005$$

At $\omega = 128$ rad/s,

$$\angle \mathbf{G} = -252.7°$$

$$-252.7° = -180° + \tan^{-1}\left(\frac{128}{1.005}\right)$$

$$- 2\tan\left(\frac{128}{p}\right)$$

$$\tan^{-1}\left(\frac{121}{p}\right) = 81.13°$$

$$p = \frac{128}{\tan 81.13°} = 19.99$$

Iterating with the new values, at $\omega = 0.25$ rad/s,

$$-167.4 = -180° + \tan^{-1}\left(\frac{0.25}{z}\right) - 2\tan\left(\frac{0.25}{19.99}\right)$$

$$z = 0.9998 \rightarrow 1.00$$

At $\omega = 128$ rad/s,

$$-252.7 = -180° + \tan^{-1} 128 - 2\tan\left(\frac{128}{p}\right)$$

$$p = 19.98 \rightarrow 20$$

Then,

$$\mathbf{G} = \frac{K(s+1)}{s^2(20+s)^2}$$

$$|\mathbf{G}|_{\omega=4} = 10^{30\,\text{dB}/20\,\text{dB}} = (10)^{1.5}$$

Then,

$$K = \frac{(10)^{1.5}(4)^2|20+j4|^2}{|1+j4|}$$

$$= 2503 \rightarrow 2500$$

$$\mathbf{G} = \frac{(6.26)(s+1)}{s^2\left(\dfrac{s}{20}+1\right)^2}$$

The low-frequency asymptote is

$$\left|\frac{6.26}{s^2}\right| \rightarrow 1 \text{ at } s = \sqrt{6.26} = 2.5$$

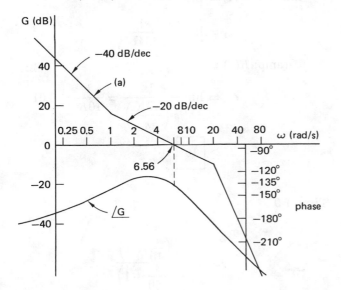

(b) The highest frequency that has $\underline{/\mathbf{G}} = -135°$ is (by iteration) 6.56 rad/s, which has a gain of 0.917. The gain can be modified to become

$$\frac{6.26}{0.917} = \boxed{6.825}$$

Timed 7

$$\mathbf{GH}(s) = \frac{K}{s(s+1)(s+5)}$$

(a) The root locus is found only after all other parts are completed, and appears at the end of the solution.

$$1 + \mathbf{GH} = 0$$

$$s(s+1)(s+5) + K = 0$$

$$s^3 + 6s^2 + 5s + K = 0$$

Break-away point:

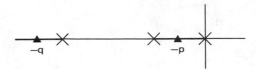

$$(s+q)(s+p)^2 = (s^2 + 2ps + p^2)(s+q)$$
$$= s^3 + (2p+q)s^2 + (p^2 + 2qp)s + p^2q$$
$$= s^3 + 6s^2 + 5s + K = 0$$

$$2p + q = 6 \text{ or } q = 6 - 2p$$

Also,

$$p^2 + 2qp = 5 = p^2 + 2p(6-2p)$$
$$p^2 + 12p - 4p^2 = 5$$
$$p^2 - 4p + \frac{5}{3} = 0$$

$$p = 2 \pm \sqrt{4 - \frac{5}{3}}$$

The minus sign must be used because $0 < p < 1$.

$$p = 0.472$$
$$q = 6 - 2p = 5.055$$

(b) $K = p^2q = \boxed{1.128}$

To find the instability in terms of ω and K, use the Routh-Hurwitz criterion.

$$s^3 + 6s^2 + 5s + K = 0$$

$$\begin{array}{c|ccc}
s^3 & 1 & 5 \\
s^2 & 6 & K \\
\hline
s^1 & \dfrac{30-K}{6} & 0 \\
s^0 & K
\end{array}$$

Entries below the dashed line are derived.

$$c_3 = \frac{\begin{vmatrix} 1 & 5 \\ 6 & K \end{vmatrix}}{-6} = \frac{K-30}{-6}$$

(c) $K = \boxed{30}$ (for instability)

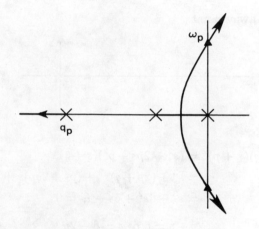

At the instability point,

$$(s+q_p)(s^2+\omega_p^2) = s^3 + 6s^2 + 5s + 30$$
$$= s^3 + q_p s^2 + \omega_p^2 s + q_p \omega_p^2$$
$$q_p = 6$$
$$\omega_p^2 = 5$$
$$K = 30 = q\omega_p^2 = (5)(6)$$
$$\omega_p = \sqrt{5} = 2.236 \text{ rad/s}$$

The root-locus has

$$\text{centroid: } \frac{-1-5}{3} = -2$$
$$\text{asymptotes: } 180° \text{ and } \pm 60°$$

(a)

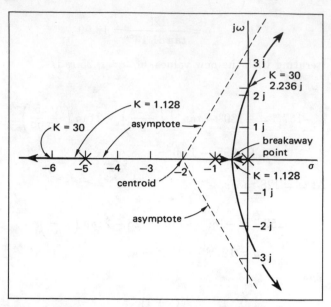

Timed 8

$$\mathbf{G} = \frac{10}{s+1}$$

To provide zero steady-state error to a step input, the system must have an integration in the loop.

To adjust to a particular percentage error for a ramp input, an adjustable gain is needed.

$$\mathbf{H} = \boxed{\dfrac{K}{s}}$$

$$\mathbf{GH} = \frac{10K}{s(s+1)}$$

$$\lim_{s\to0}(1+\mathbf{GH}) = \lim_{s\to0}\frac{10K}{s}$$

$$e_{ss} = \lim_{s\to0}\frac{sR(s)}{1+\mathbf{GH}}$$

$$\text{ramp: } R(s) = \frac{1}{s^2}$$

$$e_{ss} = \lim_{s\to0}\frac{1}{s\left(\dfrac{10K}{s}\right)} = \frac{1}{10K} \le 0.01$$

$$K \ge \boxed{10}$$

Timed 9

$$\mathbf{G}_p = \frac{A\left(\dfrac{s}{10}+1\right)}{s\left(\dfrac{s}{150}+1\right)}$$

The low-frequency asymptote is $\frac{A}{s}$.

Given $|\mathbf{G}_p| \to 1$ at $\omega = 1$,

$$|\mathbf{G}_p| = \frac{A}{\omega}$$
$$A = 1$$

Given $\mathbf{G}_c = \frac{K}{s}$,

$$\mathbf{G} = \mathbf{G}_c\mathbf{G}_p = \frac{K\left(\frac{s}{10}+1\right)}{s^2\left(\frac{s}{150}+1\right)}$$

$$\underline{/\mathbf{G}} = \tan^{-1}\left(\frac{\omega}{10}\right) - 180^\circ - \tan^{-1}\left(\frac{\omega}{150}\right)$$

Find ω where $\underline{/\mathbf{G}} = -135^\circ$.

ω	$5\frac{\text{rad}}{\text{s}}$	$10\frac{\text{rad}}{\text{s}}$	$15\frac{\text{rad}}{\text{s}}$
$\underline{/\mathbf{G}}$	-155°	-138°	-129.40°

Interpolate,

$$\frac{\omega - 10}{-135 + 138} = \frac{15 - 10}{-129.4 + 138}$$

$$\omega = 11.744 \text{ rad/s}$$
$$\underline{/\mathbf{G}} = -134.87^\circ$$

Interpolate twice more,

$$\omega = 11.690 \text{ rad/s}$$
$$\underline{/\mathbf{G}} = -135.00^\circ$$

(a) $K = \dfrac{(11.69)^2\left|1 + j\dfrac{11.69}{150}\right|}{\left|1 + j\dfrac{11.69}{10}\right|}$

$$= \boxed{89.1}$$

(b) $\mathbf{G}_c\mathbf{G}_p = \dfrac{(89.1)\left(\dfrac{s}{10}+1\right)}{s^2\left(\dfrac{s}{150}+1\right)}$

At $\omega = 11.69 \text{ rad/s}$,

$$\mathbf{G}_c\mathbf{G}_p = \mathbf{G} = 1\underline{/-135^\circ}$$

$$\frac{\mathbf{G}}{1+\mathbf{G}} = \frac{1\underline{/-135^\circ}}{1 - (0.707 + j0.707)}$$

$$= \boxed{1.307\underline{/-67.5^\circ}}$$

Timed 10

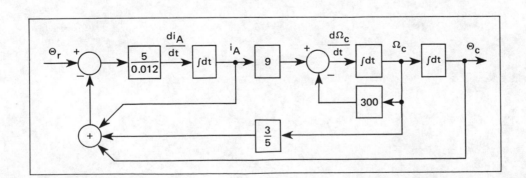

$$5(\Theta_r - \Theta_c) = 5i_A + 0.012\frac{di_A}{dt} + e_G$$

$$e_G = 3\Omega_c$$

(Note: Ω_c is angular velocity in rad/s.)

$$T = 3i_A = 0.33\frac{d\Omega_c}{dt} + 100\Omega_c$$

$$\frac{di_A}{dt} = \left(\frac{5}{0.012}\right)\left(\Theta_r - \Theta_c - i_A - \frac{3}{5}\Omega_c\right)$$

$$\frac{d\Omega_c}{dt} = \frac{3}{0.33}i_A - \frac{100}{0.33}\Omega_c$$

$$= 9i_A - 300\Omega_c$$

ILLUMINATION AND THE NATIONAL ELECTRIC CODE

Warmup 1

From Eq. 13.6,

$$RCR = (5)(24 \text{ ft} - 2.5 \text{ ft}) \left[\frac{40 \text{ ft} + 60 \text{ ft}}{(40 \text{ ft})(60 \text{ ft})} \right]$$

$$= \boxed{4.48}$$

From Eq. 13.7,

$$CCR = (5)(0.0 \text{ ft}) \left[\frac{40 \text{ ft} + 60 \text{ ft}}{(40 \text{ ft})(60 \text{ ft})} \right] = \boxed{0}$$

From Eq. 13.8,

$$FCR = (5)(2.5 \text{ ft}) \left[\frac{40 \text{ ft} + 60 \text{ ft}}{(40 \text{ ft})(60 \text{ ft})} \right] = \boxed{0.52}$$

Warmup 2

From Eq. 13.6,

$$RCR = (5)(24 \text{ ft} - 2.5 \text{ ft} - 12 \text{ ft}) \left[\frac{40 \text{ ft} + 60 \text{ ft}}{(40 \text{ ft})(60 \text{ ft})} \right]$$

$$= \boxed{1.98}$$

From Eq. 13.7,

$$CCR = (5)(12 \text{ ft}) \left[\frac{40 \text{ ft} + 60 \text{ ft}}{(40 \text{ ft})(60 \text{ ft})} \right] = \boxed{2.50}$$

From Eq. 13.8,

$$FCR = (5)(2.5 \text{ ft}) \left[\frac{40 \text{ ft} + 60 \text{ ft}}{(40 \text{ ft})(60 \text{ ft})} \right] = \boxed{0.52}$$

Warmup 3

$$\text{ceiling reflectance} = 90\% = \rho_{cc}$$

$$\text{wall reflectance} = 75\% = \rho_w$$

From Table 13.5 under base reflectance (ceiling = base) 90%, second and third columns at CR = 2.5 are

ρ_w	80%	70%
ρ_{cc}	75%	68%

Interpolating,

$$\frac{\rho_{cc} - 68\%}{75\% - 68\%} = \frac{75\% - 70\%}{80\% - 70\%}$$

The effective ceiling reflectance is

$$\rho_{cc} = \boxed{71.5\%}$$

Warmup 4

From Table 13.1 for RCR = 2 and ceiling cavity reflectance of 80%, extrapolate from wall reflectances of 50% and 30% to obtain reflectance of 75% of CU = 0.845.

Repeat for ceiling cavity reflectance of 50% to obtain CU = 0.763.

Interpolate between these values to obtain ceiling reflectance of 71.5%.

$$CU = \boxed{0.822}$$

Warmup 5

$$\text{total lm} = \frac{(100 \text{ fc})(40 \text{ ft})(60 \text{ ft})}{CU}$$

From Warmup 4, CU = 0.822, so

$$\text{total lm} = \frac{240{,}000 \text{ lm}}{0.822} = \boxed{292{,}000 \text{ lm}}$$

Warmup 6

From Table 13.3, LLD = 0.84.

From Table 13.2, LDD = 0.94.

5% ballast loss results in a loss factor of 0.95.

The voltage fluctuation for fluorescent lamps results in a 0.4-lm loss per volt, for a total of 2%, or a loss factor 0f 0.98.

$$LLF = (0.98)(0.95)(LLD)(LDD)$$

$$= (0.98)(0.95)(0.84)(0.94)$$

$$= \boxed{0.735}$$

Warmup 7

minimum no. of luminaires $= N$

$$N = \frac{(100 \text{ fc})(40 \text{ ft})(60 \text{ ft})}{\left(2 \dfrac{\text{lamps}}{\text{luminaire}}\right)(3000 \text{ initial lm})(CU)(LLF)}$$

$$= 66.2 \rightarrow \boxed{67 \text{ luminaires}}$$

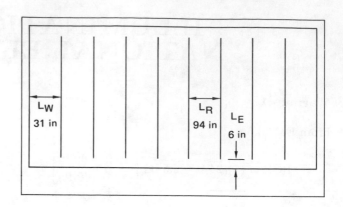

Warmup 8

With rows in the 40-ft direction (with length of 52 in), the number of luminaires per row, N_r, is

$$N_r = \frac{(40 \text{ ft})\left(12\dfrac{\text{in}}{\text{ft}}\right)}{52 \text{ in}} = 9.2 \rightarrow 9 \text{ luminaires/row}$$

$$\text{no. of rows} = \frac{67 \text{ luminaires}}{9 \dfrac{\text{luminaires}}{\text{row}}} = 7.4 \rightarrow 8 \text{ rows}$$

Row separation, L_r, is

$$L_r = \frac{\left(12\dfrac{\text{in}}{\text{ft}}\right)(60 \text{ ft})}{\left(8 - 1 + \dfrac{2}{3}\right) \text{rows}} = 93.9 \rightarrow 94 \text{ in}$$

The distance from the last luminaire in a row to the wall (in the 40-ft direction), L_e, is

$$L_e = \left(\frac{1}{2}\right)$$

$$\times \left[(40 \text{ ft})\left(12\frac{\text{in}}{\text{ft}}\right) - (9 \text{ luminaires})\left(52 \frac{\text{in}}{\text{luminaire}}\right)\right]$$

$$= 6.0 \text{ in}$$

The distance to the wall from the last row, L_w, is

$$L_w = \left(\frac{1}{2}\right)$$

$$\times \left[\left(12\frac{\text{in}}{\text{ft}}\right)(60 \text{ ft}) - (7 \text{ row spacings})\left(94 \frac{\text{in}}{\text{spacing}}\right)\right]$$

$$= 31.0 \text{ in}$$

Warmup 9

$$\text{RCR} \approx 2$$
$$\rho_{cc} = 71.5\%$$
$$\rho_w = 75\%$$

At B1, rpm = 0.51.

At B2, rpm = 0.6.

Interpolating at B1.5,

$$\text{rpm} = 0.555$$

From the bottom of Table 13.7,

RCR = 2	wall (LC$_w$)				ceiling (LC$_{cc}$)			
ρ_{cc}	80%		50%		80%		50%	
ρ_w	50%	30%	50%	30%	50%	30%	50%	30%
LC	0.232	0.127	0.209	0.115	0.222	0.190	0.130	0.113
$\rho_w = 75\%$	0.363		0.327		0.262		0.151	
$\rho_{cc} = 71.5\%$	LC$_w$ = 0.353				LC$_{cc}$ = 0.231			

From Eq. 13.11,

$$\text{RRC} = 0.285$$

With 2 lamps/luminaire, 72 luminaires, and 3000 initial lm,

$$\text{LLF} = 0.735$$

$$D_{rh} = \frac{\left(2 \dfrac{\text{lamps}}{\text{luminaire}}\right)(72 \text{ luminaires})}{2400 \text{ ft}^2} \times (3000 \text{ initial lm})(0.735)(0.285)$$

$$= \boxed{37.8 \text{ fc/ft}^2}$$

Warmup 10

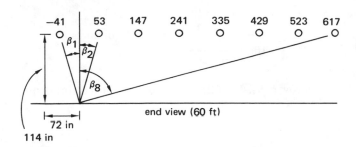

end view (60 ft)

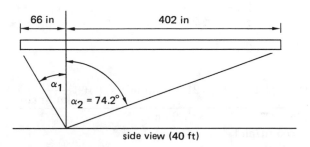

$\alpha_2 = 74.2°$

side view (40 ft)

From Table 13.7,

lateral distance (in)	β (degrees)	footcandles for $\alpha_1 = 30°$	footcandles for $\alpha_2 = 70°$	for $\alpha_2 = 80°$
−41	20*	24.1	39.7	40.3
53	25	21.6	36.4	36.9
147	52*	5.7	11.9	12.3
241	65	1.1	3.2	3.5
335	71*	0.4	1.5	1.6
429	75	0.3	0.3	0.4
523	78*	0	0.2	0.3
617	80*	0	0.2	0.3

* interpolated values

The footcandle totals are

for $\alpha_1 = 30°$, 53.2 fc

$\left.\begin{array}{l} \text{for } \alpha_2 = 70°,\ 93.4 \text{ fc} \\ \alpha_2 = 80°,\ 95.6 \text{ fc} \end{array}\right\}$ 94.3 fc (interpolated)

The total of uncorrected fc is

$$53.2 \text{ fc} + 94.3 \text{ fc} = 147.5 \text{ fc}$$

The correction, including LLF, is

$$\text{net} = (147.5 \text{ fc})\left(\frac{6 \text{ ft}}{9.5 \text{ ft}}\right)(0.735) = \boxed{68.5 \text{ fc}}$$

Concentrate 1

Using required footcandles,

$$(90 \text{ fc})(56 \text{ ft})(28 \text{ ft}) = 141,000 \text{ lm}$$

Assuming two ceiling-mounted T-12 luminaires,

$$\text{RCR} = (5)(14 \text{ ft} - 2.5 \text{ ft})\left[\frac{28 \text{ ft} + 56 \text{ ft}}{(28 \text{ ft})(56 \text{ ft})}\right]$$

$$= 3.08$$

Find the CU from Table 13.1 with 50% wall reflectance,

RCR	ceiling reflectance		extrapolate for
	80%	50%	90%
3	0.68	0.61	0.70
4	0.60	0.54	0.62*

* interpolation for RCR = 3.08: CU = 0.69

Enclosed luminaires are chosen. From Table 13.2, LDD = 0.88. From Table 13.3, use high output F48T12 lamps with multiplying factor 1.03. See end of fluorescent section of Table 13.3. Initial lm/lamp = IL.

$$\text{IL} = (4200)(1.03) = 4326 \text{ lm/lamp}$$

$$\text{LLF} = 0.80$$

Number of luminaires (2 lamps per luminaire), N_L, is

$$N_L = \frac{141,000 \text{ lm}}{\left(4326 \dfrac{\text{lm}}{\text{lamp}}\right)\left(2 \dfrac{\text{lamps}}{\text{luminaire}}\right)(0.67)(0.88)(0.80)}$$

$$= 33.5 \rightarrow 34 \text{ luminaires}$$

For the 28-ft dimension, the maximum number of luminaires per row, L_r, is

$$L_r = \frac{(28 \text{ ft})\left(12 \dfrac{\text{in}}{\text{ft}}\right)}{52 \dfrac{\text{in}}{\text{luminaire}}}$$

$$= 6.46 \rightarrow 6 \text{ luminaires/row}$$

The number of rows in the 56-ft dimension is

$$\frac{34 \text{ luminaires}}{6 \dfrac{\text{luminaires}}{\text{row}}} = 5.7 \rightarrow 6 \text{ rows}$$

For the 56-ft dimension, the maximum number of luminaires per row is

$$L_r = \frac{(56 \text{ ft})\left(12 \dfrac{\text{in}}{\text{ft}}\right)}{52 \dfrac{\text{in}}{\text{luminaire}}} = 12.92 \rightarrow 12 \text{ luminaires}$$

The number of rows in the 28-ft dimension is

$$\frac{34 \text{ luminaires}}{12 \frac{\text{luminaires}}{\text{row}}} = 2.8 \rightarrow 3 \text{ rows}$$

This requires $(3)(12) = 36$ luminaires: the same as the other arrangement. Run the rows in the 28-ft direction.

$$\left(6 \frac{\text{luminaires}}{\text{row}}\right)(6 \text{ rows}) = 36 \text{ luminaires}$$

End spacing:

$$\frac{(28 \text{ ft})\left(12 \frac{\text{in}}{\text{ft}}\right) - (6 \text{ luminaires})\left(52 \frac{\text{in}}{\text{luminaire}}\right)}{2}$$
$$= 9 \text{ in}$$

Row spacing:

$$\frac{(56 \text{ ft})\left(12 \frac{\text{in}}{\text{ft}}\right)}{\left(6 - 1 + \frac{2}{3}\right) \text{ rows}} = 118.59 \rightarrow 118.6 \text{ in}$$

Spacing to wall:

$$\frac{(56 \text{ ft})\left(12 \frac{\text{in}}{\text{ft}}\right) - (5 \text{ row-spaces})\left(118.6 \frac{\text{in}}{\text{row-space}}\right)}{2 \text{ ends}}$$
$$= 39.5 \text{ in}$$

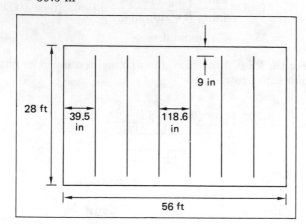

Concentrate 2

The number of luminaires required is

$$N_L = \frac{(100 \text{ fc})(06 \text{ ft})(190 \text{ ft})}{\left(3100 \frac{\text{lm}}{\text{lamp}}\right)\left(4 \frac{\text{lamps}}{\text{luminaire}}\right)(0.75)(0.62)}$$
$$= 299.7 \rightarrow 300 \text{ luminaires}$$

300 8-ft luminaires are needed.

The number of luminaires per row is

$$\frac{(180 \text{ ft})\left(12 \frac{\text{in}}{\text{ft}}\right)}{100 \frac{\text{in}}{\text{luminaire}}} = 21.6 \text{ luminaires}$$

Each row consists of 21 8-foot and one 4-foot luminaire.

The number of rows is

$$\frac{300 \text{ luminaires}}{21.5 \frac{\text{luminaires}}{\text{row}}} = 13.95 \rightarrow 14 \text{ rows}$$

End spacing:

$$\frac{(180 \text{ ft})\left(12 \frac{\text{in}}{\text{ft}}\right) - (21.5 \text{ luminaires})\left(100 \frac{\text{in}}{\text{luminaire}}\right)}{2 \text{ ends}}$$
$$= 5 \text{ in/end}$$

Row spacing:

$$\frac{(96 \text{ ft})\left(12 \frac{\text{in}}{\text{ft}}\right)}{\left(14 - 1 + \frac{2}{3}\right) \text{ rows}} = 84 \frac{1}{4} \text{ in}$$

Spacing from last row to wall:

$$\frac{(96 \text{ ft})\left(12 \frac{\text{in}}{\text{ft}}\right) - \left(84 \frac{1}{4} \frac{\text{in}}{\text{space}}\right)(13 \text{ spaces})}{2 \text{ ends}} = 28 \frac{3}{8} \text{ in}$$

(a) ┌──┐
   │ 294 8-ft luminaires and 14 4-ft luminaires are │
   │ required.   │
   └──┘

(b)

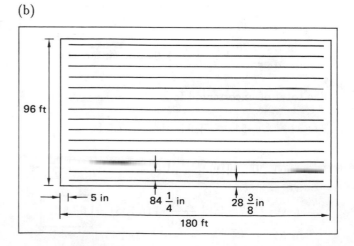

$$P = \left[\left(\frac{285 \text{ W}}{8\text{-ft luminaire}}\right)\left(21\frac{8\text{-ft luminaires}}{\text{row}}\right)\right.$$
$$\left.+ \left(\frac{190 \text{ W}}{4\text{-ft luminaire}}\right)\left(1\frac{4\text{-ft luminaire}}{\text{row}}\right)\right]$$
$$\times \text{ 14 rows}$$
$$= 86.45 \text{ kW}$$

$$W = (86.45 \text{ kW})\left(17\frac{\text{hr}}{\text{day}}\right)\left(5\frac{\text{days}}{\text{week}}\right)\left(50\frac{\text{weeks}}{\text{yr}}\right)$$
$$= 367{,}412 \text{ kW-hr}$$

(c) $\text{cost/year} = (367{,}412 \text{ kW-hr})\left(\frac{\$0.015}{\text{kW-hr}}\right)$
$$= \boxed{\$5{,}511.19}$$

Concentrate 3

From Table 13.8, MMI = 2 fc.

For a medium clean/dirty environment with cleaning once in three years, LDD = 0.77.

From Ex. 13.1, LLD = 0.91. For MH = 30 ft and a 6-ft overhang,

$$\left.\begin{array}{l}\text{CU(Ss)} = 0.35 \\ \text{CU(Hs)} = 0.02\end{array}\right\} \text{CU} = 0.37$$

Spacing for staggered or opposite, from Eq. 13.15,

$$\frac{(2 \text{ luminaires})\left(1\frac{\text{lamp}}{\text{luminaire}}\right)}{\times \left(25{,}500\frac{\text{lm}}{\text{lamp}}\right)(0.91)(0.77)(0.37)}{(2 \text{ fc})(40 \text{ ft})}$$
$$= 165.3 \text{ ft}$$

Timed 1

The total of required lumens is

$$(30 \text{ fc})(20{,}000 \text{ ft}^2) = 6 \times 10^5 \text{ lm}$$

Given CU = 0.78 and LLF = 0.72, the required lamp lumens are

$$\frac{6 \times 10^5 \text{ lm}}{(0.78)(0.72)} = 1.069 \times 10^6 \text{ lm}$$

The energy cost per kW per year is

$$\left(\frac{\$0.075}{\text{kW-hr}}\right)\left(\frac{3200 \text{ hr}}{\text{yr}}\right) = \$240/\text{kW-yr}$$

Luminaire A: 150 W incandescent

$$N_L = \frac{1.069 \times 10^6 \text{ lm}}{\left(1\frac{\text{lamp}}{\text{luminaire}}\right)\left(2600\frac{\text{lm}}{\text{lamp}}\right)} = 411 \text{ luminaires}$$

The initital cost is

$$(411 \text{ luminaires})\left(\frac{\$75}{\text{luminaire}}\right) = \$30{,}825$$

The yearly energy cost is

$$(411 \text{ luminaires})\left(0.15\frac{\text{kW}}{\text{luminaire}}\right)\left(\frac{\$240}{\text{kW-yr}}\right)$$
$$= \$14{,}796/\text{yr}$$

The yearly replacement cost is

$$(411 \text{ lamps})\left(\frac{3200\frac{\text{hr/yr}}{\text{lamp}}}{750\frac{\text{hr}}{\text{lamp}}}\right)\left(\frac{\$4.35}{\text{lamp}}\right) = \$7{,}628/\text{yr}$$

Luminaire B: 175 W mercury vapor

$$N_L = \frac{1.069 \times 10^6 \text{ lm}}{\left(1\frac{\text{lamp}}{\text{luminaire}}\right)\left(7700\frac{\text{lm}}{\text{lamp}}\right)} = 139 \text{ luminaires}$$

The initial cost is

$$(139 \text{ luminaires})\left(\frac{\$162.50}{\text{luminaire}}\right) = \$22{,}588$$

The yearly energy cost is

$$(139 \text{ luminaires})\left(0.175\frac{\text{kW}}{\text{luminaire}}\right)\left(\frac{\$240}{\text{kW-yr}}\right)$$
$$= \$5{,}838/\text{yr}$$

The yearly replacement cost is

$$(139 \text{ lamps})\left(\frac{3200\frac{\text{hr/yr}}{\text{lamp}}}{24{,}000\frac{\text{hr}}{\text{lamp}}}\right)\left(\frac{\$10}{\text{lamp}}\right) = \$185/\text{yr}$$

luminaire	A:150 W incandescent	B:175 W mercury-vapor
number of luminaires	411	139
initial cost	$30,825	$22,588
energy cost/yr	$14,796	$5,838
replacement cost/yr	$7,628	$185
annual cost	$22,124	$6,023

Timed 2

(a) A scheme with 4 lamps/pole within the lot, 1 lamp/pole in corners, and 2 lamps/pole along the edges provides reasonably uniform lighting.

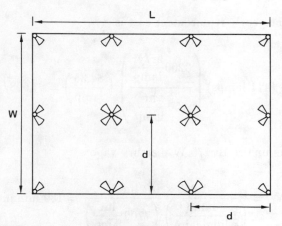

Find the number of lamps needed.

$$\text{corners}: \quad 4$$

$$\text{edges}: \quad (2)\left[(2)\left(\frac{L}{d}-1\right)+(2)\left(\frac{W}{d}-1\right)\right]$$

$$\text{interior}: \quad (4)\left(\frac{L}{d}-1\right)\left(\frac{W}{d}-1\right)$$

Adding all of these,

$$N_L = 4\,\frac{LW}{d^2}$$

With BU = 0.65, LLD = 0.74, and LDD = 0.48,

$$N_L = \frac{(6.25\text{ fc})(360\text{ ft})(420\text{ ft})}{\left(65{,}000\,\dfrac{\text{lm}}{\text{lamp}}\right)(0.65)(0.74)(0.48)} = 63\text{ lamps}$$

$$d^2 = \frac{\left(4\,\dfrac{\text{lamps}}{\text{pole}}\right)(360\text{ ft})(420\text{ ft})}{63\text{ lamps}}$$

$$d \approx 98\text{ ft}$$

$$\frac{W}{d} = \frac{360}{98} = 3.67 \rightarrow 4$$

$$\text{5 poles across}$$

$$d_l = \frac{360\text{ ft}}{4} = 90\text{ ft}$$

$$\frac{L}{d} = \frac{420}{98} = 4.29 \rightarrow 4$$

$$\text{5 poles lengthwise}$$

$$d_W = \frac{420\text{ ft}}{4} = 105\text{ ft}$$

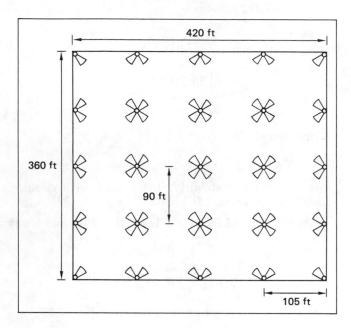

The beam angle is

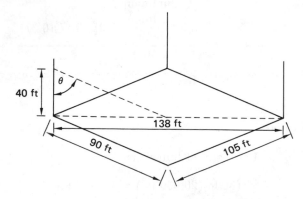

$$\theta = \tan^{-1}\left(\frac{\dfrac{138}{2}}{40}\right) = 59.9^\circ \rightarrow \boxed{60^\circ}$$

(b) There are 64 lamps. Each lamp requires a current of

$$I = \frac{1000\text{ W} + 25\text{ W}}{(220\text{ V})(0.8)} = 5.824\text{ A}$$

Each lamp must be derated by 0.8 to meet NEC, so

$$I_{rated/lamp} = \frac{5.824 \text{ A}}{0.8} = 7.28 \text{ A}$$

(c) 22 lamps are required per phase, so the total rating must be 160 A. The next highest rated breaker is 175 A, so the main breaker rating is

> three-phase 175 A at 220 V

This must permit a surge current of 280 A. This will feed three parallel load circuits.

Each phase will serve three branch circuits which must use 60 breakers. The branch circuit breakers are three-phase 60 A.

Circuit 1:

Circuit A1 has an 8-lamp load,

$$(8 \text{ lamps}) \left(7.28 \frac{\text{A}}{\text{lamp}} \right) = 58.24 \text{ A}$$

Brand circuit 1A requires AWG # 4 U.F. copper wire, as required by NEC Table 310-16.

All remaining feeders serve 7 lamps, which take 51 A and require AWG #6 U.F. copper wire.

Circuit 2: (Circuit 3 is mirror image)

All phases have seven loads. From circuit 1 calculation, all branches require AWG #6 U.F. copper wire.

ENGINEERING ECONOMICS

Warmup 1

$$F = (\$1000)(F/P, 6\%, 10)$$
$$= (\$1000)(1.7908) = \boxed{\$1790.80}$$

Warmup 2

$$P = (\$2000)(P/F, 6\%, 4)$$
$$= (\$2000)(0.7921) = \boxed{\$1584.20}$$

Warmup 3

$$P = (\$2000)(P/F, 6\%, 20)$$
$$= (\$2000)(0.3118) = \boxed{\$623.60}$$

Warmup 4

$$\$500 = A(P/A, 6\%, 7)$$
$$= A(5.5824)$$
$$A = \frac{\$500}{5.5824} = \boxed{\$89.57}$$

Warmup 5

$$F = (\$50)(F/A, 6\%, 10)$$
$$= (\$50)(13.1808) = \boxed{\$659.04}$$

Warmup 6

Each year is independent.

$$\frac{\$200}{1.06} = \boxed{\$188.68}$$

Warmup 7

$$\$2000 = A(F/A, 6\%, 5)$$
$$= A(5.6371)$$
$$A = \boxed{\$354.79}$$

Warmup 8

$$F = (\$100)[(F/P, 6\%, 10)$$
$$+ (F/P, 6\%, 8) + (F/P, 6\%, 6)]$$
$$= (\$100)(1.7908 + 1.5938 + 1.4185)$$
$$= \boxed{\$480.31}$$

Warmup 9

$$r = 0.06$$
$$\phi = \frac{0.06}{12} = 0.005$$
$$n = (5)(12) = 60$$
$$F = (\$500)(1.005)^{60} = \boxed{\$674.43}$$

Warmup 10

$$\$120 = (\$80)(F/P, r, 7)$$
$$(F/P, r, 7) = \frac{\$120}{\$80} = 1.5$$

By searching the tables,

$$r = \boxed{6\%}$$

Concentrate 1

$$\text{EUAC} = (\$17{,}000 + \$5000)(A/P, 6\%, 5)$$
$$- (\$14{,}000 + \$2500)(A/F, 6\%, 5) + \$200$$
$$= (\$22{,}000)(0.2374) - (\$16{,}500)(0.1774)$$
$$+ \$200$$
$$= \boxed{\$2495.70}$$

Concentrate 2

Assume the bridge will be there forever.

To find the cost to keep the old bridge, the generally accepted method is to consider the salvage value as a benefit lost (cost).

$$
\begin{aligned}
\text{EUAC} &= (\$9000 + \$13,000)(A/P, 8\%, 20) \\
&\quad - (\$10,000)(A/F, 8\%, 20) + \$500 \\
&= (\$22,000)(0.1019) \\
&\quad - (\$10,000)(0.0219) + \$500 \\
&= \$2522.80
\end{aligned}
$$

Find the cost to replace the old bridge.

$$
\begin{aligned}
\text{EUAC} &= (\$40,000)(A/P, 8\%, 25) \\
&\quad - (\$15,000)(A/F, 8\%, 25) + \$100 \\
&= (\$40,000)(0.0937) - (\$15,000)(0.0137) + \$100 \\
&= \$3642.50
\end{aligned}
$$

Keep the old bridge.

Concentrate 3

$$
\begin{aligned}
D &= \frac{\$150,000}{15} = \$10,000 \\
0 &= \$150,000 \\
&\quad + (\$32,000)(1 - 0.48)(P/A, r, 15) \\
&\quad - (\$7530)(1 - 0.48)(P/A, r, 15) \\
&\quad + (\$10,000)(0.48)(P/A, r, 15) \\
\$150,000 &= (\$16,640 - \$3915.60 + \$4800) \\
&\quad \times (P/A, r, 15) \\
(P/A, r, 15) &= \frac{\$150,000}{\$17,524.40} = 8.5595
\end{aligned}
$$

By searching the tables, $i = \boxed{8\%}$

Concentrate 4

(a) $\dfrac{\$1,500,000 - \$300,000}{\$1,000,000} = \boxed{1.2}$

(b) $\$1,500,000 - \$300,000 - \$1,000,000 = \boxed{\$200,000}$

Concentrate 5

The annual rent is

$$
\begin{aligned}
(12)(75) &= 900 \\
F &= (\$14,000 + \$1000)(F/P, 10\%, 10) \\
&\quad + (\$150 + \$250 - \$900)(F/A, 10\%, 10) \\
&= (\$15,000)(2.5937) - (\$500)(15.9374) \\
&= \boxed{\$30,936.80}
\end{aligned}
$$

Concentrate 6

$$
\begin{aligned}
\$2000 &= (\$89.30)(P/A, r, 30) \\
(P/A, r, 30) &= \frac{\$2000}{\$89.30} = \$22.396 \\
r &= 2\% \text{ per month} \\
i &= (1.02)^{12} - 1 = \boxed{0.2682 \text{ or } 26.82\%}
\end{aligned}
$$

Concentrate 7

(a) SL:

$$
D = \frac{\$500,000 - \$100,000}{25} = \boxed{\$16,000}
$$

(b) SOYD:

$$
\begin{aligned}
T &= \left(\frac{1}{2}\right)(25)(26) = 325 \\
D_1 &= \left(\frac{25}{325}\right)(\$500,000 - \$100,000) = \boxed{\$30,769} \\
D_2 &= \left(\frac{24}{325}\right)(\$400,000) = \boxed{\$29,538} \\
D_3 &= \left(\frac{23}{325}\right)(\$400,000) = \boxed{\$28,308}
\end{aligned}
$$

(c) DDB:

$$
\begin{aligned}
D_1 &= \left(\frac{2}{25}\right)(\$500,000) = \boxed{\$40,000} \\
D_2 &= \left(\frac{2}{25}\right)(\$500,000 - \$40,000) = \boxed{\$36,800} \\
D_3 &= \left(\frac{2}{25}\right)(\$500,000 - \$40,000 - \$36,800) \\
&= \boxed{\$33,856}
\end{aligned}
$$

Concentrate 8

$$P = -\$12{,}000 + (\$2000)(P/F, 10\%, 10)$$
$$- (\$1000)(P/A, 10\%, 10)$$
$$- (\$200)(P/G, 10\%, 10)$$
$$= -\$12{,}000 + (\$2{,}000)(0.3855)$$
$$- (\$1000)(6.1446) - (\$200)(22.8913)$$
$$= \boxed{\$ - 21{,}951.86}$$

$$EUAC = (\$21{,}951.86)(A/P, 10\%, 10)$$
$$= (\$21{,}951.86)(0.1627) = \boxed{\$3571.56}$$

Concentrate 9

Assume that the probability of failure in any of the n years is $1/n$.

$$EUAC(9) = (\$1500)(A/P, 6\%, 20)$$
$$+ \left(\frac{1}{9}\right)(0.35)(\$1500)$$
$$+ (0.04)(\$1500)$$
$$= (\$1500)[0.0872 + (0.35)\left(\frac{1}{9}\right) + 0.04]$$
$$= \$249.13$$
$$EUAC(14) = (\$1600)\left[0.1272 + (0.35)\left(\frac{1}{14}\right)\right]$$
$$= \$243.52$$
$$EUAC(30) = (\$1750)\left[0.1272 + (0.35)\left(\frac{1}{30}\right)\right]$$
$$= \$243.01$$
$$EUAC(52) = (\$1900)\left[0.1272 + (0.35)\left(\frac{1}{52}\right)\right]$$
$$= \$254.47$$
$$EUAC(86) = (\$2100)\left[0.1272 + (0.35)\left(\frac{1}{86}\right)\right]$$
$$= \$275.67$$

$$\boxed{\text{Choose the 30 year pipe.}}$$

Concentrate 10

$$EUAC(7) = (0.15)(\$25{,}000) = \$3750$$
$$EUAC(8) = (\$15{,}000)(A/P, 10\%, 20)$$
$$+ (0.10)(\$25{,}000)$$
$$= (\$15{,}000)(0.1175) + (0.10)(\$25{,}000)$$
$$= \$4262.50$$
$$EUAC(9) = (\$20{,}000)(0.1175) + (0.07)(\$25{,}000)$$
$$= \$4100.00$$
$$EUAC(10) = (\$30{,}000)(0.1175) + (0.03)(\$25{,}000)$$
$$= \$4275$$

$$\boxed{\text{It is cheapest to do nothing.}}$$

Timed 1

$$EUAC(1) = (\$10{,}000)(A/P, 20\%, 1) + (\$2000)$$
$$- (\$8000)(A/F, 20\%, 1)$$
$$= (\$10{,}000)(1.2000) + \$2000$$
$$- (\$8000)(1.0000)$$
$$= \$6000$$
$$EUAC(2) = (\$10{,}000)(A/P, 20\%, 2) + \$2000$$
$$+ (\$1000)(A/G, 20\%, 2)$$
$$- (\$7000)(A/F, 20\%, 2)$$
$$= (\$10{,}000)(0.6545) + \$2000$$
$$+ (\$1000)(0.4545)$$
$$- (\$7000)(0.4545)$$
$$= \$5818.00$$
$$EUAC(3) = (\$10{,}000)(A/P, 20\%, 3)$$
$$+ \$2000 + (\$1000)(A/G, 20\%, 3)$$
$$- (\$6000)(A/F, 20\%, 3)$$
$$= (\$10{,}000)(0.4747) + \$2000$$
$$+ (\$1000)(0.8791)$$
$$- (\$6000)(0.2747)$$
$$= \$5977.90$$
$$EUAC(4) = (\$10{,}000)(A/P, 20\%, 4)$$
$$+ \$2000 + (\$1000)(A/G, 20\%, 4)$$
$$- (\$5000)(A/F, 20\%, 4)$$
$$= (\$10{,}000)(0.3863) + \$2000$$
$$+ (\$1000)(1.2742)$$
$$- (\$5000)(0.1863)$$
$$= \$6205.7$$

$$\text{EUAC}(5) = (\$10{,}000)(A/P, 20\%, 5)$$
$$+ \ \$2000 + (\$1000)(A/G, 20\%, 5)$$
$$- \ (\$4000)(A/F, 20\%, 5)$$
$$= (\$10{,}000)(0.3344) + \$2000$$
$$+ \ (\$1000)(1.6405) - (\$4000)(0.1344)$$
$$= \$6446.9$$

(a) $\boxed{\text{Sell at the end of the second year.}}$

(b) From Eq. 14.8,

$$\text{cost} = \$6000 + (0.20)(\$5000) + (\$5000 - \$4000)$$
$$= \boxed{\$8000}$$

Timed 2

The man should charge his company only for the costs due to the business travel.

Insurance: $\$300 - \$200 = \$100$
Maintenance: $\$200 - \$150 = \$50$

Salvage: ($\$1000 - \$500$) in 5 years
$$(\$500)(A/F, 10\%, 5) = (\$500)(0.1638)$$
$$= \$81.90$$

Gasoline: $\dfrac{(\$5000)(0.60)}{15} = \$200$

$$\text{EUAC per mile} = \frac{\$100 + \$50 + \$81.9 + \$200}{\$5000}$$
$$= \$0.0864$$

(a) $\boxed{\$0.107 > \$0.0864, \text{ so the reimbursement is adequate.}}$

(b) $0.10x = (\$5000)(A/P, 10\%, 5) + \$250 + \$200$
$$-(\$800)(A/F, 10\%, 5) + \left(\frac{x}{15}\right)(0.60)$$
$$= (\$5000)(0.2638) + \$250 + \$200$$
$$- \ (\$800)(0.1638) + 0.04x$$
$$0.10x = 1637.96 + 0.04x$$
$$0.06x = 1637.96$$
$$x = \boxed{27{,}299 \text{ mi}}$$